3.00
N.T.

THE UNIVERSE
AROUND US

SIR JAMES JEANS
THE UNIVERSE AROUND US

FOURTH EDITION
REVISED AND RESET

CAMBRIDGE
AT THE UNIVERSITY PRESS
1969

PUBLISHED BY
THE SYNDICS OF THE CAMBRIDGE UNIVERSITY PRESS

Bentley House, 200 Euston Road, London, N.W. 1
American Branch: 32 East 57th Street, New York 22, N.Y.

First Edition	1929
Reprinted	1929
	1930
Second Edition	1930
Reprinted	1930
	1931
Third Edition	1933
Reprinted	1938
Fourth Edition	1944
Reprinted	1945
	1946
	1953
	1960
	1969

PRINTED IN THE U.S.A.

PREFACE

The present book contains a brief account, written in simple language, of the methods and results of modern astronomical research, both observational and theoretical. Special attention has been given to problems of cosmogony and evolution, and to the general structure of the universe. My ideal, perhaps never wholly attainable, has been that of making the entire book intelligible to readers with no special scientific knowledge.

Parts of the book cover the same ground as various lectures I have recently delivered to University and other audiences, including a course of wireless talks I gave last autumn. It has been found necessary to rewrite these almost in their entirety, so that very few sentences remain in their original form, but those who have asked me to publish my lectures and wireless talks will find the substance of them in the present book.

J. H. JEANS

DORKING

1 *May* 1929

PREFACE TO SECOND EDITION

In preparing a second edition, I have taken advantage of a great number of suggestions made by correspondents and reviewers, to whom I offer my sincerest thanks. I have also inserted discussions of the new planet Pluto, the rotation of the galaxy, the apparent expansion of the universe, and other subjects which have become important since the first edition was published, and in general have tried to bring the book up to date.

J. H. JEANS

DORKING

2 *August* 1930

FROM THE PREFACE TO THIRD EDITION

The three years which have elapsed since the second edition of this book appeared have been more than usually eventful for those parts of science with which the book deals.

At the sub-atomic end of the scale of nature, the uncharged neutron and the positively-charged electron have been discovered. At the other end of the scale there is much new knowledge, both observational and theoretical, on the expansion of the universe and cosmic radiation. In the intermediate parts of the scale, in addition to a large mass of new observational material, we find new spectroscopic methods for investigating the constitution and rotations of the stars, and new theoretical discussions of their structure. From these and other causes, the present edition is substantially longer than its predecessors.

J. H. JEANS

DORKING

7 *October* 1933

PREFACE TO FOURTH EDITION

In the interval since the third edition appeared, astronomy has continued its triumphal progress. Perhaps the most noteworthy single episode has been the discovery that the physics of atomic nuclei can not only give a satisfactory account of the radiation of the sun and stars, but can also explain many hitherto puzzling stellar characteristics; the largest and smallest ingredients of nature—the star and the atomic nucleus—have met and thrown light on one another, to the great improvement of our understanding of both. This and other outstanding advances have necessitated many changes in and additions to my book. A large part of it has been re-written, while most of the remainder has been substantially amended.

J. H. JEANS

DORKING

September 1943

CONTENTS

PLATES

The Study of Astronomy

On the evening of January 7, 1610, a fateful day for the human race, Galileo Galilei, Professor of Mathematics in the University of Padua, sat in front of a telescope he had made with his own hands.

More than three centuries previously, Roger Bacon, the inventor of spectacles, had explained how a telescope could be constructed so as "to make the stars appear as near as we please." He had shown how a lens could be so shaped that it would collect all the rays of light falling on it from a distant object, bend them until they met in a focus, and then pass them on through the pupil of the eye on to the retina. Such an instrument would increase the power of the human eye, just as an ear trumpet increases the power of the human ear by collecting all the waves of sound which fall on a large aperture, bending them, and passing them through the orifice of the ear on to the ear drum.

Yet it was not until 1608 that the first telescope had been constructed by Lippershey, a Flemish spectacle-maker. On hearing of this instrument, Galileo had set to work to discover the principles of its construction and had soon made himself a telescope far better than the original. His instrument had created no small sensation in Italy. Such extraordinary stories had been told of its powers that he had been commanded to take it to Venice and exhibit it to the Doge and Senate. The citizens of Venice had then seen the most aged of their Senators climbing the highest bell-towers to spy through the telescope at ships which were too far out at sea to be seen at all without its help. The telescope admitted about a hundred times as much light as the unaided human eye, and Galileo claimed that it showed objects fifty miles distant as clearly as though they were only five miles away.

Perhaps it need hardly be said that this power is quite insignificant in comparison with that of modern instruments. The telescope of 100-inch aperture at Mount Wilson, California, the largest at present in existence, admits 2500 times as much light as Galileo's tiny instrument, and so 250,000 times as much light as the unaided eye. The telescope of double this aperture, which is now being built in California, will admit four times as much light as the 100-inch instrument, or about a million times as much light as the unaided eye.

The absorbing interest of his new instrument had almost driven from Galileo's mind a problem to which he had at one time given much thought. Over two thousand years previously, Pythagoras and Philolaus had taught that the earth is not fixed in space but rotates on its axis every twenty-four hours, thus causing the alternation of day and night. Aristarchus of Samos, perhaps the greatest of all the Greek mathematicians, had further maintained that the earth not only turned on its axis, but also described a yearly journey round the sun, this being the cause of the cycle of the seasons.

Then these doctrines had fallen into disfavour. Aristotle had pronounced against them, asserting that the earth formed a fixed centre to the universe. At a later date Ptolemy had explained the tracks of the planets across the sky in terms of a complicated system of cycles and epicycles; this explanation had again supposed that the planets moved around an immoveable earth. The Church had given its sanction and active support to these doctrines. Indeed, it is difficult to see what else it could have done, for it seemed almost impious to suppose that the great drama of man's fall and redemption, in which the Son of God had Himself taken part, could have been enacted on any lesser stage than the very centre of the Universe.

Yet, even in the Church, the doctrine had not gained universal acceptance. Oresme, Bishop of Lisieux, and Cardinal Nicholas of Cusa had both declared against it, the latter writing in 1440:

I have long considered that this earth is not fixed, but moves as do the other stars. To my mind the earth turns upon its axis once every day and night.

At a later date such views incurred the active hostility of the Church, and in 1600 Giordano Bruno was burned at the stake, one of the counts against him being his insistence on the doctrine of the plurality of worlds. He had written:

It has seemed to me unworthy of the divine goodness and power to create a finite world, when able to produce beside it another and others infinite; so that I have declared that there are endless particular worlds similar to this of the earth; with Pythagoras I regard it as a star, and similar to it are the moon, the planets and other stars, which are infinite in number, and all these bodies are worlds.

The most weighty attack on orthodox doctrine had, however, been delivered by the Polish ecclesiastic and astronomer, Nicolaus Copernicus (1473–1543). In his great work *De revolutionibus orbium coelestium* Copernicus had shown most of Ptolemy's elaborate structure of cycles and epicycles to be unnecessary, because the tracks of the planets across the sky could be explained in a much simpler manner by supposing that the earth and the planets all moved round a fixed central sun. The sixty-six years which had elapsed since this book was published had seen these theories hotly debated, but they were still neither proved nor disproved. And although Galileo found himself powerfully attracted to them, he had hitherto thought it the more prudent course to keep his opinions to himself.

Galileo had already found that his new telescope provided a means of testing astronomical theories. As soon as he had turned it on to the Milky Way, a whole crowd of legends and fables as to the nature and structure of this object had vanished into thin air; it proved to be nothing more than a swarm of faint stars scattered like golden dust on the black background of the sky. Another glance through the telescope had disclosed the true nature of the moon. On it were mountains which cast shadows, so that it proved to be a world like our own, as Giordano Bruno had maintained. What if the telescope should now in some way prove able to decide between the orthodox doctrine that the earth formed the hub of the universe, and the revolutionary new doctrine that the earth was only one of a number of bodies, all circling round the sun like moths round a candle-flame?

And now Galileo catches Jupiter in the field of his telescope and sees four small bodies circling around the great mass of the planet—like moths round a candle-flame. What he sees is an exact replica of the solar system as imagined by Copernicus, and it provides direct visual proof that such systems are at least not alien to the architectural plan of the universe. On January 30th he writes to Belisario Vinta that these small bodies move round the far greater mass of Jupiter "just as Venus and Mercury, and perhaps the other planets, move round the sun."

Any lingering doubts that Galileo may have felt as to the significance of his discovery were removed nine months later when he observed the phases of Venus; the shining surface of the planet was seen to pass through the same cycle of shapes as the moon—from crescent through semicircle to a full circle, and then, reversing the paths, back through semicircle to crescent. This of course showed at once that the planet was not self-luminous, since had it been so, its surface would always have appeared as a full circle of light. But even when it was known that the planet was not self-luminous, two distinct alternatives remained. If Venus moved round the earth in a Ptolemaic epicycle, then, as Ptolemy had himself pointed out, she could never show more than half her surface illuminated. If, on the other hand, she moved round the sun in a circle, while the earth also moved round the sun in a larger circle, as the new Copernican view required, then the shining surface of Venus ought to exhibit the complete sequence of phases shown by the moon, the surface of the planet appearing completely dark at the moment when it passed between the earth and the sun. And the same ought to be true also of Mercury. It had indeed been urged as an objection to the Copernican theory that neither Venus nor Mercury exhibited this full cycle of phases.

Galileo's telescope now showed that, precisely as Copernicus had foretold, Venus passed through the full cycle of phases, so that, in Galileo's own words, we "are now supplied with a determination most conclusive, and appealing to the evidence of our senses, of two very important problems, which up to this day have been discussed by the greatest intellects with different conclusions. One is that the planets are not self-

luminous. The other is that we are absolutely compelled to
say that Venus, and Mercury also, revolve around the sun,
as do also all the rest of the planets, a truth believed indeed
by the Pythagorean school, by Copernicus, and by Kepler,
but never proved by the evidence of our senses, as is now proved
in the case of Venus and Mercury."

These discoveries of Galileo made it clear that Aristotle,
Ptolemy and the majority of those who had thought about
these things in the last 2000 years had been utterly and hopelessly wrong. In estimating his position in the universe, man
had up to now been guided mainly by his own desires, and his
self-esteem; long fed on boundless hopes, he had spurned the
simpler fare offered by patient scientific thought. Inexorable
facts now dethroned him from his self-arrogated station at the
centre of the universe; henceforth he must reconcile himself
to the humble position of the inhabitant of a speck of dust,
and adjust his views as to the significance and importance of
human life accordingly.

The adjustment was not made at once. Human vanity,
reinforced by the authority of the Church, contrived to make
a rough road for those who dared draw attention to the earth's
insignificant position in the universe. Galileo was forced to
abjure his beliefs. Well on into the eighteenth century the
ancient University of Paris was teaching that the motion of
the earth round the sun was a convenient *but false* hypothesis,
while the newer American Universities of Harvard and Yale
taught the Ptolemaic and Copernican systems of astronomy
side by side as though they were equally tenable. Yet men
could not keep their heads buried in the sand for ever, and
when at last its full implications were accepted, the revolution
of thought initiated by Galileo's observations of January 7,
1610, proved to be the most catastrophic in the history of
the race. The cataclysm was not confined to the realms of
abstract thought; henceforth human existence itself was to
appear in a new light, and human aims and aspirations would
be judged from a different standpoint.

This oft-told story has been told once again, in the hope
that it may serve to explain some of the interest taken in
astronomy to-day. The more mundane sciences prove their

worth by adding to the amenities and pleasures of life, or by
alleviating pain or distress, but it may well be asked what
reward astronomy has to offer. Why does the astronomer
devote arduous nights, and even more arduous days, to studying
the structure, motions and changes of bodies so remote that
they can have no conceivable influence on human life?

In part at least the answer would seem to be that many
have begun to suspect that the astronomy of to-day, like that
of Galileo, may have something to say on the enthralling
question of the relation of human life to the universe in which
it is placed, and on the beginnings, meaning and destiny of the
human race. Bede records how, some twelve centuries ago,
human life was compared in poetic simile to the flight of a
bird through a warm hall in which men sit feasting, while the
winter storms rage without.

The bird is safe from the tempest for a brief moment, but immediately passes from winter to winter again. So man's life appears
for a little while, but of what is to follow, or of what went before,
we know nothing. If, therefore, a new doctrine tells us something
certain, it seems to deserve to be followed.

These words, originally spoken in advocacy of the Christian
religion, describe what is perhaps the main interest of astronomy to-day. Man
only knowing
Life's little lantern between dark and dark

wishes to probe farther into the past and future than his brief
span of life permits. He wishes to see the universe as it existed
before man was, as it will be after the last man has passed
again into the darkness from which he came. The wish does
not originate solely in mere intellectual curiosity, in the desire
to see over the next range of mountains, the desire to attain
a summit commanding a wide view, even if it be only of a
promised land which he may never hope himself to enter; it
has deeper roots and a more personal interest. Before he can
understand himself, man must first understand the universe
from the dust of which his body has been formed, and from
the events of which all his sense perceptions are drawn. He
wishes to explore the universe, both in space and time, because
he himself forms part of it, and it forms part of him.

We may well admit that science cannot at present hope to say anything final on the questions of human existence and human destiny, but this is no justification for not becoming acquainted with the best that it has to offer. It is rare indeed for science to give a final "Yes" or "No" answer to any question propounded to her. When we are able to put a question in such a definite form that either of these answers could be given in reply, we are generally already in a position to supply the answer ourselves. Science advances rather by providing a succession of approximations to the truth, each more accurate than the last, but each capable of endless degrees of higher accuracy. To the question, "where does man stand in the universe?" the first attempt at an answer, at any rate in recent times, was provided by the astronomy of Ptolemy: "at the centre." Galileo's telescope provided the next, and incomparably better, approximation: "our home in space is only one of a number of small bodies revolving round a huge central sun." Nineteenth-century astronomy swung the pendulum still farther in the same direction, saying: "there are millions of stars in the sky, each similar to our sun, each doubtless surrounded, like our sun, by a family of planets on which life may be kept in being by the light and heat received from its sun." Twentieth-century astronomy suggests, as we shall see, that the nineteenth century had swung the pendulum too far; less of the universe seems likely to be suited for life than our fathers thought, or would have thought if they had given free play to their intellects.

We are setting out to explain the approximation to the truth provided by twentieth-century astronomy. No doubt it is not the final truth, but it is a step on towards it, and unless we are greatly in error it is very much nearer to the truth than was the teaching of nineteenth-century astronomy. It claims to be nearer the truth, not because the twentieth-century astronomer claims to be better at guessing than his predecessors of the nineteenth century, but because he has incomparably more facts at his disposal. Guessing has gone out of fashion in science; it was at best a poor substitute for knowledge, and modern science, eschewing guessing severely, confines itself, except on very rare occasions, to ascertained facts and the inferences which, so far as can be seen, follow unequivocally from them.

It would of course be futile to pretend that the whole interest of astronomy centres round the questions just mentioned. Astronomy offers at least three other groups of interest which may be described as utilitarian, scientific and aesthetic.

Astronomy, like the other sciences, was originally studied for mainly utilitarian reasons. It provided measures of time, and enabled mankind to keep a tally on the flight of the seasons; it taught him to find his way across the trackless desert and, later, across the trackless ocean. In the guise of astrology, it held out hopes of telling him his future. There was nothing intrinsically absurd in this, for even to-day the astronomer is largely occupied with foretelling the future movements of the heavenly bodies, although not of human affairs—a considerable part of the present book will consist of an attempt to foretell the future, and in so doing to predict the final end, of the material universe. Where the astrologers went wrong was in supposing that terrestrial empires, kings and individuals formed such important items in the scheme of the universe that the motions of the heavenly bodies could be intimately bound up with their fates. As soon as man began to realise, even faintly, the measure of his own insignificance in the universe, astrology died a natural and inevitable death, at least among educated people.

The utilitarian aspect of astronomy has by now shrunk to very modest proportions. The national observatories still broadcast the time of day, and help to guide ships across the ocean, but the centre of astronomical interest has shifted so completely that the remotest nebulae arouse incomparably more enthusiasm than "clock-stars," and the average astronomer almost completely neglects our nearest neighbours in space, the planets, and gives his main attention to stars so distant that their light takes hundreds, thousands, or even millions, of years to reach us.

Recently, astronomy has acquired a new scientific interest through establishing its position as an integral part of the general body of science. The various sciences can no longer be treated as distinct; scientific discovery advances along a continuous front which extends unbroken from electrons of a fraction of a millionth of a millionth of an inch in diameter to nebulae whose diameters are measured in hundreds of thousands of millions of millions of miles. A gain of astronomical knowledge may add to our knowledge of physics and chemistry, and *vice versa*. The stars have long ago ceased to be treated as mere points of light. Each is now regarded as an experiment on a heroic scale, a high-temperature crucible in which nature herself operates through ranges of temperature and pressure utterly beyond any available in our laboratories, and permits us to watch the results. In so doing, we may happen upon properties of matter which have eluded the terrestrial physicist, owing to the small range of physical conditions at his command. For instance matter exists in nebulae with a density at least a million times lower than anything we can approach on earth, and in certain stars at a density nearly a million times greater. How can we expect to understand the whole nature of matter from laboratory experiments in which we can command only one part in a million million of the whole range of density known to nature?

Even more recently, astronomy has become of direct importance to philosophy through the light it has shed on the metaphysical concepts of space and time. It has provided weighty evidence in support of the central doctrine of the theory of relativity—that space and time form a single indissoluble whole. Indeed, whatever may have been the case with the world of professional scientists, it was the results obtained by astronomers at the eclipse of 1919 which first focused general interest on the theory of relativity, and thus led to our present understanding of the relations between space and time. The even more recent evidence as to the possible expansion of space itself may be found to contain a new and still more profound message as to the meaning of our fundamental metaphysical concepts.

Yet for each one who feels the scientific or philosophical appeal of astronomy, there are probably a dozen who are attracted by its aesthetic appeal. Many even of those who seek after knowledge for its own sake, driven by that intellectual curiosity which provides the fundamental distinction between themselves and the beasts, find their main interest in astronomy, as being the most poetical and the most aesthetically gratifying of the sciences. Others, living in a world tortured by wars and conflicts, want to exercise their imaginations on something remote from the horrors of everyday life, and find they can obtain satisfaction and relaxation in contemplating the serene immensities of the outer universe. To many, astronomy provides something of the vision without which the people perish.

Before proceeding to describe the results of the modern astronomer's survey of the sky, let us try to envisage in its proper perspective the platform from which his observations are made.

In Chapters III and VI, we shall see how the earth was born out of the sun, something like 3000 millions of years ago. It was born in a form in which we should find it hard to recognise the solid earth of to-day with its seas and rivers, its rich vegetation and overflowing life. Our home in space came into being as a globe of intensely hot gas on which no life of any kind could either gain or retain a foothold.

Gradually this globe of gas cools down, becoming first liquid, then plastic. Finally its outer crust solidifies, rocks and mountains forming a permanent record of the irregularities of its earlier plastic form. Vapours condense into liquids, and rivers and oceans come into being, while an atmosphere is formed out of the so-called "permanent" gases—oxygen, nitrogen, helium, neon. Gradually the earth assumes a condition suited to the advent of life, which finally appears, we know not how, whence or why.

It is not easy to estimate the time since life first appeared on earth, but it can hardly have been more than a small fraction of the whole 3000 million years or so during which the earth seems to have been in existence. Still, there was probably life on earth at least 300 million years ago, and possibly as far back as 1000 million years ago. The first life appears to have been wholly aquatic, but gradually fishes changed into reptiles, reptiles into mammals, and finally man emerged from mammals. The evidence favours a period of from 300,000 to 1,000,000 years ago for this last event. Thus life has in-

habited the earth for only a fraction of its existence, and man
for only a tiny fraction of this fraction. To put it in another
way, the astronomical time-scale is incomparably longer than
the human time-scale—the generations of man, and even the
whole of human existence, are only ticks of the astronomer's
clock.

Most of the 10,000 or more generations of men who connect
us up with our ape-like ancestry must have lived lives which
did not differ greatly from those of their animal predecessors.
Hunting, fishing and warfare filled their lives, leaving but
little time or opportunity for intellectual contemplation. Then,
at last, man began to awaken from his long intellectual slumber,
and, as civilisation slowly dawned, felt the need for occupa-
tions other than the mere feeding and clothing of his body.
He began to discover revelations of infinite beauty in the
grace of the human form or the play of light on the myriad-
smiling sea, which he tried to perpetuate in carefully chiselled
marble or exquisitely chosen words. He began to experiment
with metals and herbs, and with the effects of fire and water.
He began to notice, and try to understand, the motions of the
heavenly bodies, for to those who could read the writing in
the sky, the nightly rising and setting of the stars and planets
provided evidence that beyond the confines of the earth lay
an unknown universe built on a far grander scale.

In this way the arts and sciences came to earth, bringing
astronomy with them. We cannot quite say when, but compared even with the age of the human race, they came but
yesterday, while in comparison with the whole period of the
earth's existence, their age is but a twinkling of the eye.

Scientific astronomy, as distinguished from mere star-gazing,
can hardly claim an age of more than 3000 years. It is less
time than this since Aristarchus and others explained to a
little-heeding and mainly incredulous world that the earth
moved around a fixed sun. Yet the really significant figure
for our present purpose is not so much the time since men
began to make conjectures about the structure of the universe,
as the time since they began to unravel its true structure by
the help of ascertained fact. The important length of time
is that which has elapsed since that evening in 1610 when

Galileo first turned his telescope on to Jupiter—a mere three centuries or so.

We begin to grasp the true significance of these round-number estimates when we re-write them in tabular form. We have:

Age of earth	about	3,000,000,000	years
Age of life on earth	more than	300,000,000	,,
Age of man on earth ...	more than	300,000	,,
Age of astronomical science	about	3,000	,,
Age of telescopic astronomy	,,	300	,,

When the various figures are displayed in this form we see what a very recent phenomenon astronomy is. Its total age is less than a hundredth part of the age of man, less than a hundred-thousandth part of the time that life has inhabited the earth. During more than 99,999 parts out of the 100,000 of its existence, life on earth was hardly concerned about anything beyond the earth.

But whereas the past of astronomy is to be measured on the human time-scale, a hundred generations or so of men, we may hope that its future will be measured on the astronomical time-scale. For it is reasonable to expect that the future of our race will be terminated by astronomical causes. Thus as the earth has already existed for 3000 million years, it is *a priori* reasonable to suppose that it will exist for at least something of the order of 3000 million years yet to come, and humanity and astronomy with it. Actually we shall find reasons for expecting it to last longer than this. If so, astronomy is still at the very opening of its existence. This is why its message can claim no finality—we are not describing the mature convictions of a man, so much as the first impressions of a new-born babe which is just opening its eyes. Even so they are better than the idle introspective dreamings in which it indulged before it had learned to look around itself and away from itself.

And so we set out to learn what astronomy has to tell us about the universe in which we live our lives. Our inquiry will not be entirely limited to this one science. We shall call upon other sciences—physics, chemistry and geology—as well as the more closely allied sciences of astrophysics and cosmogony, to give what help they can in interpreting the message of observational astronomy. The information we shall obtain will be fragmentary. If it must be compared to anything, let it be to the pieces of a jig-saw puzzle. Could we get hold of all the pieces, they would, we are confident, form a single complete consistent picture, but many of them are still missing. It is too much to hope that the incomplete series of pieces we have already found will disclose the whole picture, but we may at least collect them together, arrange them in some sort of methodical order, fit together pieces which are obviously contiguous, and perhaps hazard a guess as to what the finished picture will prove to be when all its pieces have been found and finally fitted together.

CHAPTER I

Exploring the Sky

We have seen how man, after inhabiting the earth for at least 300,000 years, has within the last 300 years or so—the last one-thousandth part of his life on earth—become possessed of an optical means of studying the outer universe. In the present chapter we shall try to describe the first impressions he has formed with his newly-awakened eyes. The description will be arranged in a very rough chronological order. This is also an order of increasing telescopic power, or again of seeing farther and farther into space, so that our order of arrangement might equally be described as one of increasing distance from the sun. We shall not attempt any sort of continuous record, but shall merely mention a few landmarks so as to show in broad outline the order in which territory was won and consolidated in man's survey of the universe.

THE SOLAR SYSTEM

We may conveniently start with the solar system, the structure of which was unravelled by Galileo and his successors.

The sun's family of planets falls naturally into distinct groups. Near to the sun are the four small planets, Mercury, Venus, the Earth and Mars. At much greater distances are the four great planets, Jupiter, Saturn, Uranus and Neptune. Beyond all these lies the recently discovered planet Pluto, the outermost member of our system so far known.

Mercury is nearest of all to the sun; next comes Venus. The orbits of these two planets lie between the earth's orbit and the sun. As seen from the earth, these planets appear to describe relatively small circles round the sun, so that they necessarily appear near to the sun in the sky. As a consequence, they can only be seen either in the early morning, if they happen to rise just before the sun, or in the evening if they set after the sun. The ancients, not altogether recognising that the same planets could appear both as morning and evening stars, gave them different names according as they figured as the one or the other. As a morning star Venus was called Phosphoros by the Greeks and Lucifer by the Romans; as an evening star it was called Hesperus by both.

Next beyond these planets, as we proceed outward from the sun into space, comes the Earth, and then Mars, completing the group of small planets. Mars, Venus and Mercury are all smaller than the earth in size, although Venus is only slightly so.

There is a wide gap between the orbit of Mars, the last of the small planets, and that of Jupiter, the first of the great planets. This is not empty; it is occupied by the orbits of thousands of tiny planets known as asteroids. None of these approaches the earth in size; Ceres, the largest, is less than 500 miles in diameter, and only four are known with diameters of more than 100 miles. The planets Mercury, Venus and Mars have all been known from remote antiquity, but the asteroids only entered astronomy with the nineteenth century, Ceres, the first and largest, having been discovered by Piazzi on January 1, 1801.

Beyond the asteroids come the four great planets Jupiter, Saturn, Uranus and Neptune, all far larger than the earth. Jupiter, the largest, is nearly 90,000 miles in diameter, or more than eleven times the diameter of the earth; fourteen hundred bodies of the size of the earth could be packed inside Jupiter, and leave room to spare. Saturn, which comes next in order, makes a good second to Jupiter in size, having a diameter of about 70,000 miles. These two are by far the largest of the planets.

Uranus and Neptune have each about four times the diameter, and so about sixty-four times the volume, of the earth. The size of Pluto is not yet known with accuracy; the most recent indications are that it contains about as much substance as the earth, but it may quite possibly be smaller in size.

Jupiter and Saturn form such conspicuous objects in the sky that they have been known from the earliest times, but Uranus and Neptune are comparatively recent discoveries. Sir William Herschel discovered Uranus quite accidentally in

1781, while looking through his telescope with no motive other than the hope of finding something interesting in the sky. By contrast, Neptune was discovered in 1846 as the result of intricate mathematical calculations, which many at the time regarded as the greatest triumph of the human mind, at any rate since the time of Newton. It was a triumph of youth. The honour must be apportioned in approximately equal shares between an Englishman, John Couch Adams, then only 27 years old, who was afterwards Professor of Astronomy at Cambridge, and a young French astronomer, Urbain J. J. Leverrier, who was only eight years his senior. Both attributed certain vagaries in the observed motion of Uranus to the gravitational pull of an exterior planet, and both set to work to calculate the orbit in which this supposed outer planet must move to explain these vagaries.

Adams finished his calculations first, and informed observers at Cambridge as to the part of the sky in which the new planet ought to lie. As a result, Neptune was observed twice, although without being immediately identified as the wanted planet. But before the identification had been established at Cambridge, Leverrier finished his computations and communicated his results to Galle, an assistant at Berlin, who was able to identify the planet at once, Berlin possessing better starcharts of the region of the sky in question than were accessible at Cambridge.

Gradually it emerged that the gravitational pull of Neptune was inadequate to account for all the vagaries in the motions of Uranus, while similar vagaries began to appear in Neptune's own motion. This pointed to the existence of yet another planet, farther out·even than Neptune. Just as Adams and Leverrier had done on the former occasion, so Dr Percival Lowell, of Flagstaff Observatory, Arizona, computed the orbit in which the conjectured new planet ought to move, but many years of careful search were necessary before the Flagstaff observers discovered, in March 1930, the planet to which they subsequently gave the name of Pluto (Plate I). The new planet was found to be moving in almost precisely the orbit which Lowell had predicted fifteen years previously. On the other hand, Lowell's calculations had suggested that the unknown

PLATE I

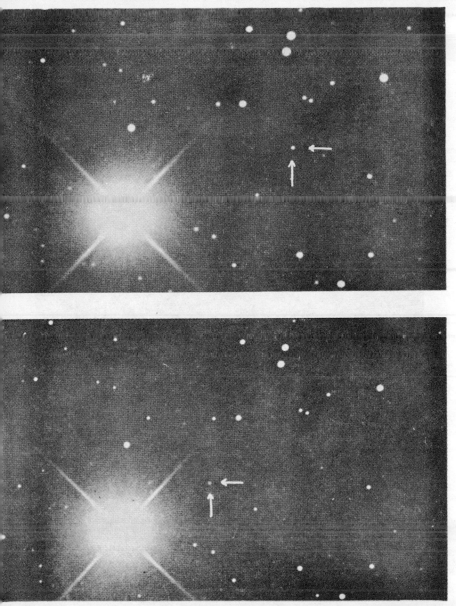

The Discovery of Pluto

The two photographs were taken at the Lowell Observatory on the nights of March 2 and 5, 1930. The object indicated by arrows was seen to have moved considerably in the interval, and this proved that it was of planetary character.

The bright object in the bottom left-hand corner is the star δ Geminorum (see footnote to p. 170).

PLATE II

Franklin-Adams Chart

The Milky Way in the neighbourhood of the Southern Cross

planet ought to be more than six times as massive as the earth, whereas Pluto has only about the same mass as the earth. For this and other reasons, some astronomers are inclined to think that the agreement between Lowell's predictions and the actual orbit of Pluto was largely accidental.

Galileo's discovery of the four satellites of Jupiter in 1610 was followed in time by the discovery of further satellites moving round all the planets except the extreme members of the Solar System, namely the two small planets Mercury and Venus which lie nearest the sun, and the small planet Pluto which lies farthest away from the sun. In 1655 Huyghens discovered Titan, the largest of Saturn's satellites, and by 1684 Cassini had discovered four more. Then, after the lapse of a full century, Sir William Herschel discovered two satellites of Uranus in 1787 and two more satellites of Saturn in 1789. We shall discuss the full system of planetary satellites and also the smaller bodies of the solar system—comets, meteors and shooting-stars—in a later chapter, when we come to deal with the way they came into being.

THE GALACTIC SYSTEM

As our next landmark we may take the survey of the stars by the two Herschels, Sir William Herschel, the father (1738–1822) and Sir John Herschel, the son (1792–1871). What Galileo had done for the solar system, the two Herschels set out to do for the huge family of stars—the "galactic" system, bounded by the Milky Way—of which our sun is a member.

On a clear moonless night the Milky Way is seen to stretch, like a great arch of faint light, from horizon to horizon. Travellers find that what we see is only part of a full circle of light—the galactic circle—which stretches completely round the earth and divides the sky into two equal halves. It thus forms a sort of celestial "equator," with reference to which astronomers are accustomed to measure latitude and longitude in the sky. As Galileo's telescope first showed, it consists of a crowd of faint stars, each too dim to be seen individually without telescopic aid (see Plates II, III and IV). And, as might be expected, the proper interpretation of this great belt

of faint stars has proved to be fundamental to a proper understanding of the architecture of the universe.

If stars were scattered uniformly through infinite space, we
should at last come to a star in whatever direction we looked,
so that the sky would appear as a uniform blaze of intolerable
light. It is true that this would not be the case if light were
dimmed or blotted out after travelling a certain distance, but
even then, the sky would appear the same in all directions,
for there would be no reason why one part of the sky should
be more lavishly spangled with stars than another. Thus the
existence of the Milky Way suggests that the system of the stars
does not extend uniformly to infinity. The system must have
a definite structure, and it was the architecture of this structure
that Sir William Herschel set himself to unravel. The work he
did for the northern half of the sky was subsequently extended
to the southern hemisphere by his son, Sir John Herschel.

We shall best understand the method employed by the
Herschels if we first imagine all the stars in the sky to be
intrinsically similar objects. Each would then emit the same
amount of light, so that the nearer stars would appear bright,
and the farther stars faint, merely as an effect of distance. If
there is no absorption of light in space, the way in which
apparent brightness decreases with distance is of course well
known; the law is that of the "inverse square of the distance,"
which means that the apparent brightness decreases just as
rapidly as the square of its distance increases; a star which is
twice as distant as a second similar star appears only a quarter
as bright, and so on. Thus if all stars emitted the same amount
of light, we could estimate their relative distances from their
relative brightnesses. By calculating the relative distances of
various stars, cutting wires proportional to these lengths, and
pointing them in the directions of the stars to which they
referred, we could form a model of the arrangement of the stars
in the sky. We should, in fact, know the whole structure of
the system of stars except for its scale. To represent the faint
stars of the Milky Way, a great number of very long wires
would be needed. In the model these would all point towards
different parts of the Milky Way, forming a flat wheel-like
structure.

PLATE IV

E. E. Barnard

The richest part of the Milky Way—the Star-cloud in Sagittarius

PLATE III

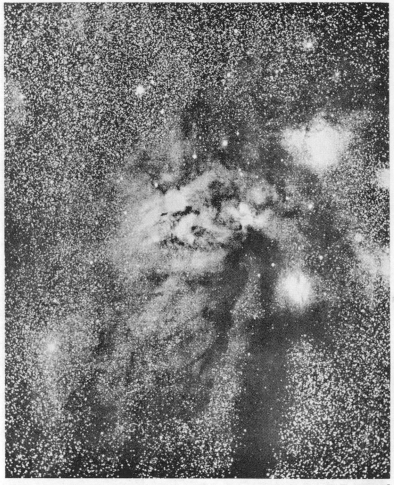

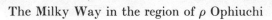

E. E. Barnard

The Milky Way in the region of ρ Ophiuchi

The problem which confronted Sir William Herschel was more intricate than this, because he knew that the stars were of different intrinsic brightness as well as at different distances, and both factors combined to produce differences of apparent brightness. One of the main difficulties of the problem lay in the fact that these two factors have to be disentangled before any definite conclusions can be reached.

Herschel found that the number of stars visible in his telescope-field varied enormously with different directions in space. It was of course greatest when the telescope was pointed at the Milky Way, and fell off, steadily and rapidly, as the telescope was moved away from the Milky Way. Generally speaking, two telescope-fields which were at the same angular distance from the Milky Way contained about the same number of stars. In the technical language of astronomy, the richness of the star-field depended mainly on the galactic latitude—just as the earth's climate depends mainly on the geographic latitude—and not to any great extent on the longitude.

Fields in different galactic latitudes—i.e. at different angular distances from the Milky Way—were found to differ in quality as well as in number of stars. The brightest stars of all occurred about equally in all fields; the fields differed mainly in their faint stars. These, and particularly the faintest stars of all, became enormously more abundant as the Milky Way was approached.

Sir William Herschel rightly interpreted this as showing that the system of stars surrounding the sun began to thin out within distances reached by his telescope, and that it began to thin out soonest in directions farthest away from the Milky Way. From this he concluded that the general shape of the galactic system of stars must be that of a wheel or a biscuit or a watch, the stars being most thickly scattered near the centre, and occurring more sparsely in the outer regions. The plane of the Milky Way of course formed the central plane of the structure. The fact that the Milky Way divides the sky into two almost exactly equal parts suggested to Herschel that the sun must be very nearly in this central plane, a view which is entirely confirmed by modern investigations. The fact that parts of the sky which were equidistant from the Milky Way appeared about equally bright, suggested to him that the sun not only lay in the central plane of the system, but was very near to its actual centre, a view which is now known to be untenable (see pp. 60, 65, below).

Fig. 1 shews in cross-section the general kind of structure which Sir William Herschel attributed to the galactic system, the sun being placed at its centre. A structure of this type would obviously account for the general appearance of the sky. Generally speaking those stars which appear brightest of all are the nearest, and are so near that there is no appreciable thinning out of stars before they are reached. This explains why the brightest stars of all are seen in about equal numbers in all directions in the sky. But the stars which appear very faint are mostly very distant, being in fact so distant that

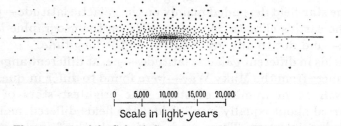

Fig. 1. The structure of the Galactic System according to Herschel and Kapteyn.

the great depth of the system in directions in and near to the galactic plane is brought into play. In these directions, and these only, do we find very faint stars in great profusion; layer after layer of distant stars, ranged almost endlessly one behind the other, give rise to the apparent concentration of faint stars which we describe as the Milky Way.

The detailed arrangement shown in fig. 1 is that which Kapteyn assigned to the system at a later date (1922). In the scale of dimensions shown below it, as always in astronomy, a light-year means the distance that light travels in a year. As the speed of light is about 186,000 miles a second, a light-year is about six million million miles.

The way by which Kapteyn arrived at the details of this proposed scheme was highly technical; but its general principles are easily understood. With a telescope having an aperture of three inches—i.e. one which collects all the light falling on a circle three inches in diameter—I may be able to see a certain number of stars—say 100—within a small area of the sky. If I replace my telescope by one having an aperture of six inches, my eye will receive four times as much light as before, so that I shall now be able to see stars like those I previously saw up to double the distance of these latter in space—in brief, the telescope can probe twice as far into space as its predecessor of half its aperture.

Thus eight times as large a volume of space has become open to my observation, and I may reasonably expect to see eight times as many stars as before. If I do not see so many, I shall conclude that the new region of space is less thickly populated with stars than the original region, and from the extent of the deficiency I shall be able to form some idea of the extent to which the stars have become thinned out.

Actual counts of stars convinced Herschel, Kapteyn and innumerable other investigators that the stars begin to thin out in every direction immediately we leave the vicinity of the sun, so that the sun must be at a point at which the density of the stellar population is a maximum. This is why Kapteyn, like Herschel, placed the sun at the centre of a distribution such as is shown in fig. 1. The extent to which actual star-counts deviated from those predicted by the simple law just explained provided the material for the detailed con-struction of fig. 1.

Some such view of the structure of the galactic system prevailed until fairly recently, but modern investigations (pp. 63 ff.) have shown quite convincingly that it needs modification in two respects—the dimensions of the system are substantially greater than the scale attached to fig. 1 indicates, and the sun is not at the centre of the system, or anywhere near it. But, subject to these two modifications, the scheme proposed by Herschel and Kapteyn still stands as providing a first approximation, at least, to the truth.

The final acceptance of the Copernican view of the structure of the solar system was in a large measure due to Galileo's discovery of the similar system of Jupiter, which happened to be so situated in space that a terrestrial observer could obtain a bird's-eye view of it as a whole. We can never obtain a bird's-eye view of the solar system as a whole because we can only see it from inside, so that visual confirmation that such systems could exist was only to be obtained through the discovery of other similar systems, which we could see from outside.

Sir William Herschel believed he had obtained a similar visual confirmation of his view of the structure of the galactic system. He thought he had discovered systems of the same kind, of which he could obtain a bird's-eye view because they were entirely extraneous to the galaxy. They were shaped much as he believed the galactic system to be shaped. He believed them to be clouds of stars and spoke of them as "island universes." He found it impossible to distinguish the separate stars in them, but believed that sufficient telescopic power would make this possible, just as it had enabled Galileo to see the stars in the Milky Way. In this he was right; the separate stars can now be seen (cf. Plate V, opposite).

These objects form only one of the many classes of astro-nomical objects to which the name nebula has been assigned, because of their indefinite cloudy appearance (nebula = a cloud). They are generally known as "extra-galactic nebulae" because they are outside the galactic system, and entirely detached from it, but we shall frequently find it convenient to use the briefer term "great nebulae," to which their immense size fully entitles them. Before describing them in detail, it will be well to give a brief preliminary account of the various types of object which astronomy includes under the general name of nebulae.

NEBULAE

A telescope exhibits a planet as a disc of appreciable size, and an eye-piece which magnifies 60 times will make Jupiter look as large as the moon. Yet an eye-piece which magnifies 60 times, or any greater number of times, can never make a star look as large as Jupiter. Apart from an exception which will be noted immediately, no magnification within our com-mand causes any star to appear as anything other than a mere point of light. Most stars are of course enormously

PLATE V

Magnification of a part (left-hand top corner) of the Great Nebula *M* 31 in Andromeda, which is shown complete in Plate X (p. 25).

PLATE VI

N.G.C. 2022

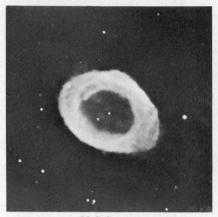

N.G.C. 6720

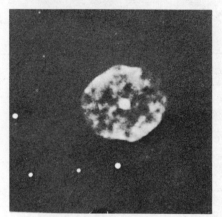

N.G.C. 1501

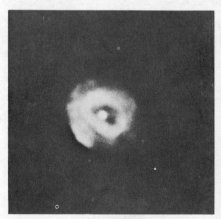

N.G.C. 7662

Mt Wilson Observatory

Planetary Nebulae

larger than Jupiter, but they are also enormously more distant, and it is the distance that wins.

The telescope nevertheless shows a number of objects, other than stars, which appear bigger than mere points of light. Apart from the moon and planets, they are all faint and hazy in appearance, and so have received the general name of "nebulae." Detailed investigation has shown that they fall into three distinct classes.

PLANETARY NEBULAE. The first class are known as "Planetary Nebulae." There is nothing of a planetary nature about them beyond the fact that, like the planets, they appear as discs of distinct size, and not as mere points, in a telescope. Only a few hundreds of these objects are known; four typical examples are illustrated in Plate VI. They prove to be comparatively faint and near objects, at any rate in comparison with other nebulae we shall be discussing. Van Maanen estimated that 21 which he studied are at an average distance of about 4500 light-years, which places them well within the galactic system, and that on the average they give out about ten times as much light as the sun.

We shall discuss their physical structure below (p. 182). For the moment, it is enough to say that they are merely exceptionally hot stars which, just because of their extreme heat, are surrounded by luminous atmospheres of enormous extent. Thus they form an exception to our general statement that no star ever appears as anything but a point of light in a telescope.

GALACTIC NEBULAE. The second class are generally described as "Galactic Nebulae," examples being shewn in Plates VII, VIII and IX (following p. 24). These also lie within the galactic system. They are completely irregular in shape, their general appearance being that of huge glowing wisps of gas stretching from star to star. And this is pretty much what they are. Even a cursory glance shows that each irregular nebula contains several stars enmeshed within it; careful telescopic examination often extends the dimensions of the nebula almost indefinitely, so that the whole of a constellation may be wrapped up in a single nebula.

There is but little doubt as to the physical nature of these nebulae. A mass of evidence shows that the space between the stars is not utterly void of matter, but is occupied by a cloud of tenuous gas. Here and there this cloud may be denser than usual; here and there it may be lighted up and made to incandesce by the radiation of the stars within it, and may either reflect the light of these stars, or be raised to incandescence and so emit its own light. We know that this is the true origin of the light of these nebulae, for their light reproduces the character of the light of the stars in the nebulae. For instance, the well-known group of the Pleiades is found to be embedded in a vast faintly luminous nebula, whose light provides "a true copy of the light of the star Merope and of the other bright stars of the Pleiades."

In other places the nebula may be entirely opaque to light, lying like a black curtain across the sky. Variations of density, opacity and luminosity combine to produce all the fantastic shapes and varied degrees of light and shade we see in the galactic nebulae.

A similar opacity is responsible for the dark patches which occur in the general arrangement of the stars. A conspicuous example occurs in the part of the Milky Way shewn in Plate II (p. 17); the dark patch which looks at first like a hole in the system of stars is graphically described as "The Coal Sack." Other and similar dark patches can be seen in Plates III and IV (pp. 18, 19), and also on Plates VIII and IX. These black patches in the sky cannot possibly represent actual holes, since it is inconceivable that there should be so many empty tunnels through the stars all pointing exactly earthward, so that we are compelled to interpret them as veils of obscuring matter which dim or extinguish the light of the stars behind them. This obscuring matter is of great importance to modern astronomy, as we shall soon see.

EXTRA-GALACTIC NEBULAE. Nebulae which belong to the third class are of an altogether different nature. They are mostly of definite and regular shape, and show various other characteristics which make them easy of identification. Many of them have a spiral structure; these are called "spiral nebulae." The most conspicuous of all the spiral nebulae is also the nearest; it is the Great Nebula M 31 in Andromeda,

PLATE VII

Mt Wilson Observatory

The Nebula in Cygnus

PLATE VIII

Mt Wilson Observatory

The Trifid Nebula *M* 20 in Sagittarius

PLATE IX

Mt Wilson Observatory

The "Horse's Head" in the Nebula in Orion

PLATE X

Yerkes Observatory

The Great Nebula *M* 31 in Andromeda with its two companions—*M* 32 directly above the centre of the main nebula, and N.G.C. 205 in the lower left-hand corner. An enlargement of the upper left-hand corner of *M* 31 is shown in Plate V (p. 22), and an enlargement of the central region in Plate XVII (p. 68).

shown in Plate X, which is just visible to the naked eye. The astronomer Marius, observing it telescopically in 1612, described it as looking "like a candle-light seen through horn." Plate XI shows a second example, which is probably very similar in its physical structure but is viewed from another angle, so that we see it almost exactly edge-on, while Plate XII shows yet a third nebula of the same general type, but viewed from a direction perpendicular to its central plane.

Nebulae of this type all lie outside the galactic system, so that the term "extra-galactic nebulae" provides a suitable name for them. Their size is colossal; any one of the photographs shown in Plates X to XII would have to be enlarged to the size of the whole of Europe before a body of the size of the earth became visible in it, even under a powerful microscope. Their general shape is similar to that which Sir William Herschel assigned to the galactic system, and it was this that led him to think they were similar to the galactic system of stars, and to describe them as "island universes." We shall see later how his conjecture has been confirmed by recent research; the extra-galactic nebulae, or some at least of them, are systems of stars like our own galactic system. Thus a view of an extra-galactic nebula may give us a very good idea of what our own system would look like if we could see it from outside. The nebula shown in Plate X is probably very similar in shape, size and structure to our own, and the same is true of the nebula in Plate XI, which is viewed from such a direction that the system is seen edge-on. We notice that the disc of stars is very flat, and this is a common feature in nearly all extra-galactic nebulae. Wyse and Mayall have measured six nebulae which we see edge-on, and find that their length is never less than 8·9 times the thickness, the average ratio being 12·3. Thus, except for the boss of matter at the centre, we must think of a galaxy as a very flat disc of stars.

THE DISTANCES OF THE STARS

The year 1837 may well provide our next landmark; it is the year in which the distance of a star was first measured.

In the second century after Christ, Ptolemy had argued that the earth could not be moving through space, since if it were its position relative to the surrounding stars would continually change. As the earth swung round the sun, its inhabitants would be in the position of a child in a swing. And, just as the swinging child sees the nearer trees, persons and houses oscillating rhythmically against a remote background of distant hills and clouds, so the inhabitants of the earth would see the nearer stars continually changing their position against their background of more distant stars. Yet night after night the constellations remained the same, or so at least Ptolemy believed; the same stars circled eternally in the same relative positions around the pole, and conspicuous groups of stars such as the seven stars of the Great Bear, the Pleiades or the constellation of Orion showed no signs of change. For aught the unaided human eye could tell, the stars might be spots of luminous paint on a canvas background, with the earth forming an unmoving pivot around which the whole structure swung.

In opposition to this, the Copernican theory of course required that the nearer stars should be seen to move against the background of the more distant stars, as the earth performed its yearly journey round the sun. But year after year, and even century after century, passed without any such motion being detected. The old Ptolemaic contention that the earth formed the fixed centre of the universe might almost have regained its former position, had it not been that various lines of evidence had begun to show that even the nearest stars were necessarily very distant—so distant, indeed, that their apparent want of motion need cause no surprise. The child in a swing cannot expect to have optical evidence of its own motion if the nearest object it can see is twenty miles away.

The most direct evidence that the stars are very remote is of course their faintness; if the stars are similar bodies to the sun, then the difference in apparent brightness between the stars and the sun will give a measure of the difference between the distances of the stars and the sun. For instance, we receive 11,500 million times as much light from the sun as from Sirius, the brightest star in the sky. Now the brightness of a luminous object falls off as the square of our distance

PLATE XI

The Nebula N.G.C. 891 in Andromeda seen edge-on

PLATE XII

The Nebula N.G.C. 7217

from it, whence it follows that if the Sun and Sirius were exactly similar bodies, the distance of Sirius would be 107,000 times that of the sun—for 11,500 million is the square of 107,000. Actually Sirius is considerably more luminous than the Sun, so that its distance is even greater than we have calculated. But our rough calculation will have shown that even those stars which look brightest must be very distant indeed, and it is not surprising that for a long time astronomers met with no success in their attempts to detect the apparent swinging motion of the stars—"parallactic motion," as it is technically called—which results from the earth's orbital motion.

Finally, in the year 1837, Struve detected a parallactic motion of Vega. From it he deduced the distance of Vega to be about 26 light years (p. 20), but his observations were not very consistent with one another, and their discrepancies suggested that the estimated distance might well be in error by at least half of its amount; we now know that it was actually less than half of the true distance. In the next year, Bessel observed a parallactic motion of 61 Cygni. Here the different observations were in good agreement with one another, and Bessel's estimated distance of 10·5 light-years agreed well with modern measurements, which fix the distance at 11·1 light-years. In the same year Henderson measured the distance of the very near star α Centauri as about $3\frac{1}{4}$ light-years, the true value, as we now know, being 4·31 light-years. Although these various values were not very accurate when judged by modern standards, they provided impressive evidence of the stupendous scale on which the universe is built.

Let us pause for a moment to consider the series of processes by which these immense distances are measured. The first step is to select a convenient base-line a few miles in length on the surface of the earth, and to measure this in terms of standard yards or metres. Starting out from this base-line, a geodetic survey maps out a long narrow strip of the earth's surface, preferably running north and south, and measures it in terms of the base-line. The difference of latitude at the two ends is then measured by astronomical methods, as for instance by noticing the difference in the altitude of the pole-star at the two places. As the length of the strip is already known in miles, this immediately gives the dimensions of the earth.

The method is identical with that used by the earliest Greek geometers. By its use Eratosthenes of Alexandria (*ca.* 276–195 B.C.) estimated the circumference of the earth to be 250,000 stadia, which, on any reasonable conjecture as to the length of the stadion, was fairly near the truth. According to the values adopted by the International Geodetic Association, the earth's equatorial radius is 6378·388 kilometres, or

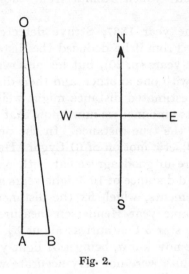

Fig. 2.

3963·34 miles, its polar radius being 6356·912 kilometres or 3949·99 miles.

Having determined the size of the earth, the next step is to determine the distances of the nearer astronomical objects outside the earth. That of the nearest of all, the moon, is found with comparative ease.

The method is simply that by which the terrestrial surveyor measures the distance of an inaccessible object. Suppose that when he stands at a point *A*, he finds that the object *O* is due north of him. He may then move to a point *B* a mile to the east of *A*, and find that the object now lies 5° to the west of north. He now knows the shape of the triangle *AOB*—its angles are 90°, 5° and 85°. He also knows the length of one of its sides, namely $AB = 1$ mile. A simple drawing or calculation now shows that the lengths of the other sides are $AO = 11.43$ miles and $BO = 11.47$ miles, which gives him the information he wants. The line *AB* is called the base-line, and it is easy to see that difficulties arise if it is too small in comparison with the distances to be measured; small errors in the measurement of angles and directions may then result in the calculated distances being seriously in error.

When the inaccessible object O is the moon, the astronomer takes his base-line *AB* to be the distance between two observatories several thousands of miles apart. Simultaneous observations at the two observatories then give the angles of the triangle *AOB*, and the moon's distance is easily calculated. As the moon does not move in an exact circle round the earth, this distance is found to vary between the limits of 222,000 to 253,000 miles, the average distance being about 238,900 miles, or rather less than 60 times the radius of the earth.

It would be very difficult to determine the distance of the sun directly by this method, partly because the distance is more than 20,000 times the radius of the earth, and so more than 10,000 times the length of any possible base-line, but even more because of technical difficulties arising from the brightness of the sun. The relative distances of the sun and planets are, however, known with considerable accuracy, so that if any one distance can be determined, that of the others follows at once. Thus attempts have been made to measure the distances of the nearest planets Venus and Mars, and, more recently, of various asteroids (p. 15) which come still nearer to the earth. The asteroid Eros, which was discovered in 1898, has proved particularly useful for this purpose; not only does it approach occasionally to within 14 million miles of the earth, but it is also a quite minute body, only about 16 miles in diameter, so that when viewed out in the depths of astronomical space, it forms an ideal "point" of which to observe the position. In 1931, when it approached to within 16,000,000 miles of the earth, measurements were taken at a great number

of observatories, and from these Spencer Jones finds that the
sun's distance must be very near to 93,000,000 miles; the actual
number he gives is 93,003,000, with an estimated accuracy of
about one part in 10,000.

The next, and biggest problem of all, is to determine the
distances of the stars. Any base-line on the surface of the
earth would be so minute in comparison with the distances
to be measured as to be entirely useless. Nothing less than the
whole diameter of the earth's orbit around the sun—about
186,000,000 miles—is of any use as a base-line, and even this
proves to be distressingly small.

The first step in this progression, that from the standard
yard or metre to the measured base-line on the earth's surface,
involves an increase of several thousand-fold in length. The
increase involved in the next step, from the base-line to the
earth's diameter, is again one of thousands. And again the
next step, from the diameter of the earth to that of the earth's
orbit involves an increase of thousands. But the last step of
all, from the earth's orbit to stellar distances, is found to involve
a million-fold increase.

For recent measurements show that the nearest stars are
almost exactly a million times as distant as the nearest planets.
At its nearest approach to the earth, Venus is 26 million miles
distant, while the nearest star, Proxima Centauri, is 25,000,000
million miles away; this latter star is a faint companion of the
well-known bright star α Centauri in the southern hemisphere.
The distances of the three nearest planets when at their
nearest, and of the three nearest stars, are shown in the following table:

PLANETS		STARS		
Name	Distance (miles)	Name	Distance (miles)	Distance (light-years)
Venus	26,000,000	⎰ Proxima Centauri	25,000,000 million	4·27
		⎱ α Centauri		4·31
Mars	35,000,000	Munich 15040	35,000,000 „	6·04
Mercury	47,000,000	Wolf 359	48,000,000 „	8·14

It is almost impossible to visualise a million, so that the
bare statement that the stars are a million times as remote

PLATE XIII

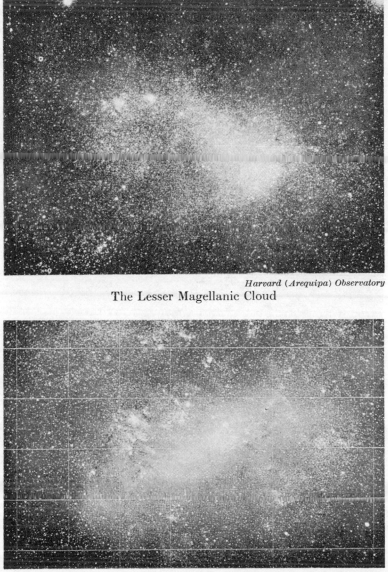

Harvard (Arequipa) Observatory

The Lesser Magellanic Cloud

Franklin-Adams Chart

The Greater Magellanic Cloud

PLATE XIV

Dominion Astrophysical Observatory, B.C.

The Globular Cluster *M* 13 in Hercules

as the planets gives only a feeble indication of the immensity of the gap that divides the solar system from its nearest neighbours in space. Perhaps the apparent fixity of the stars can be made to convey a more vivid impression of their remoteness.

The earth performs its yearly journey round the sun at a speed of about $18\frac{1}{2}$ miles a second, which is about 1000 times the speed of an express train. The sun moves at a similar rate through the group of stars surrounding it, and, broadly speaking, the nearer planets and the majority of the nearer stars move with comparable speeds. We shall not obtain a bad approximation of the truth if we imagine that all these astronomical bodies move with exactly equal speeds. If so, their distances would be betrayed by the speed with which they appear to move across the sky—the slower their apparent motion the greater their distances, and *vice versa*. Actually the astronomer uses this method to help him pick out the nearest stars.

Now the planets move across the sky so rapidly that it is quite easy to detect their motion from night to night and even from hour to hour; the stars move so slowly that, except with telescopic aid, no motion can be detected from generation to generation, or even from age to age. Even the conspicuous constellations in the sky, which on the whole are formed of the nearest stars of all, have retained their present appearance throughout the whole of historic times. The contrast between the planets which change their positions every hour, and the stars which fail to show any appreciable change in a century, gives a vivid impression of the extent to which the stars are more distant than the planets.

It is far more difficult to visualise the actual distances of the stars. The statement that even the nearest of them is 25,000,000 million miles away hardly conveys a definite picture to the mind, but we may fare better with the alternative statement that the distance is four and a quarter light-years—the distance that light, travelling at 186,000 miles a second, takes four and a quarter years to traverse.

Light travels at the same speed as wireless signals because both are waves of electric disturbance. Incidentally this speed is just about a million times that of sound. The enormous disparity in the speeds of sound and of electric waves is vividly brought out in the ordinary process of broadcasting. When a speaker broadcasts from London his voice takes longer to travel 3 feet from his mouth to the microphone as a sound wave, than it does to travel a further 500 miles to the north of Scotland as an electric wave. Wireless listeners in Australia hear the music of a concert broadcast from London sooner than an ordinary listener at the back of the London concert hall who relies on sound alone; they hear it a fifteenth of a second after it is played. Yet these same wireless waves, travelling with the speed of light, take four and a quarter years to reach the nearest star, so that the inhabitants of Proxima Centauri would be over four and a quarter years late in hearing a terrestrial concert. And in time we shall have to consider other and even more distant stars which terrestrial music would not yet have reached had it started on its journey before the Norman Conquest, before the Pyramids were built, before man appeared on earth—perhaps even before life of any kind appeared on earth.

SPECTRUM ANALYSIS

As our next landmark we may suitably take the application of spectrum analysis to astronomy.

All light is a blend of lights of different colours, and just as Newton, with his famous prism, analysed sunlight into all the colours of the rainbow, so the spectroscope analyses the light from a star, or indeed from any source whatever, into its various constituent colours. The instrument spreads out the light into a strip of light of continuously graduated colour, which is described as a "spectrum." The colours are those of the rainbow, and are arranged in the same order, running from violet through blue, green, yellow and orange to red. The reason for this is that the rainbow is itself a "spectrum" of light. Indeed the simplest spectroscope in the world consists of a single globule of water, such as a drop of dew or a raindrop. A multitude of such globules—a patch of dewy lawn or a shower of rain—forms a better spectroscope, which breaks up the light just as a laboratory spectroscope does.

There is of course a physical reason underlying the invariable sequence of colours. We shall see later (p. 129) that

PLATE XV

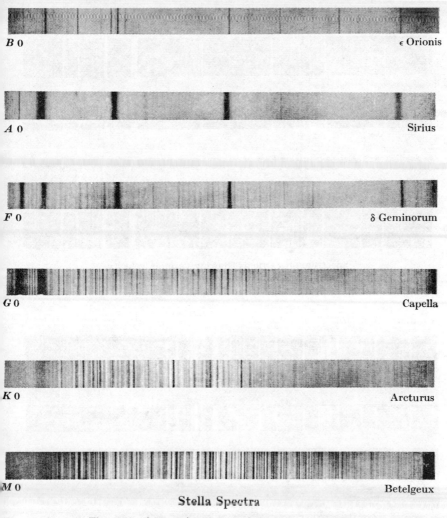

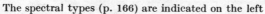

Stella Spectra

The spectral types (p. 166) are indicated on the left

PLATE XVI

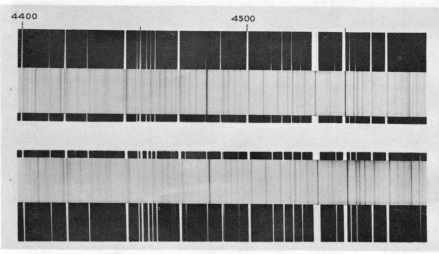

Spectrum of μ Orionis showing variable velocity

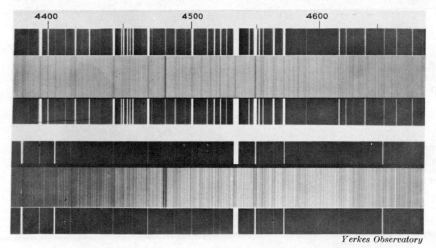

Yerkes Observatory

Spectrum of ζ Ursae Majoris showing lines doubled

The Doppler Effect in Stellar Spectra

many of the more important properties of light are explained by supposing that light consists of a succession of waves—like the ripples which the wind blows up on a pond—and that the different colours of light result from waves of different lengths, red light being produced by the longest waves, and violet light by the shortest. The colours in the spectrum occur in the order of their wave-lengths, from the longest (red) to the shortest (violet).

In 1814 Fraunhofer repeated Newton's analysis of sunlight, and found that the spectrum was crossed by a number of dark lines, which meant that certain short ranges of colour were either deficient or entirely missing from the light of the sun. These lines are still known as the Fraunhofer lines. We shall come upon the physical reason for their existence later (p. 136).

It has since been found that the spectra of all stars are crossed by somewhat similar lines. As examples, the spectra of a few well-known stars are shown in Plate XV (p. 32). The exact position of the lines conveys a wealth of information to the astronomer. In favourable cases they may tell him the temperature (p. 166), density (p. 158) and chemical composition (p. 34) of the atmosphere of a star; the star's distance from us (p. 58), and the speed with which that distance is increasing or decreasing (p. 36); and possibly even the weight of the star (p. 80) and the rate at which it is rotating (p. 36).

THE CHEMICAL COMPOSITION OF THE STARS. When the light from a simple chemical substance, such as sodium or calcium, is broken up spectroscopically, it is not found to give a continuous band of light of continuously varying colour, but rather a pattern, in which bright and dark places alternate. This pattern is found to be characteristic of the substance, so that an examination of the pattern makes it possible to deduce the nature of the substance emitting the light. Two spectroscopists Kirchhoff and Bunsen are said to have examined the light from a distant fire in Mannheim through a spectroscope, and, detecting the characteristic pattern of the element strontium in the spectrum of the fire, concluded that there must be strontium in the burning material. It was then a simple step to reason: If we can detect the nature of this distant burning material, why not also that of the material of the sun and stars?

It has proved possible to do this; the dark lines observed in the spectra of the stars can mostly be identified with the lines which make the characteristic patterns of the various chemical elements. In the spectra given on Plate XV, it is possible to identify the characteristic lines of such chemical elements as helium, hydrogen, calcium and iron. By the year 1862, Sir William Huggins had already observed the spectra of about 40 stars, and recognised the known spectral patterns of many known chemical substances in them. A few years later, the Italian astronomer Secchi had observed about 4000 stellar spectra and classified them into distinct types, which he designated as types I, II, III and IV.

Thus it is possible to tell the chemical constitution of the atmosphere of a star with considerable accuracy from a study of its spectrum; the composition of the interior layers is of course not accessible to observation. With a few insignificant exceptions, the whole spectral pattern can be identified as arising from substances which are known on earth, so that we may conclude that, as regards their outer layers at least, the stars are built of the same chemical elements as the earth.

We shall return later (p. 163) to a detailed discussion of the chemical composition of the stars, when we come to consider the various types of stars revealed by observation.

SPECTROSCOPIC VELOCITIES. When a star's distance is known, its motion across the sky tells us its speed in a direction at right angles to the line along which we look at it—i.e. across the line of sight—but provides no means of discovering its speed along this line. We cannot see the motion of a body which is coming straight towards us, and a star moving at a million miles a second in a direction exactly along the line of sight would yet appear to be standing still in the sky. The spectroscope makes good the deficiency, and enables the astronomer to evaluate velocities along the line of sight. The method is as follows.

When the light received from a star is analysed in a spectroscope, the characteristic pattern of lines or bands may be found to be shifted bodily in one direction or the other from its normal position. If the shift is towards the red end of the spectrum, the light emitted by the star is reaching us in a redder state than that in which it ought normally to be, and since red light has the longest wave-length, this means that every wave of light is longer—more drawn out—than normal.

As all light travels through space with the same speed, this means that fewer waves reach us than would normally be the case. This may be because we are receding from the star, or it from us, or a mixture of both reasons. In any case when the spectral pattern is displaced towards the red end of the spectrum we know that the distance between ourselves and the star is increasing. In the same way, a displacement towards the violet end shows that the distance between ourselves and the star is decreasing, or in brief, the star is approaching. The shift of a spectrum resulting from the motion of the body which emits it is generally described as the "Doppler Effect."

Examples of this are shown in Plate XVI (p. 33). The topmost of the four lines on the plate shows a portion of the violet-blue region of three spectra, the middle one being that of the star μ Orionis while the other two above and below (which are identical) are "comparison" spectra, which show the normal positions of the lines of certain terrestrial substances. From the approximate identity of these lines with lines in the spectrum of the star, we deduce that the star contains the substances in question. This being so, the comparison spectra must show the normal positions of certain spectral lines of a star of this type—i.e. the position when the star is neither advancing towards us nor receding from us. Careful inspection shows that the stellar spectrum is displaced slightly to the right—i.e. towards the red end of the spectrum—showing that the star must be receding from us.

The line below this shows the spectrum of the same star taken at a different date. Again we notice the displacement towards the red end, but we see that it is greater than before. When this second spectrogram was taken the star must have been receding more rapidly than when the first was taken.

When the amount of displacement of the lines of the spectrum of any object can be measured with accuracy, a surprisingly simple calculation will tell us the speed with which the object is moving towards or away from us. For instance, if each line or band in a stellar spectrum is found to represent a wave-length a hundredth of one per cent. longer than that usually associated with it, then the star is receding from us with a speed of a hundredth of one per cent. of the velocity of light, or 18·6 miles a second—and similarly for all other displacements.

SPECTROSCOPIC ROTATION. By watching the motions of sun-spots across the surface of the sun, we find that the sun's atmosphere, in the proximity of its equator, rotates approximately once every 24¾ days. It follows that every point on the sun's equator is moving round the sun's centre with a speed of, roughly, 6000 feet a second. This means that points at the western end of the sun's equator are receding from us at 6000 feet a second while points at the eastern edge are advancing towards us at the same speed. If the sun stood still, its light would show the normal spectrum for a star of its type; actually, as the result of its rotation, half of its surface emits light in which the spectral pattern is displaced towards the red end, while the other half emits light in which the pattern is displaced in the other direction. The consequence is that every line of the normal spectrum is broadened out into a band of appreciable width. And if we had no other means—such as that just mentioned—of studying the sun's rotation, it would be possible, by studying the observed widths of these lines, to calculate the speed of motion of points on the sun's equator, and hence to deduce the sun's rate of rotation.

Quite recently this method has been applied to the rotations of stars other than the sun, and it is now possible to state the speeds of equatorial motion of a great number of stars. We shall see later how it is also possible to calculate the sizes of the stars; when these are known it is an easy matter to deduce the periods of rotation of the stars.

THE PHOTOGRAPHIC EPOCH

If we were only allowed to select one more landmark in the progress of astronomy, we might well choose the application of photography to astronomy in the closing years of the nineteenth century; this opened the floodgates of progress more thoroughly than anything else had done since the invention of the telescope. Hitherto the telescope, after collecting and bending rays of light from the sky, had projected the concentrated beam of light through the pupil of the human eye on to the retina; in future it was to project it on to the incomparably more sensitive photographic plate. The eye can retain an impression only for a fraction of a second; the photographic plate adds up all the impressions it receives for hours or even days, and records them practically for ever. The eye can only measure distances between astronomical objects by the help of an intricate machinery of cross-wires, screws and verniers; the photographic plate records distances automatically. The eye, betrayed by preconceived ideas, impatience or hope, can and does make every conceivable type of error; the camera cannot lie.

And so it comes about that if we try to pick out landmarks in twentieth-century astronomy we find that, in a sense, it consists of nothing but landmarks; the slow, arduous methods of conquest of the nineteenth century have given place to a sort of gold-rush in which claims are staked out, the surface scratched, the more conspicuous nuggets collected, and the excavation abandoned for something more promising, all with such rapidity that any attempt to describe the position is out of date almost before it can be printed. We can only attempt a general impression of the new territory, and with this will be inextricably mixed a discussion of old territory seen in the light of new knowledge.

GROUPS OF STARS AND BINARY SYSTEMS

A glance at the sky, or, better, at a photograph of a fragment of the sky, suggests that, in the main, the stars are scattered at random over the sky, except for the concentration of faint stars in and towards the Milky Way, which we have already considered. Any small bit of sky does not look very different from what it would if bright and faint stars had been sprinkled haphazard out of a celestial pepperpot.

Yet this is not quite the whole story. Here and there groups of conspicuous stars are to be seen, which can hardly have come together purely by accident. Orion's belt, the Pleiades, Berenice's hair, even the Great Bear itself, do not look like accidents, and in point of fact are not. It is the existence of these natural groups of stars that lies at the root of, and justifies, the division of the stars into constellations. We shall explain later how the physical properties of the stars are studied; for the present it is enough to remark that physical study shows that groups such as those just mentioned are, generally speaking, true families, and not mere accidental concourses, of stars. The members of any one group, such as the Pleiades, not only show the same physical properties, but also have identical motions through space; they are journeying perpetually through the sky in one another's society. As the stars of such a group are both physically similar, and travel in company, they might appropriately be described as a family of stars. The astronomer, however, prefers to call them a "moving cluster."

These families are of almost all sizes, the smallest and commonest type consisting of only two members. After this the next commonest type consists of three members; the three stars which are nearest to us in space, Proxima Centauri and the two stars of α Centauri (p. 30), form such a triple system. Then come systems of four, five and six members, and so on indefinitely.

Let us first turn our attention to families consisting of only two members. Even if the stars had been sprinkled on to the sky at random out of a pepperpot, the laws of chance would require that in a certain number of cases pairs of stars should appear very close together. And a study of a photograph of any star-field shows that a large number of such close pairs actually exist. The number is, however, greater than can be explained by the laws of chance alone. The apparent closeness of some pairs may be attributed to chance, but a physical cause is needed to account for the remainder. We can unravel the mystery by photographing the field at intervals of a few years and comparing the various results obtained. Some of the stars which originally appeared as close pairs will be found to move steadily apart. These are the pairs of stars which, although they appeared close together in the sky, were not so in space; one star merely happened to be almost exactly in line with the other as seen from the earth. Other pairs are found not to break up with the passage of time; although the two components change their relative positions, they never become completely separated. Each star is found to be describing an orbit about the other, just as the earth does round the sun, and the moon round the earth, and for precisely the same reason: gravitation keeps them together.

Such pairs of stars are known as "binary systems." They are by no means rare freaks in the sky. Kuiper estimates that 68 per cent. of the stars which are more massive than the sun are of this type.

THE LAW OF GRAVITATION. Drop a cricket ball from your hand and it falls to the ground. We say that the cause of its fall is the gravitational pull of the earth. In the same way, a cricket ball thrown into the air does not move on for ever in the direction in which it is thrown; if it did it would leave the earth for good, and voyage off into space. It is saved from this fate by the earth's gravitational pull which drags it gradually down, so that it falls back to earth. The faster we throw it, the farther it travels before this occurs; a similar ball projected from a gun would travel for many miles before being pulled back to earth.

The law governing all these phenomena is quite simple. It is that the earth's gravitational pull causes all bodies to fall 16 feet earthward in a second. This is true of all bodies which are free to fall, no matter how they are moving; every body which is not in some way held up against gravitation is 16 feet lower at the end of any second than it would have been if gravitation had not acted through that second.

To illustrate what this means, let the big circular curve $B'A'C'$ in fig. 3 represent the earth's surface, and imagine that a shot is fired horizontally from A, the top of an elevation AA'. If the shot were not pulled earthwards by gravitation, it would travel indefinitely along the line AB out into space. If AB is the distance it would travel in a second under these imaginary conditions, the end of a second's actual flight does not find it at B, but at a point 16 feet nearer the earth, gravitation having pulled it down this 16 feet during its flight. For instance, if *BB'* in fig. 3 should happen to be 16 feet, the shot would strike the earth at *B'* after a flight of precisely one second.

As another example, let us suppose that the 16-foot fall below *B* does not drag the shot down to earth but only to a point *b*, which is at precisely the same height above the earth's surface as the point *A* at which the shot started. If gravitation were not acting, so that the shot travelled along the line *AB*,

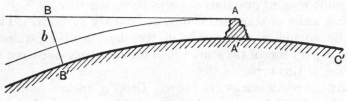

Fig. 3.

its height above the earth would continually increase. Actually in the case we are now considering, gravitation pulls the shot down at just such a rate as to prevent any increase of height occurring, so that the shot neither increases nor decreases its height; it neither flies off into space nor drops to earth, but continues to describe circles round the earth indefinitely.

A simple geometrical calculation shows that for the distance *Bb* to be 16 feet, the distance *AB* travelled in one second must be 25,880 feet or 4·90 miles.* Thus, if we could fire a shot

---

* Let *C* be the centre of the earth, and *bCD* the diameter through *b*. Then $BA^2 = Bb \times BD$, where $Bb = 16$ feet, and BD, which is 16 feet more than the

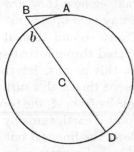

Fig. 4.

earth's diameter = 41,900,000 feet. From this we readily calculate that $BA = 25,880$ feet. This calculation of course neglects the height of the hill *AA'* by comparison with the earth's diameter.

horizontally with a speed of 4·90 miles a second, it would describe endless circles round the earth, the earth's gravitational pull exactly neutralising the natural tendency of the shot to fly away along the straight line *AB*.

In 1665 Newton began to suspect that this same gravitational pull might be the cause of the moon describing a circular orbit around the earth instead of running away at a tangent into space. The moon's distance from the earth's centre is 238,900 miles, or 60·27 times the radius of the earth. As the moon describes a circle of this size every month (27 days 4 hours 43 minutes 11·5 seconds), we can calculate that its speed in its orbit is 2300 miles an hour. After one second it will have travelled 3370 feet, and if it kept to a strictly rectilinear course this would carry it 0·0044 feet farther away from the earth. Thus, to keep in an exact circular orbit around the earth, it must fall 0·0044 feet in a second. This is far less than the 16 feet that a body falls in a second at the earth's surface, but Newton conjectured that the force of gravity must weaken as we recede from the earth's surface. Actually a body at the earth's surface falls 3632 times as far in a second as the moon's earthward fall in its orbit. Now 3632 is the square of 60·27 (or 3632 = 60·27 × 60·27), whence Newton saw that the moon's fall would be of exactly the right amount if the force of gravity fell off as the inverse square of the distance— that is to say, if it decreased just as rapidly as the square of the distance increased. As we shall see later, astronomical observation confirms the truth of this law in innumerable ways. This led Newton to put forward his famous law of gravitation according to which the gravitational pull of any body, such as the earth, falls off inversely as the square of the distance from the body.

The pull which the earth exerts on any object at its surface is proportional to the amount of substance the object contains, or, as we say, to the "mass" of the object. For instance, the pull on two tons of substance is twice the pull on one ton. But the pull depends also on the mass of the earth, and if this were suddenly reduced to half, the earth's gravitational pull on every object would also be reduced to half.

Various experimenters have measured the gravitational pull

which a few tons of lead exert in the laboratory, and, with this knowledge, it is easy to calculate how many tons of substance the earth must contain so as to exert its observed gravitational pull on bodies outside it. It is found that the mass of the earth must be just under six thousand million million million tons,* or, as we shall write it, 6×10^{21} tons.†

Just as the earth's gravitational pull keeps the moon perpetually moving in a circular path round it, so the sun's gravitational pull keeps the earth and the other planets moving in paths around the sun which are either circular or nearly so. Knowing the distance of any planet from the sun, and also its speed in its orbit, we can calculate the distance this planet falls towards the sun in a second. This tells us the amount of the sun's gravitational pull, and from this we can calculate that the sun's mass must be about 332,000 times the mass of the earth, or almost exactly 2×10^{27} tons. Whichever of the planets we use, we obtain exactly the same mass for the sun. This not only gives us confidence in our result, but it also confirms the law of gravitation, for if this law were inexact or untrue, the different planets would not all tell exactly the same story as to the sun's weight. The theory of relativity shows that the law cannot be absolutely exact, but the amount of inexactness is inappreciable except for the nearest planet, Mercury, and even here it is so exceedingly small that we need not trouble about it for our present purpose.

Just as we can weigh the sun and earth by studying the motion of a body gripped by their gravitational pull—or "in their gravitational fields," as the mathematician would say—so we can weigh any other body which keeps a second small body moving round it by its gravitational attraction. For instance, from the motions of Jupiter's satellites we can calcu-

* Here, as throughout the book, we use the French or metric ton of a million grammes or 2204·5 lbs. The English ton of 2240 lbs. is equal to 1·0160 French tons.

† The notation 6×10^{21} stands for the number formed by a 6 followed by 21 zeros, this shorthand notation being essential, in the interests of brevity, in discussing astronomical numbers. A million is 10^6, a million million is 10^{12} and so on.

A similar notation is needed to express very small numbers. The expression 10^{-21} is written for $\dfrac{1}{10^{21}}$ and so on. Thus 6×10^{-6} stands for $\dfrac{6}{1,000,000}$ or 0·000006.

late that the mass of Jupiter must be about $1·92 \times 10^{21}$ tons, which is 317 times the mass of the earth, although still only $\frac{1}{1047}$ of that of the sun. Similarly the mass of Saturn is found to be $5·71 \times 10^{23}$ tons or about 94·9 times that of the earth.

WEIGHING THE STARS. And now we come to a striking application of the principles just explained—when we observe two stars in the sky describing orbits about one another, we can weigh the stars from a study of their orbits. Generally the problem is not quite so simple as those we have just discussed. For its adequate treatment, we must once again levy toll on the mathematical work of Newton.

We have seen that a projectile fired horizontally with a speed of 4·90 miles a second would describe endless circles round the earth. What would happen if it were fired in some other direction and with some other speed?

Newton showed that when a small body is allowed to move freely under the gravitational pull of a big body, it will run away altogether if its speed exceeds a certain critical amount; in this case its orbit is the curve called a hyperbola. But if its speed is less than this critical amount, its orbit will always be an ellipse—a sort of pulled out circle or oval curve* (fig. 5, p. 44). Many years before Newton proved this, Kepler had found that the actual paths of the planets round the sun were not exact circles but ellipses; for the most part they were ellipses which did not differ greatly from circles, being what the mathematician calls "ellipses of small eccentricity." Now

---

* The simplest definition of an ellipse is that it is the curve drawn by a moving point P which moves in such a way that the sum of its distances PS, PT from two fixed points S, T remains always the same. In practice we can most easily draw an ellipse by slipping an endless string $SPTS$ round two drawing pins S, T stuck into a drawing board. Stretch the string tight with a pencil at P, and on letting the pencil move round, keeping the string always tight, we shall draw an ellipse. If the pins S, T in the drawing board are placed near to one another the curve described by the pencil P is nearly circular. The ratio of the distance ST to the length of the remainder of the string $SP+PT$ is called the "eccentricity" of the ellipse; it is necessarily less than unity, because two sides of a triangle are together greater than the third side.

In the limiting case in which the eccentricity is made zero, the ellipse becomes a circle. If the eccentricity is nearly as large as unity, the ellipse is very elongated. All the different shapes of ellipses are obtained by letting the eccentricity change from 0 to 1, and these represent all the different shapes of orbit that a small body can describe around a heavy gravitating mass. The points S, T are called the foci of the ellipse, and the big attracting body always occupies one or other of the two foci of the ellipse.

it can be proved that if the force of gravitation were to fall off in any way other than according to Newton's law of the inverse square of the distance, the orbits of the planets would not be elliptical, so that Kepler's discovery provided confirmation of the truth of Newton's law of gravitation.

When the astronomer studies the motions of a binary system in the sky, he again finds that, generally speaking, the two components do not move in circles about one another but in ellipses.* Once again, Newton's law is confirmed, and we are entitled to assume that the forces which keep binary stars together are the same gravitational forces as keep the moon from running away from the earth, or the planets from the sun. Assuming this, a study of these ellipses makes it

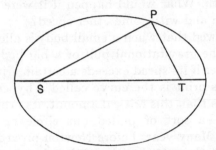

Fig. 5. The oval curve is an ellipse; the points *S*, *T* are its "foci."

possible to weigh the stars. If one of the component stars were enormously more massive than the other, the former would stand still while the lighter component described an ellipse around it, the motion being essentially similar to that of a planet around the sun. But in actual binary systems the two components are usually comparable in mass, and this brings new complications into the question. There is no need to enter into mathematical details here. Suffice it to say that neither star stands still, the two components describing ellipses of different sizes, and from a study of these two ellipses the weights of both the components can be determined.

The first three columns in the following table show the

* What he actually observes is the "projection" of the orbit on the sky, but it is a well-known theorem of geometry that the projection of an ellipse is always an ellipse.

result of weighing the four binary systems nearest the sun in this way, the sun's mass being taken as unity:

Stellar Masses

Binary systems near the sun.

Star	Distance in light-years from the sun	Masses of components in terms of sun's mass	Luminosity (see p. 46)
α Centauri *A*	4·31	1·10	1·14
” *B*		0·89	0·32
Sirius *A*	8·65	2·35	24
” *B*		0·98	0·0024
Procyon *A*	10·5	1·48	6·6
” *B*		0·46	0·0005
Kruger 60 *A*	12·7	0·27	0·0015
” *B*		0·14	0·0004

We see that the masses of these stars do not differ greatly from that of the sun, although naturally the whole of space provides a greater range than the four stars of our table which happen to be near the sun. But even in the whole of space, no star is known for certain to have a mass less than that of Kruger 60 *B*. This does not imply that there may not be in-numerable stars with still smaller masses, for stars of small mass are mostly very faint, and the stars of the smallest mass of all are probably all too faint to be seen by us. But stars can be detected by other means than sight. Just as Uranus showed irregularities in its motion which were attributed to the gravitational disturbance of another and hitherto unseen planet (Neptune, p. 16), so the binary system 61 Cygni shows irregularities in its motion which appear to be caused by the gravitational pull of another body, completely invisible to us, with only about a sixtieth of the mass of the sun (p. 175), while the binary 70 Ophiuchi shows similar irregularities which suggest the disturbing influence of a dark body having only about one-hundredth of the mass of the sun. It is at present impossible to say whether such dark objects as these should be regarded as stars or as planets—if as the former, they are by far the least massive stars so far known.

At the other end of the scale, many stars are known to have masses which are far greater than any in our table. Of

stars whose masses are known with fair accuracy, the star
H.D. 1337 (Pearce's star) is certainly one of the most massive,
its components having 36·3 and 33·8 times the mass of the sun.
The star β Lyrae is still more massive; the masses of its components are not known separately with any accuracy, but their
total cannot be less than the mass of 95 suns—perhaps they
are about 60 and 45 suns. Plaskett's star B.D. 6° 1309 must
be more massive still; again the masses of the two components
are not known with accuracy, but they cannot be less than
75 and 63 times that of the sun (p. 51).

This way of estimating stellar masses is of course available
only for binary or multiple systems; it can never tell us the
mass of a single isolated star. The theory of relativity has
presented us with a way of calculating stellar masses (p. 80)
which is not limited in this way, but unhappily it is only
workable in a very limited number of instances. It is mentioned here because it can be applied to a class of exceedingly
luminous stars known as the Trumpler stars which prove to
have masses of the order of 100 times that of the sun. Here,
so far as is at present known, is the upper limit to stellar
masses.

We might have expected that the stars would be found to
have all sorts of masses; there is no obvious reason why there
should not be stars with either millions or millionths of times
the mass of the sun. The fact that the masses are found to lie
within fairly narrow limits suggests that a star is a definite
species of astronomical product, and not a mere haphazard
chunk of luminous matter.

The average constituent mass in the above very short table
is 0·96 times that of the sun, which suggests provisionally that
the sun is of slightly more than average mass; more detailed
studies (p. 177, below) will, however, show that the sun is
substantially more massive than most stars.

LUMINOSITY. The last column of the table on p. 45 gives
the "luminosities" of the stars, which means their candle-
powers measured on an astronomical scale, in which the candle-
power of the sun is taken as unity. For instance, the entry
24 for Sirius means that Sirius, regarded as a lighthouse in
space, has 24 times the candle-power of the sun. The lumi-

nosities of the stars show an enormously greater range than their masses. In a general way the most massive stars prove to be the most luminous, as we might perhaps have anticipated. But what we could not have foreseen is that, generally speaking, those stars which are the most massive also emit most luminosity per unit mass; for most stars the luminosity is nothing like proportional to the mass, but more nearly to the cube of the mass—a star which is twice as massive as the sun will probably be eight times as luminous, and so on.

Here we come upon one of the central facts of physical astronomy which until recently seemed to provide one of the outstanding puzzles of the subject, but the solution has now been found, and we shall come upon a full and convincing explanation later (p. 202).

SPECTROSCOPIC BINARIES. The two components of a binary system will usually be moving with different speeds, so that the normal spectrum of a binary system will consist of the superposition of two distinct spectra, these exhibiting the different displacements appropriate to the speeds of the two components.

An example is shown in the lower half of Plate XVI, which exhibits the spectrum of the binary star ζ Ursae Majoris on two separate occasions. It is well to look at the lower line first. As before, the top and bottom spectra are identical, and show the normal positions of the spectral lines of certain terrestrial substances, which are used for purposes of comparison. The middle spectrum is that of the star, and in it we see each line of the "comparison" spectrum replaced by two distinct lines—one from each constituent of the binary system; the amounts of their displacements of course tell us the speeds of motion of the constituents (p. 35). In the upper line, the spectral lines are no longer distinct, showing that this spectrum was photographed at a moment when the two constituents were advancing or receding at approximately equal speeds.

If an astronomer were acquainted with the orbital motions of the two components of a binary system, he might proceed to calculate with what speeds these components would move in the direction of the line of sight, and could then predict to what extent the two spectra ought to be displaced if the light from the system were analysed in a spectroscope; the spectroscope would of course confirm his prediction.

It is more instructive to imagine the reverse process. Suppose that on analysing the light from a star, the astronomer obtains a composite spectrum in which the lines are doubled—as in the lower line on Plate XVI—and are found to shift rhythmically backwards and forwards about their normal positions. The fact that there are two spectra tells him that he is dealing with a binary system; if the rhythmic shift repeats itself every two weeks, he knows that its orbit takes two weeks to complete. He studies the star by direct vision and finds it is a binary system in which the constituents revolve about one another every two weeks.

He examines another spectrum, and finds that it shifts rhythmically every two days. On looking directly at this star he can see only a single point of light. In spite of this he knows that there must be two stars, but the mere fact that they move around one another in so short a time as two days proves that they must be very close to one another, and he need feel no surprise that his telescope has failed to separate the image into two distinct points of light. Systems of this kind, which the spectroscope shows to be binary, but which the telescope usually shows as a single point of light, are called "spectroscopic binaries." Over a thousand such systems are known.

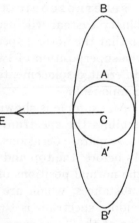

Fig. 6. The little orbit AA' and the big orbit BB' give the same velocities along the line of sight CE.

If the astronomer tries to construct the orbit of such a system from the spectroscopic observations alone, he finds himself in difficulties. His observations only tell him the velocities along the line of sight, and these depend both on the actual speed of the star in its orbit and on the orientation of this orbit in space; the same velocity may arise either from a big orbit in a plane nearly at right angles to the line of sight, or from a much foreshortened little orbit. For this reason, it is impossible to calculate the actual orbit or the weights of the stars from spectroscopic observation alone.

ECLIPSING BINARIES. There is one exception. Suppose that a star's light is seen to diminish in amount at regular intervals and to return to its original strength after each diminution. The obvious interpretation of the diminution of light is that one component of the system is eclipsing the other, and this can only happen if the orbit is so completely foreshortened that its plane passes through, or at least very close to, the earth. In such a case it is possible to reconstruct the whole orbit, and thence to calculate the weights of the two components. Not only so, but the length of time during which the eclipses last tells us the actual sizes of the two components, so that it is possible to draw a complete picture of the system. Diagrams of the dimensions and orbits of two typical eclipsing binaries are shown in fig. 7; these are drawn to the same scale, this being indicated by the small circle representing the sun.

In many eclipsing binaries the fluctuations of light can be adequately explained by treating the constituents as globular masses which pass in front of and behind one another. In other cases such explanations prove inadequate, showing that the stars must be treated as more complicated structures. Indeed, it is clear that if the two constituents are only a small distance from one another, each will raise substantial tides on the other, which may even be so high as entirely to alter the shapes of the stars. In such cases, the phenomena can usually be explained on the supposition that the masses are of ellipsoidal, instead of globular, shape.

But the stars may be so close that, when the orbits are calculated in this way, the constituents are found to overlap. The obvious physical interpretation of this is that a common atmosphere envelops both. We are no longer dealing with two stars revolving freely round one another in empty space, but with two bodies pushing their ways through a resisting medium. And the resistance of this medium may have observable results, both dynamical and spectroscopic.

The star β Lyrae shows effects of this kind, and a series of studies by Kopal, O. Struve, Kuiper and others have suggested that the star is of the kind just described. Its period of 12·916 days is getting gradually longer, at the rate of 9·38 seconds a year, as though something were interfering with the free motion of its components, while the spectrum shows extreme complications, which Struve thinks can be explained as caused by streams of gas, some of which pass from one star to the other, while others pass off into space.

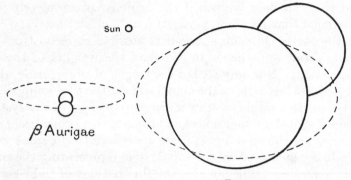

Fig. 7. Components and orbits of Eclipsing Binaries. (The broken lines represent the orbit of the smaller component round the larger.)

Another interesting class of eclipsing binary is typified by the star ζ Aurigae, in which one component is a compact bright star while the other is enormously larger and surrounded by an extensive atmosphere of tenuous gas. When the small bright star passes behind its far larger companion, it does not suffer immediate eclipse but continues to shine for more than a day, although with steadily diminishing intensity, through the diffuse atmosphere of the larger star. As its light gradually diminishes its spectrum undergoes changes which not only give information as to the chemical composition of the atmosphere of the larger star, but also as to the way in which various chemical substances are distributed in this atmosphere. Here we can really study the interior of a star by shining a light through it—or rather, by watching what happens when nature shines a light through it.

When no eclipse occurs in a spectroscopic binary, there is no means of knowing how much the orbit observed is foreshortened, but we can obtain a general idea of the masses of the components by assuming an average degree of foreshortening. If we assume different degrees of foreshortening in turn, we shall find that the computed masses come out least when the plane of the orbit is assumed to pass through the earth— i.e. when the orbits are computed as though the system were an eclipsing one. Thus, although we cannot discover the actual masses of the components of a non-eclipsing binary, we can always state limits above which they must lie, namely the masses computed as though the system were an eclipsing one. This is how we know that the two components of Plaskett's star (p. 46) must have more than 75 and 63 times the mass of the sun.

VARIABLE STARS

The majority of stars shine with a perfectly steady light, so that we can say that a star is of so many candle-power. The sun, for instance, emits a light of $3\cdot23 \times 10^{27}$ candle-power.

But there are also stars in which the light flickers up and down. In some, as in the eclipsing binaries just described, the light-fluctuations are quite regular, repeating themselves with such precision that the stars might well be used as time-keepers. In others the fluctuations, though not perfectly regular, are nearly so, while still others exhibit fluctuations which appear at present to be completely irregular, although the changes in these may perhaps be reduced to law and order in due course. For our present discussion, the various types of irregular variables are not of great importance.

CEPHEID AND CLUSTER VARIABLES. The really interesting stars are those of a certain class of regular variable, generally called "Cepheid variables," after their prototype, the star δ Cephei. The physical nature of these stars and the mechanism of their light-fluctuation are still not completely understood; we shall consider this problem below (p. 206).

But, whatever the mechanism of their light-fluctuation may be, observation shows that these stars possess a certain definite property, which proves to be of the utmost value. This being so, we may accept it gratefully without troubling as to its

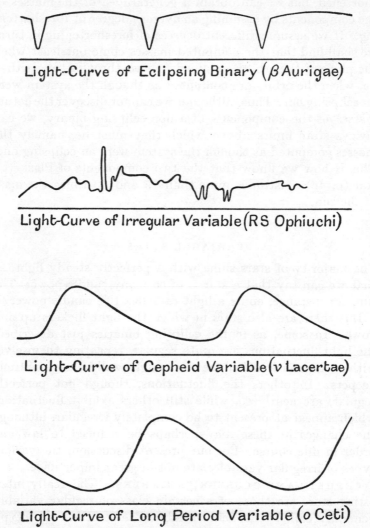

Light-Curve of Eclipsing Binary (β Aurigae)

Light-Curve of Irregular Variable (RS Ophiuchi)

Light-Curve of Cepheid Variable (ν Lacertae)

Light-Curve of Long Period Variable (o Ceti)

Fig. 8. Light-curves of typical Variable Stars of different classes.

why and wherefore. The perfectly regular light-fluctuations of the eclipsing binaries would make them useful for measuring time even though we did not understand the mechanism behind these fluctuations. In the same way the fluctuations of Cepheid variables possess a quality which makes them useful for measuring space—we can use them as measuring-rods with which to survey the distant parts of the universe. In brief, this property is that we can deduce the intrinsic brightness of these stars, and so their distances, from their observed light-fluctuations.

The light-fluctuations are so distinctive as to make the stars easy of detection and recognition. There is a rapid increase of light, followed by a slow gradual decline; then again the same rapid increase and slow decline as before. It is as though someone were throwing armfuls of fuel on to a bonfire at perfectly regular intervals.

Another class of variable stars, generally known as "long-period variables," shows somewhat similar light-fluctuations, but the two classes are easily distinguished by their very different periods of light-fluctuation. The light-fluctuations of the long-period variables usually occupy about a year; those of the Cepheid variables are far more rapid, the complete cycle seldom occupying more than about a month, and more generally being a matter only of a few days or hours. A specially rapid type of Cepheid variables is often found in Globular Clusters (p. 58); these are described as "Cluster variables," and frequently complete their cycles in periods of six to ten hours. But some are even more rapid; one in the cluster ω Centauri has a period of less than an hour and a half.

Fig. 8 (p. 52) shows light-curves of typical variable stars of the different classes. In each diagram the progress of time is represented by motion across the page from left to right; the higher the fluctuating curve is above the horizontal line at any instant, the brighter the star at that instant.

STELLAR DISTANCES

Out near the boundary of the galactic system is a cluster of stars known as the Lesser Magellanic Cloud (Plate XIII, p. 30), in which Cepheid variables occur in great profusion. In 1912 Miss Leavitt of Harvard found that the light of the brighter Cepheid variables in this cloud fluctuated more slowly than the light of the fainter ones. Whatever was responsible for turning the stellar lights up and down, it acted more rapidly for feeble than for brilliant lights. If a number of Cepheid variables were at different distances from the earth, their apparent brightnesses would of course depend only in part on their intrinsic brightness or candle-power, but the stars in the Magellanic Cloud are all, nearly enough, at the same distance from the earth. Thus differences in the apparent brightnesses of stars in this cloud could only represent real differences of intrinsic brightness, and Miss Leavitt's discovery could be stated in the form that the period of light-fluctuation of a Cepheid depended on its candle-power. Although this was at first only proved to be true for the Cepheids in the Magellanic Cloud, it has since been abundantly established for all Cepheids.

It follows that if two Cepheids A, B in different parts of the sky are found to fluctuate with equal rapidities, then their intrinsic candle-powers must be equal. Any difference in their apparent brightness must then be traceable to a difference in their distances from us; if A looks a hundred times as bright as B, then B must be at ten times the distance of A. In the same way, a third Cepheid C may prove to be at ten times the distance of B. We now know that C is a hundred times as remote as A. And if D can be found ten times as distant as C, we know that D is a thousand times as remote as A. So we can go on constructing and ever extending our measuring-rod; there is no limit until we reach such distances that even Cepheid variables, which are exceptionally bright stars, fade into invisibility.

This method can only inform us as to the comparative distances of Cepheids. The absolute distances of a few of the nearer Cepheids have, however, been determined by the parallactic method already explained—i.e. by measuring their apparent motion in the sky, resulting from the earth's motion round the sun. Taking any one of these stars as our original Cepheid A, we can step continually from one Cepheid to another, and so calculate the absolute distances of all the Cepheid variables in the sky.

In this way the observed relation between the period of fluctuation and the brightness of Cepheid variables—commonly known as the "period-luminosity law"—can be made to provide a scale on which the absolute luminosity, or candlepower, of a Cepheid can be read off directly from the observed period of its light-fluctuations. The Cepheid variables may be regarded as lighthouses set up in distant parts of the universe. We can recognise them, just as a sailor recognises lighthouses, by the quality and regular fluctuations of their light. We can read off their candle-power from the period of these fluctuations as easily as the sailor could read off the candle-power of a lighthouse from an Admiralty chart. The apparent brightness of the Cepheid then informs us as to its distance from us.

For instance, Cepheids whose light fluctuates in a period of 40 hours are known to be approximately 200 times as luminous as the sun, and so are of 6.46×10^{29} candle-power; a period of ten days indicates a luminosity 1600 times that of the sun, or a candle-power of 5.17×10^{30}, and so on. If a star in a distant astronomical formation is observed to be a Cepheid variable fluctuating with a period of ten days, we know that its actual candle-power must be 5.17×10^{30}. Its apparent brightness is observed to be that of a star of, say, magnitude 16, which, stripped of technicalities, means that we receive as much light from it as from a single candle at a distance of 570 miles. The difference between one candle and 5.17×10^{30} candles accordingly results from the difference between 570 miles and the distance of the object in question, whence, since light falls off as the inverse square of the distance, we calculate that the distance of the object must be about 220,000 light-years. But such a calculation needs some correction to allow for the dimming effect of the obscuring matter in space.

It would be difficult to over-estimate the importance of all this to modern astronomical science. It provides us with a means for surveying, if not the whole of the universe, at least those parts of it in which Cepheid variables are visible. Actually this last reservation is unimportant, for Cepheid variables are very freely scattered in space. Naturally the method is of most value for the exploration of the more distant parts of the universe; here it achieves triumphant success where other methods fail completely. The parallactic method begins to fail when we try to sound distances of more than about a hundred light-years. The apparent path in the sky, which a star at this distance describes in consequence of the earth's motion round the sun, is of the size of a pin-head two miles away. With all their refinements, modern instruments find it difficult enough to detect so small a motion as this, and it is practically impossible to measure it with accuracy.

The difficulties of measurements based on the "period-luminosity" law are of a different kind. Even the nearest Cepheids are so remote that it is difficult to determine their absolute distances with any great accuracy, either by the parallactic or by any other method. Thus the "period-luminosity" law makes it possible to measure the relative distances of Cepheid variables—and also, of course, of the objects in which they occur—with great accuracy, but the absolute distances cannot be determined with equal accuracy. Still, it is unlikely that the most recent determinations will prove to be in error by as much as 10 per cent.

Because of this uncertainty, all large distances given in the present book, and in astronomical literature in general, must be read as being subject to an error of perhaps 10 per cent. from this cause alone. Even so, it is still true that the "period-luminosity" law measures the distances of objects up to a million light-years away, with a smaller percentage of error than is to be expected in the parallactic measures of stars only a hundred light-years away.

SOUNDING SPACE

This by no means exhausts the list of modern methods of surveying space. Any standard type of astronomical object, which is easily recognisable and emits the same amount of light no matter where it occurs, provides an obvious means of measuring astronomical distances, for when once the intrinsic luminosity of such an object has been determined, the distance of every example of it can be estimated from its apparent brightness.

Although Cepheid variables of assigned periods provide the most striking instance of such standard objects, three others are available, although they are not so generally useful as Cepheids. First comes another type of variable star, the "long-period variables" already mentioned, which are generally similar to Cepheids except that their light fluctuates much more slowly. These stars are intrinsically far more luminous even than Cepheids, many of them being 10,000 times as luminous as the sun. They are accordingly visible at enormous distances, and may ultimately be found to provide a means of sounding depths of space so remote that even Cepheids are lost to sight.

Next come novae or new stars. Every now and then an ordinary star in the sky suddenly bursts out in a phenomenal blaze of light, shining with perhaps a thousand times its original brilliance. The cause of these violent outbursts is still a matter for debate, and no thoroughly convincing explanation has as yet been given. A study of comparatively near novae has, however, disclosed the surprising fact, for which no explanation has yet been found, that most novae attain to approximately the same maximum luminosity—about 25,000 times that of the sun. An exception is provided by a quite distinct type of novae, known as "supernovae," which are differentiated from ordinary novae by an abnormal brightness; for a brief period they shine with the luminosity of hundreds of millions of suns (p. 179). Disregarding these, we may say that ordinary novae, when at their brightest, provide standard objects of the kind required, and as novae appear in various parts of the sky, and particularly in the extra-galactic nebulae, they provide a rough means of measuring stellar and nebular distances.

Blue stars (p. 169) provide yet another method. These are exceedingly luminous, and blue stars of the same spectral type are found to show only a small range of luminosity *inter se*. Thus these also are objects of standard luminosity, and this makes it possible to determine the distances of blue stars, and so of course of the astronomical objects in which they occur.

There are still two other possible ways of determining stellar distances. W. S. Adams and others have found that certain definite peculiarities in the spectra of certain classes of stars convey information as to the density of the atmosphere of the star emitting them. This density is related to the star's physical structure and this in turn to its absolute luminosity; knowing this, it is easy to estimate the star's distance from its apparent brightness. This is sometimes described as the method of "Spectroscopic Parallaxes"—an unhappy and misleading bit of jargon, since a parallax is an angle, and the method has nothing to do with angles.

Finally the diffuse cloud of nebular matter which is spread through interstellar space (p. 24) is found to affect the quality of light travelling through it in such a way that a star's spectrum gives some slight indication of the amount of cloud through which the light of the star has travelled, and this again provides a rough means of estimating distances inside the galactic system.

GLOBULAR CLUSTERS. The law of Cepheid luminosity was first used by Hertzsprung to estimate the distance of the Lesser Magellanic Cloud, the study of which had been responsible for the original discovery of the law. Shapley subsequently used it to determine the distances of the rather mysterious groups of stars known as "Globular Clusters." A typical example of these is shown in Plate XIV (p. 31). About 100 of these clusters are known and they all look pretty much alike, except for differences in apparent size. Even these can be traced mainly to differences of distance, so that the globular clusters are probably almost identical objects, and Plate XIV might almost be regarded as a picture of any one of them.

As Cepheid variables abound in all of these, it is possible to measure their distances from the earth—if not with absolute accuracy, at least to the degree of accuracy explained on p. 56. The nearest cluster ω Centauri is found to be about 22,000 light-years distant, while the next nearest 47 Toucani is only 3 per cent. farther away. But the farthest known cluster N.G.C. 7006 is at a distance of about 186,000 light years. At such distances the parallactic method of measuring distances would of course fail hopelessly. The parallactic orbit of a star at 186,000 light-years' distance is about the size of a pin-head held the other side of the Atlantic; no telescope on earth could detect, still less measure, such an orbit.

Such figures as 186,000 light-years can convey but little
conception of the distance of this remotest of star-clusters
from us. We may apprehend it better if we reflect that the
light by which we see the cluster started on its long journey
from it to us at a time when primaeval man still roamed over
the earth. Through the childhood, youth and age of thousands
of generations of men, through the long prehistoric ages,
through the slow dawn of civilisation and through the whole
span of time which history records, through the rise and fall
of dynasties and empires, this light has travelled steadily on
its course, covering 186,000 miles every second, and is only

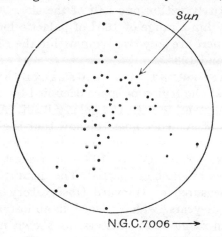

Fig. 9. The arrangement of the Globular Clusters.

just reaching us now. And yet this enormous stretch of space
does not carry us to the confines of the universe; quite
possibly it has barely carried us to the confines of the galactic
system.

Shapley mapped out the complete system of the globular
clusters, and found that they occupy an oblong region, lying
on both sides of the plane of the Milky Way, its two greatest
diameters lying in this plane, and its transverse diameter
being considerably shorter. The general arrangement is shown
in fig. 9, in which the page of the book represents the plane
of the Milky Way, and the various dots represent the points
in this plane which are nearest to the different clusters. Thus

the diagram exhibits the system of globular clusters as they would appear to an observer out in space who viewed it from a direction perpendicular to the galactic plane. All the globular clusters except N.G.C. 7006 lie within a circle of about 115,000 light-years' radius, having its centre at about 50,000 light-years from the sun.

As the diagram shows, the arrangement lies fairly symmetrically about a diameter of the circle; this is found to be the line pointing to galactic longitude 325°. The sun lies at the edge of the region within which the clusters lie, which explains why the clusters, as seen from the earth, appear to lie almost entirely within one half of the sky. Actually most of them lie within a range of 130° of galactic longitude (235° to 5°), while there are only two lying within the 152° of latitude between 41° and 193°.

THE ARRANGEMENT OF THE GALACTIC SYSTEM. We now know that the region of space occupied by these globular clusters is co-extensive with the galaxy itself. A considerable accumulation of evidence goes to show that the centre of the galaxy lies in a massive star-cloud in the constellation of Sagittarius (see Plate IV, p. 19)—the richest part of the Milky Way, as might be expected. The distance of this star-cloud was measured at Harvard Observatory and found to be 47,000 light-years, which placed it almost at the centre of the system of globular clusters, as shown in fig. 9. This and other evidence to be mentioned later show that the sun is about 40,000 light-years from the centre of the galactic system. How, then, did Herschel and Kapteyn make the mistake of supposing it to be at the centre?

ABSORBING MATTER IN SPACE. We have seen on Plates II and IX (pp. 17 and 24) how some parts of the sky are so thickly veiled by obscuring matter that it is impossible to see through the veil to the stars beyond. Such regions are certainly exceptional, but it is now recognised that no parts of the sky are entirely free from obscuring matter, which dims, when it does not entirely obliterate, the light from the stars beyond. We live in a patchy fog which prevents distant objects being seen in their full brilliance, and results in very distant objects not being seen at all unless they are exceptionally bright. When we walk in the open on a foggy day, our vision is restricted to the same distance in every direction and, if we did not know otherwise, this might easily mislead us into thinking that we were at the centre of things. It was thus that Herschel and Kapteyn were deceived into supposing that we were at the centre of the galaxy.

The celestial fog is densest in and near the plane of the galaxy, as might perhaps have been anticipated. Here light is usually halved in intensity after travelling through the fog for about 3000 years—i.e. after traversing about 3000 light-years thickness of the fog. Thus a journey through the 40,000 light-years which separate us from the central regions of the galaxy, reduces light to a mere 10,000th part of what it would otherwise have been, and this means extinction for all except the brightest of lights. As most objects in the galaxy are at more than 40,000 light-years distance, it follows that the majority of galactic objects cannot be seen at all. For the same reason, no extra-galactic nebulae are to be seen in or close to the galactic plane, and no globular clusters in a slab which extends for about 4000 light-years on either side of this plane—not necessarily because there are none to see, but simply because the general obscuration of light prevents our seeing any that there may be.

The recognition that this foggy veil permeates the whole of the galactic system has made it necessary to reduce the distances formerly assigned to faint objects. It used to be assumed that faint objects appeared faint as the result of their distance alone, so that when the luminosity of a distant object was known, its faintness informed us as to its distance. We now know that faintness arises from a combination of two causes, and it is not generally possible to apportion it accurately between the two. But it is certain that distant objects as a whole are considerably nearer than we thought some years ago.

THE LOCAL SYSTEM OF STARS

For a time another factor was believed to have been partly responsible for the error of supposing that the sun was at the centre of the galaxy. Various astronomers thought they had found evidence of a local concentration of stars—millions in number, and many of them of more than average brightness—surrounding the sun. They described this as the "local system" or "local cluster." It was supposed to have the same flattened shape as the main galaxy, but it did not lie exactly in the galactic plane, being inclined at about 12° to it. There seems to be no doubt that the sun lies very near to the central plane of the galactic system; Seares has found that it can hardly lie more than 25 light-years from it, and whether to the south or north it is impossible to say. But the sun was found to lie distinctly to the north in the supposed local system, perhaps 150 light-years to the north of its central plane, according to one estimate. Fig. 10 shows a cross-section of the system as it was supposed to lie. The confusion of this local cluster with the main galactic system was thought to have been responsible for earlier erroneous views as to the architecture of the galaxy.

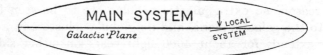

Fig. 10. Diagrammatic scheme of cross-section of the Galactic System. The sun is at the head of the arrow.

But the very existence of this local cluster is now in doubt; the cosmical fog just mentioned may have been partly or wholly responsible for the conviction that such a cluster existed. By obliterating the more distant, but not the nearer, stars of the galaxy, it could easily give the impression that we are at the centre of a region where the stars are exceptionally bright and exceptionally numerous. Bok and others, re-discussing the problem in the light of our present knowledge of the cosmical fog, still believe that a local cluster exists, Bok estimating its diameter at about 5000 light-years. On the other hand Oort, making a different allowance for the cosmical fog, finds that the density of stars near the sun is not abnormally high but abnormally low—we are not in a local concentration of stars, but in a local scarcity of stars. It is of course obvious that if we attribute too little obscuring power to the cosmical fog, there will still appear to be a local concentration of stars, and *vice versa*, so that it is perhaps significant that Bok assumes a lower value than most astronomers for the density of the fog.

In any case, the direct evidence for a local cluster of stars has become very uncertain. Partly because of this, and partly for another reason which will be mentioned almost immediately (p. 65), it seems highly probable that the idea of a local cluster must be abandoned.

THE ROTATION OF THE GALAXY

We have already compared the shape of the galactic system to that of a wheel. Obviously the system could not retain this shape if the stars which formed it were standing still in space. For the gravitational pull of the inner stars would cause the outermost stars—the rim of the wheel—to fall inwards, and the system would end as a confused jumble of stars somewhere in the vicinity of the hub of the wheel. In 1913 Poincaré suggested that the galactic "wheel" might escape this fate if it were in a state of rotation. Just as the earth's motion saves it from falling into the sun—or, to take a rather closer analogy, just as the rotation of Saturn's rings saves the particles which form the rings from falling on to Saturn—so, Poincaré suggested, the stars which form the rim of the wheel might be saved from falling into the hub, by a motion of rotation of the whole wheel. A rough calculation suggested that it would be necessary for the wheel to rotate at the rate of a complete revolution about every 500 million years.

Naturally it is no simple matter to detect so slow a rotation. It was first suspected to occur in the following way. We know that when a spinning-top or gyroscope is set in rapid rotation, a considerable force is needed to twist the top or gyroscope about in space. This is the principle underlying the action of the gyroscopic compass such as is used to steer ships. A gyroscope, a sort of big steel spinning-top, is kept spinning with its two ends pivoted in a swinging frame. No matter how the ship turns, the motion of the gyroscope keeps the frame pointing always in the same direction, and by the help of this

fixed direction the ship is kept on its course. Now the solar
system has many of the properties of a huge spinning-top, the
revolutions of the planets corresponding to the spin of the top.
As there is no twist impressed on this "spinning-top" from
outside, its axis of rotation must always point in the same
direction, thus providing a sort of "gyroscopic compass" to
give us our bearings in space.

In 1913 Charlier believed he had found that this "gyroscopic compass" was turning round against the distant background of the Milky Way, at the rate of a complete rotation
every 370 million years, a period which subsequent measurements increased to 530 million years. Eddington then suggested that it might be the background rather than the
gyroscopic compass that was turning, the Milky Way actually
rotating in the way imagined by Poincaré, and at just about
the rate which Poincaré had calculated.

Recent investigations by Oort, Plaskett, Lindblad and others
prove beyond doubt that such a rotation really occurs, although it is of a more complicated type than the simple "cartwheel" rotation we have so far discussed. In the solar system
the innermost planets move more rapidly than the outermost:
they must do so if the motion of each planet is to counteract
the sun's attraction, since this attraction is greatest in the
regions nearest to the sun. In the same way, if the rotational
motion of the galaxy is to counteract the gravitational attraction of the innermost stars, the inner parts of the galaxy must
rotate faster than the outer. Thus the sun ought to be over-
taking those stars which lie outside it on the galactic wheel,
while being itself overtaken by those which lie inside it.
A careful analysis of stellar motions has disclosed just such
a motion.

At first sight the stars seem to be moving at random—with
all sorts of speeds and in every possible direction. But instead
of looking at the stars individually, let us look at them in
groups; let us fix our attention on groups of stars which are
all near to one another in space, and determine the motion
of each group as a whole by averaging the motions of all its
members. We shall find that all the groups are moving round
a centre which is found to lie in exactly the direction which

Shapley assigned to the centre of the galaxy from his study of the globular clusters.

The amount of this motion can be measured with fair accuracy, and measurement discloses that the galaxy is in rotation in the way just described, the inner parts rotating most rapidly. The average speed with which the stars move round the centre of the galaxy is found to increase by 1 km. a second for every 200 light-years that we move towards the centre.

From this single datum it is easy to deduce that the sun must take about 250 million years to complete its journey around the centre of the galaxy. The earth being about 3000 million years old, the sun has probably travelled round the galaxy about a dozen times since the earth came into existence.

This rotation makes it difficult to believe in the local cluster of stars mentioned on p. 63. For the different parts of such a cluster would be forced to revolve around the centre of the galaxy at different rates, according to their different distances from the centre, so that after a few rotations the stars of the cluster would become scattered through the whole galaxy; in brief, such a cluster could not be a permanent structure.

To obtain further information about the galactic rotation, we must introduce some second datum—as, for instance, the actual speed with which the sun moves on its journey. To measure this, we need some fixed standard of reference. We may, for instance, take the more distant of the globular clusters, since, even if they are revolving round the centre of the system, they are unlikely, on account of their great distance, to be revolving at anything like the speed of the sun. A spectroscopic study of the speeds (p. 35) at which the sun is approaching towards, or receding from, these clusters suggests that the group of stars in the proximity of the sun is moving round the centre of the galaxy at a speed of about 270 km. a second. A simple calculation now shows that the whole length of orbit must be about 230,000 light-years, so that the radius of the orbit—the distance of the sun from the centre of the galaxy—must be about 36,000 light-years.

No great accuracy can be claimed for this figure, which is only a lower limit at best. For the distant globular clusters are likely to have some motion of revolution round the sun and the speed of this motion ought to be added to the estimated speed of 270 km. a second. Indeed, when Stromberg tried to determine the speed of the sun's motion from the nearest of the extra-galactic nebulae instead of from the farthest of the globular clusters, he obtained figures ranging from 360 to 500 km. a second.

Any increase in the estimated speed of the sun's motion must obviously increase the length of the sun's orbit, and so also the distance of the sun from the centre of the galaxy. With this in mind, the estimated distance of 36,000 light-years must be considered to be in satisfactory agreement with the estimates of 50,000 and 47,000 light-years already mentioned.

With this knowledge of the size of the sun's orbit, we can calculate what gravitational force the other stars must exert on the sun to keep it moving in this orbit. In other words, we can weigh all the matter inside the orbit of the sun, using precisely the same method as we use to weigh Jupiter when we know the motion of its satellites. It appears that the total matter inside the orbit of the sun must have a mass equal to that of about 150,000 million suns. Other estimates of the mass of the galaxy have been made, mostly with results similar to the foregoing. Two estimates by Lindblad, for instance, give the total mass of the galaxy as 110,000 and 180,000 million suns respectively. Part of this may of course arise from interstellar dust or gas. Nevertheless, as the average star weighs only about half as much as the sun (p. 177), the total number of stars in the galactic system may well be of the order of 300,000 million. This estimate of course includes all stars, dark as well as luminous.

Again we are confronted with the difficulty of visualising such large numbers. With perfect eyesight on a clear moonless night we can see about 3000 stars. Imagine each of these 3000 stars to spread out into a complete sky-full of 3000 new stars, and we are contemplating 9 million stars, which is still only the number visible in a telescope of 5 inches aperture. We probably cannot ask our imagination to play the same trick for us a second time, but if it can be persuaded to do so, and if we can think of each of these 9 million stars as again generating a whole sky-full of stars, we still have only 27,000 million stars within our purview—a number which is still far below any permissible estimate of the total number of stars in the galactic system. Or again, let us notice that the number of stars photographically visible in the 100-inch telescope, namely 1500 million, is about equal to the number of men, women and children in the world. Each inhabitant of the earth—each man, woman and child living in the five continents or travelling on the seven seas—can be allowed to choose his own particular star, and can then repeat the process tens, and more probably hundreds, of times without going outside the galactic system.

After this we can still go exploring outside the galactic system and find more and ever more stars. The galactic system, with its hundreds of thousands of millions of stars, no more contains all the stars in space than one house contains all the inhabitants of Great Britain. There are millions of other houses and millions of other families of stars; the other houses are the extra-galactic nebulae, the faint nebulous objects we have already described (p. 24), and which Herschel designated, somewhat conjecturally, as "island universes."

THE EXTRA-GALACTIC NEBULAE

THE NEARER NEBULAE. With the most powerful of modern telescopes it is possible to study the nearer nebulae in great detail; they are found to consist, in part at least, of huge clouds of stars. A powerful microscope shows that a puff of cigarette smoke, in spite of its appearance of continuity, consists of a cloud of minute but quite distinct particles. In just the same way, a powerful telescope breaks up the light from the outer regions of these nebulae into distinct spots of light; the nebula is resolved into a cloud of shining particles, just as the Milky Way was in Galileo's tiny telescope of three centuries ago. We have already seen this in Plate V (p. 22), which represents a magnification of a small area in the top left-hand corner of the Great Nebula M 31 in Andromeda shown in Plate X; the resolution into distinct spots of light is unmistakable. We know that some at least of these spots of light are stars; Hubble has found that many of them are Cepheid variables, their light showing the unmistakable characteristic fluctuations of the familiar Cepheid variables nearer home. The other shining points of light are of comparable brightness and show about the range of brightness above and below that of the Cepheids which is needed to justify us in supposing that they are ordinary stars. Not only so, but Hubble has observed outbursts in no fewer than 85 stars in this nebula which exactly reproduce the familiar characteristics of the outbursts of novae in the galactic system. He has also found stars which reproduce all the well-known features of long-period variables, and objects precisely similar to the globular clusters of the galactic system. Thus, there is little room for doubt that the nebula, as regards its outer regions at least, is essentially a cloud of stars, with many similarities to our own galactic system.

The central region of the nebula is shown in Plate XVII, and the structure of this is more doubtful. No stars have so far been detected here, although novae occasionally flash out, and a small number of stars have been detected in the corresponding regions of other nebulae. It may be that stars are present but are hidden in a fog of obscuring matter, or it may be that the central regions of this and similar nebulae consist of clouds of gas which have not yet condensed into stars (p. 223), the stars which are occasionally seen being wanderers from the more starry parts.

We have seen how Shapley was able to estimate the distances of the globular clusters by observing the periods of the Cepheid variables he found in them, and the use of the "period-luminosity" law (p. 58). Hubble has estimated the distances of the nearer nebulae in the same way, although his original estimates, like those of Shapley, call for some revision —partly to allow for the obscuring matter lying in and near the galactic plane of our own system, and partly on account of subsequent adjustments to the period-luminosity law.

The nearest nebula of all proves to be the Great Nebula in Andromeda just described, its distance being about 680,000 light-years. As this is nearly four times the distance of the furthest globular cluster, the "extra-galactic" nebulae are

PLATE XVII

Mt Wilson Observatory

Magnification of the central region of the Great Nebula *M* 31 in Andromeda of which the whole is shown on Plate X (p. 25).

PLATE XVIII

Mt Wilson Observatory

The Nebula *M* 33 in Triangulum

seen to be entirely detached from the galactic system; the adjective is justified.

Shapley found that the nearest globular cluster, ω Centauri, was closely followed by a second, 47 Toucani, at only three per cent. greater distance. It is the same with the nebulae; the Great Nebula $M\,31$ in Andromeda, shown in Plate X, is closely followed by the nebula $M\,33$ in Triangulum which is shown in Plate XVIII, the distance again being only a few per cent. greater.

Double and triple nebulae are almost as frequent in the sky as binary and triple stars. Often a large main nebula will be found to have one or two smaller satellite nebulae in attendance, although sometimes it will have a companion equal in size and importance with itself. An example of a pair of nebulae of equal size and importance will be found on Plate XXIII (p. 76), while our own galaxy provides a good example of the former type of combination; it may properly be regarded as the main nebula of a triple system, the two satellite nebulae being the Greater and Lesser Magellanic Clouds shown on Plate XIII (p. 80).

These are visible to the naked eye as two approximately circular clouds, in the sky of the southern hemisphere. They show many of the characteristics of true galaxies, but their distance from our galaxy—centre to centre—is only some 90,000 light-years. In a sense, then, they are the galaxies nearest to our own, unless their small size is thought to disqualify them from ranking as independent galaxies—for their diameters are only about 12,000 and 6000 light-years.

The Great Nebula in Andromeda is also accompanied by two satellite nebulae, $M\,32$ and N.G.C. 205, both of which can be seen on Plate X. Their distances from the centre of the main nebula are unknown, and may be anything above 5000 and 7500 light-years respectively, while their diameters are only about 800 and 1600 light-years.

MORE DISTANT NEBULAE. We have seen how longer and ever longer measuring-rods have been needed to conduct the survey of space. A standard metre rod, a base-line on the earth's surface, the radius of the earth's orbit, the distances of the nearest stars, the distances of the Cepheid variables—

each is adequate up to a certain distance and then has to give place to a successor of greater length. Finally even the Cepheid variables fail; the faintest nebulae are obviously far beyond the distance at which we may hope to detect these stars.

Hubble has devised a new measuring-rod to serve after the Cepheid measuring-rod fails. If a nebula is visible at all, it is possible to measure its apparent total brightness, and also the area of the sky it occupies. As regards nebulae of any one shape, Hubble finds that their apparent total brightness is very approximately proportional to the area they occupy in the sky, so that they are equally bright per unit of surface. This suggests that they are similar structures, differences of apparent brightness and size resulting merely from differences of distance. Here again then we have a series of standard objects, all of equal or approximately equal luminosity, and once again, as on p. 56, we can estimate the distance of any individual from its apparent brightness or faintness, or—even more simply—from its apparent dimensions if these are large enough to measure with accuracy. For instance, Plate XIX shows a cluster of nebulae in Pegasus, together with the single nebula N.G.C. 7331 (in the centre of the Plate), which appears substantially larger. We know that this must be of approximately the same size as nebulae of the same shape in the cluster. As it appears about ten times larger in diameter, we know it must be ten times nearer.

In this way, we can calculate the distance of even the faintest of the nebulae, and study the distribution of the nebulae in space.

About 2,000,000 of these faint extra-galactic nebulae can be seen in the great 100-inch telescope at Mount Wilson. Their distribution in space can be studied by the method that Herschel used (p. 21) in his studies of the distribution of stars in the galactic system. Doubling the aperture of our telescope enables us to see twice as far into space, so that, if the nebulae were uniformly distributed through space, we should see eight times as many nebulae. Actually this is what is found to happen, up to the largest telescope apertures at present available. Thus the nebulae shew no thinning out at great distances; the majority are found to be scattered through space with a

PLATE XIX

Mt Wilson Observatory

The Nebula N.G.C. 7331 in Pegasus and a remote
Cluster of faint Nebulae

PLATE XX

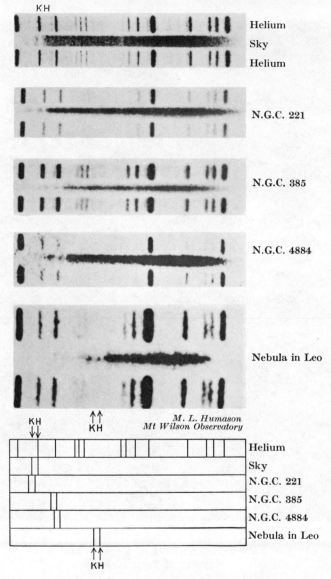

Nebular Spectra showing Displacements

tolerable approach to uniformity, at distances apart which average about 1,500,000 light-years, although here and there this uniformity is broken by clouds and clusters of nebulae in which the average distance is substantially less. For instance, a small and compact cluster, in the constellation of Pegasus, is shown in Plate XXII (p. 75). The sky is remarkably rich in nebulae in the constellations of Virgo and Coma Berenices. Here, at a distance of some ten million light-years from the sun, Shapley finds that a cloud of about 300 nebulae is collected within a space having only from five to ten times the dimensions of the galactic system. The same region of the sky also contains three other and more remote clouds. It has been suggested that our galactic system, the Andromeda nebula and other near nebulae, may constitute a similar cloud.

A still better way of estimating nebular distances has recently become available. We have seen (p. 35) how the motion of a star will cause the spectrum of the star to be displaced bodily from its normal position—towards the red end of the spectrum if the star is receding from us, and towards the violet if the star is advancing towards us. The spectra of the nebulae show displacements which are, to all appearances, of a similar nature although usually larger in amount. Whether these displacements are caused by real motions of the nebulae or in some entirely other way is still a matter for debate.

Examples of spectra of both types are shown on Plate XX opposite. In each case the central spectrum is that of the nebula, the upper and lower spectra (which are identical) forming a "comparison" spectrum (p. 35)—in this case the spectrum of helium. As these spectra are not easy to interpret, a key is provided at the bottom of the Plate. This shows only the position of the two lines H and K of calcium, all other lines and confusing details being omitted. The displacements are seen to be immense.

These displacements could not in any case represent the motions of the nebulae through space, but motions relative to our moving earth. And we have already seen that the rotation of the galaxy causes the earth to move round the centre of the galaxy with a speed of perhaps 270 km. a second; it is approaching these nebulae which lie in front of it and receding from those nebulae which lie behind it at this speed. We must allow for this motion in discussing the motions of the nebulae in space.

The spectra of the nearer nebulae are found to be displaced towards the red and towards the violet in about equal numbers. The obvious inference would seem to be that some of these nearer nebulae are advancing towards us and some receding from us.

As we pass from the nearer to the more distant nebulae, displacements towards the red begin to preponderate, until ultimately the displacements are all towards the red. It looks, on the face of it, as though all the more distant nebulae were receding from us.

A detailed study shows that the displacements of nebular spectra in general consist of two sets of displacements superposed:

(1) random displacements which may be in either direction.

(2) systematic displacements which are invariably towards the red.

The random displacements no doubt indicate random motions, half of the nebulae advancing towards us while half recede from us. But at a few million light-years' distance, these random displacements become insignificant in amount compared with the systematic displacements towards the red, so that these latter can now be studied by themselves without being complicated by the random displacements.

Humason and Hubble discovered the remarkable law that the amount of the systematic displacement is proportional to the distance of the nebula from us. The law is so exact that it provides the most reliable method we have for estimating the distances of the most remote nebulae. Whether the systematic displacement is really caused by a motion of recession of the nebulae is unknown, but this does not affect its utility as a means of estimating nebular distances; whatever the origin of the displacement may be, the distances derived by its help appear to be entirely trustworthy.

If the displacements are really caused by motion, the speeds of these motions are immense. The two largest so far measured belong to two clusters, one in Boötes and one in Ursa Major, and the corresponding speeds are 24,500 and 26,000 miles a second respectively. This is about a seventh of the velocity of light; a particle moving at such a speed would pass completely round the earth's equator in about a second. The distances of the clusters—which are deduced from their indisputable spectral displacements and not from their hypothetical speeds of motion—are 230 million and 240 million light-years.

Even this is not the greatest distance which the human eye—or rather the telescopic eye—has so far seen into space, but it is the greatest distance from which light has come in sufficient strength to permit of spectroscopic analysis. Still fainter nebulae can be discerned which, judging from their faintness, may be at distances of from 500 million to 1000 million light-years from us. The 230,000 light-years which formed the diameter of the galactic system (p. 60) seemed staggeringly large at first, but we are now speaking of distances thousands of times greater. For 99·9 per cent. or more of its long journey, the light by which we see the faintest of visible nebulae travelled towards an earth uninhabited by man. Just as it was about to arrive, man came into being on earth, and built telescopes to receive it. So at least it appears when viewed on the astronomical scale. Yet even this last 0·1 per cent. or less of the journey covers the lives of tens of thousands of generations of men, through all of which, as well as through a thousand times as great a span of time, the light has been travelling steadily onward at 186,000 miles a second.

NEBULAR MASSES. We might attempt to estimate the total number of stars in these nebulae by counting those visible in a selected average small area, but more precise methods are available. Just as we have supposed the outermost stars in the galactic system to be describing orbits under the gravitational attraction of the galaxy as a whole, so we must suppose that the outermost stars in a nebula are describing orbits under the gravitational attraction of the nebula as a whole; the forces which keep them from running away from the nebula are similar to those which keep the earth moving in its orbit round the sun. We can now weigh the nebulae, precisely in the same way as we weigh the sun (p. 42) or the galactic system (p. 66).

Hubble originally estimated that the mass of the Great Nebula *M* 31 in Andromeda, shown in Plate X (p. 25), must be about 3500 million times that of the sun, while the nebula N.G.C. 4594 in Virgo, shown in Plate XXI, must have about 35,000 million times the mass of the sun, but we now know that these estimates referred only to fractions of the nebulae. Careful studies of parts of the sky surrounding the nebulae have shown, quite convincingly, that the nebulae extend much farther out than appears even on long-exposure photographs such as those shown on Plates X, XI and XII. These plates only show the regions in which stars are numerous enough to affect the photographic plate in a way which can be seen by our unaided eyes. But when the plates are studied with instrumental aid, it is found that they would have to be extended to three or four times their present dimensions before they could show the whole of the nebular structures. In confirmation of this, globular clusters can sometimes be detected in these outer regions, just as in the outer regions of our own galaxy. All this makes it clear that until recently astronomers have not been studying the nebulae, but only their bright central portions. The nebulae, which were long supposed to be much smaller than our galaxy, now prove to be at least comparable in size. And we shall see immediately that they are also comparable in mass.

The motions of the different parts of a nebula can be studied spectroscopically in the way explained on p. 34. Many nebulae are found to contain a dense central region which rotates like a cartwheel or other rigid body, the speed of its motion at any point being simply proportional to the distance of the point from the centre, while out beyond this lies a less dense region in which the velocity of motion decreases as we recede from the centre—as it does with the planets of the solar system or with those parts of our own galaxy which are near to the sun. Near to the extremities of these outer regions, the velocities and periods of rotation are found to be comparable with those of the sun in our galaxy. Babcock has found a rotation-period of 92 million years in the outer arms of the Andromeda nebula *M* 31, while Mayall and Allen have found a rotation-period of 200 million years and a velocity of motion

PLATE XXI

The Nebula N.G.C. 4594 in Virgo

PLATE XXII

A compact Cluster of faint Nebulae in Pegasus

of 120 km. a second in the nebula M 33 in Triangulum. These may be compared with the velocity of 270 km. a second and the rotation-period of 250 million years found for the sun in the galactic system.

As these quantities are so similar, it is not surprising to find that the estimated masses of these nebulae also are very similar to that of our own system. Three different investigations have given the mass of the nebula M 31 in Andromeda as 95,000 million, 102,000 million and 200,000 million suns. On the other hand, the mass of the nebula M 33 in Triangulum has been estimated at only 17,000 million suns.

Nebular masses can be estimated in another way. When the speeds of motion of members of a cluster, such as those shown in Plates XIX and XXII, are measured spectroscopically, it is found that the members of the same cluster do not all move at precisely the same speed. The cluster as a whole may be moving at a speed of, say, 10,000 miles a second, but superposed on to this general motion of recession, the separate nebulae move inside the cluster, more or less at random, with speeds of several hundreds of miles a second.

Now if it were not for the gravitational attractions of the nebulae for one another, these random motions would soon result in the break-up of the cluster; each member of the cluster would simply continue on its present path, and would shortly be leaving the other members behind it at a speed of several hundreds of miles a second. This disintegrating tendency is of course checked by the gravitational pull which the cluster as a whole exerts on each of its members. Knowing the speeds of motion of the individual nebulae, we can calculate the gravitational pull which must be holding the cluster together so that it stands as a permanent structure; knowing this we can calculate the mass of the whole cluster, and hence deduce the average mass of the nebulae of which it is composed. Sinclair Smith has studied a cluster of 32 nebulae in Virgo by this method and finds that the average mass of its members must be of the order of 200,000 million suns. Other investigators have found comparable values for the masses of the nebulae of other clusters.

Apart from these clusters there are many pairs of nebulae

in which the two constituents appear to be revolving about one another like the two constituents of a binary star. A good example is shown on Plate XXIII opposite. The nebulae of such a pair may be weighed in almost the same way as the stars of a binary system, and the average nebular mass is again found to be of the order already mentioned.

All this seems to show that the extra-galactic nebulae are essentially similar to our own galaxy in size, mass and internal motion. The nearest nebulae of all are perhaps rather smaller in size and mass than our galaxy, but very few are near enough for accurate estimates to be made, and it is quite possible that, without going at all far out into space, we might come upon nebulae larger than our galaxy.

THE STRUCTURE OF THE UNIVERSE

So far every increase of telescopic power has carried us deeper and deeper into space, and the space open to our observation has seemed to expand at an ever-increasing rate. We may well ask whether this expansion is destined to go on for ever: are there any limits at all to the extent of space?

Even a generation ago, I think most scientists would have answered this last question in the negative. They would have argued that space could be limited only by the presence of something which is not space. We, or rather our imaginations, could only be prevented from journeying for ever through space by running up against a wall of something different from space. And, hard though it may be to imagine space extending for ever, it is far harder to imagine a barrier of something different from space which could prevent our imaginations from passing into further space beyond.

The argument is not a sound one. For instance, the earth's surface is of limited extent, but there is no barrier which prevents us from travelling on and on as far as we please. A traveller who did not understand that the earth's surface is spherical, would naturally expect that longer and longer journeys from home would for ever open up new tracts of country awaiting exploration. Yet, as we know, he would necessarily be reduced in time to repeating his own tracks.

PLATE XXIII

The twin Nebulae N.G.C. 4567–8

PLATE XXIV

The Nebula M 81 in Ursa Major

As a result of its curvature, the earth's surface, although unlimited, is finite in extent.

THE THEORY OF RELATIVITY

Einstein's original relativity theory of gravitation was based on the supposition that space also, although unlimited, is finite in extent. The total volume of space in the universe is of finite amount just as the surface of the earth is of finite amount, and for the same reason—both bend back on themselves and close up. The analogy is valid and useful only so long as we are careful to compare the whole of space to the *surface* of the earth, and not to its *volume*. The volume of the earth is also finite in amount, but for quite different reasons. A mole which burrowed on and on through the earth in a straight line would come in time to something which is not earth—it would emerge into the open air; but we can go on and on over the surface of the earth without ever coming to anything which is not the surface of the earth. The properties of space are those of the surface, not of the volume of the earth.

In the present book we can only glance very briefly at the steps by which the theory of relativity has led to this conclusion.

It is a matter of common observation that a moving body tends to persist in its motion unless something intervenes to check it: this describes the property of matter which we associate with the word "inertia." Newton enunciated this property of matter in his first law of motion:

Every body perseveres in its state of rest, or of uniform motion in a right line, unless it is compelled to change that state by forces impressed thereon,

and extended it in his second law to the case in which forces are in operation:

The alteration of motion is ever proportional to the motive force impressed, and is made in the direction of the right line in which that force is impressed.

When objects such as cricket-balls or planets are seen to describe paths which are not straight, Newton concluded that there must be a force acting on them; in these two cases, it is the force of gravitation, which we have already discussed on p. 39. Newton's second law, just quoted, provided a means of measuring the amount of this force, telling us that the force is proportional to the rate at which the moving body changes its speed. For more than two centuries this system of laws was believed to give a perfectly consistent and exact description of the processes of nature. Then, as the nineteenth century was approaching its close, certain experiments, commencing with the famous Michelson-Morley experiment, showed that the whole scheme was meaningless and self-contradictory.

Newton had measured force in terms of the change it produced in the speed of a moving body. Before we can measure a change of speed, we must be able to measure the speed itself, and to do this, we need some sort of background against which to measure it. Nineteenth-century science had imagined such a background to be provided by an ether which filled all space. This all-pervading ether, in conjunction with the supposed steady onward roll of an ever-flowing river of time, provided all that was necessary for measuring speed, and so also changes of speed and force. The river of time rolled on for a second, as measured by a clock; at the end of this second the moving body was found to have advanced, let us say, ten feet through the ether, as measured by a measuring-rod, and we could then say its speed was ten feet a second.

The experiments in question showed all these concepts to be illusory. No evidence could be found, either of an ethereal background to provide a standard of fixity in space, or of a uniformly-flowing river of time to provide a standard of speed. It became necessary to abandon the old scheme which had hitherto seemed to give an exact description of nature, and to introduce a new scheme as required by the experiments. In this new scheme, the phenomena of nature appeared as a picture painted in an entirely new space of four dimensions. This proved to be a purely mathematical and therefore probably a wholly fictitious space; in it the space and time of our everyday life are inextricably bound together into a new space of four dimensions, in which they then appear more or less as equal partners. There are innumerable ways in which space and time can be blended together to form such a space, but

there is one specially simple way in which they can be blended
so that they figure as absolutely equal partners.

To be precise, there are four equal partners. The first three
are the three dimensions of ordinary space—breadth, width
and height, or, if we prefer to take a more geographical arrangement, north-south, east-west and up-down. The fourth
is ordinary time measured in a way appropriate to the way
in which we have measured our space (a year of time corresponding to a light-year of distance in space, and so on), and
then multiplied by the square-root of -1. This last multiplica-
tion by the square root of -1 is of course the remarkable
feature of the whole affair. For the square-root of -1 has
no real existence; it is what the mathematician describes as
an "imaginary" number. No real number can be multiplied
by itself and give -1 as the product. Yet it is only when
time is measured in terms of an imaginary unit of $\sqrt{(-1)}$ years
that there is true equal partnership between space and time.
This shows that the equal partnership is purely formal—it is
nothing but a convenient fiction of the mathematician. Indeed,
had it been anything more, our intuitive conviction that time
is something essentially different from space could have had
no basis in experience and so would have vanished ere now.

The discovery that nature treated space and time as equal
partners, in the sense just explained, led to the conclusion that
motion and change of motion no longer had any strict scientific
meanings, and as a consequence the concept of force had to
be discarded. Einstein, dismissing the appearance of force as
a mere illusion, attributed the apparent curvatures in the
paths of projectiles of all kinds to their efforts to keep a straight
track through a space which was intrinsically curved. He then
found it necessary to suppose that this curvature caused space
ultimately to bend back on itself like the earth's surface, so
that the total volume of space became finite.

The general theory of relativity accounted at once for
phenomena of planetary motion which Newton's law of gravitation had entirely failed to explain—in particular the rotation
in space of the elliptical orbit of the planet Mercury. It also
predicted other phenomena—the apparent displacements of
stars near the sun at an eclipse, resulting from the light by

which we see them being bent as it passes through the sun's gravitational field, and a certain displacement of stellar spectra towards the red end. The amount of this displacement depends on the intensity of the gravitational field through which the starlight passes on its journey from the star to us, being greatest for stars which are very small or very massive or both. The phenomenon was entirely unsuspected when the predictions were first made, but has since been fully confirmed by observation. Indeed, it has qualified as one of the ordinary working tools of astronomy. It has been used to measure the diameter of the small faint star Sirius B, the companion to Sirius (p. 174), and to calculate the masses of the excessively bright and excessively massive stars which are known as the Trumpler stars (p. 46), as well as to test the nature of the stars at the centres of the "planetary nebulae" (p. 188).

On the other hand, the application of the theory of relativity to the universe as a whole does not stand on the same secure basis, with the result that several alternative views as to the structure of the universe have been, and still are, under consideration and discussion. We must review some of these in turn.

THE COSMOLOGY OF EINSTEIN. Einstein originally supposed that the dimensions of space were fixed by the amount of matter it contained, or again by the mean density of matter in space. We have no means of estimating how much matter may exist outside those regions of space which are within the reach of our telescopes, but within these regions matter seems to be fairly uniformly distributed in the form of extragalactic nebulae.

We have already seen (p. 75) how the weights of these vast bodies can be estimated, and we also know their average distances apart (p. 71). Confining ourselves to the roundest of round numbers, we may perhaps suppose the average nebula to have a mass of 100,000 million suns, and to be at an average distance of a million light-years from its neighbours. This gives an average density of matter in space of about 2.4×10^{-28} grammes per cubic centimetre, a density at which there are about 200 atoms of hydrogen, or only one atom of mercury, to the cubic metre of space. If we use Hubble's more precise estimate of 1,500,000 light-years for the average nebular distance in our part of space, this density must be reduced to 0.7×10^{-28}, but we ought then to add something to allow for the tendency of nebulae to form clusters. On the whole, we may perhaps take 10^{-28} as a reasonable round-number estimate of the average density of matter in space. If the whole of space were filled with matter of this density, Einstein's original cosmology would fix the radius of space quite definitely at 3300 million light-years. This is about twelve times the farthest known nebular distance, although probably only two or three times the distance of the farthest visible nebula.

Nevertheless, the general theory of relativity did not lead up to this cosmology in a unique way; it was perfectly possible for the former to be true and the latter false. The theory fixes the attributes of any small fraction of the universe quite definitely, but leaves open several alternative ways in which these small fractions can be pieced together to form a whole. Einstein's particular view of the cosmos could not therefore claim the prestige which attaches to his general theory of relativity as a whole. And indeed for some years it fell somewhat into disfavour, and appeared likely to be superseded by an alternative cosmology which de Sitter of Leiden propounded and developed in some detail in 1917.

THE COSMOLOGY OF DE SITTER. Let us first try to understand the essential differences between these two cosmologies.

Einstein's cosmology had supposed that the size of the cosmos was determined by the amount of matter it contained. If it had been decided, at the creation, to create a universe containing a certain amount of matter which was to obey certain natural laws, then space must at once have adjusted itself to the size suited for containing just this amount of matter and no more. Or, if the size of the universe and the natural laws were decided upon, the creation of a certain definite amount of matter became an inevitable necessity. De Sitter's universe was less simple, or, if we prefer so to put it, allowed more freedom of choice in its creation. After the laws of nature had been fixed, it was still possible to make a universe of any size, and to put any amount of matter, within limits, into it. Looked at from the strictly scientific point of view, Einstein's universe had one element of arbitrariness fewer than de Sitter's universe, and to this extent it had the advantage of greater simplicity.

On the other hand, this simplicity was acquired at a price. The fundamental corner-stone of the whole theory of relativity is the equal partnership of space and time in the sense already explained. Einstein's cosmology had gained its simplicity only at the expense of supposing that this equality of partnership disappears when we view the cosmos as a whole. It supposed space and time to be indistinguishable (in the purely formal sense already indicated) only to a being whose experience is limited to a small fraction of the universe; they become utterly distinct for a being who can range through the whole of space and time. It is not altogether clear how much weight ought to be attached to this objection, if objection it is. Real space and real time undoubtedly are distinct. Even if we deny the reality of both, they still remain distinguishable as modes of perception. What reproach, then, could it be to a cosmology that it admits that, in the last resort, when the universe is contemplated on the grand scale, space and time resolve themselves into distinct types of entity? Somehow we knew it already, before ever we began to contemplate the universe on the grand scale.

Whatever the answer to this last question may be, de Sitter's cosmology avoided all possible reproach by maintaining a completely equal partnership of space and time, not only in individual fractions of the cosmos, but throughout the cosmos as a whole. It will of course be understood that we are still speaking of equal partnership in the purely formal sense already explained, a light-year of distance entering the cosmology on the same footing as the square-root of -1 years of time. Even de Sitter's cosmology could not pretend that a light-year (9·46 million million kilometres) was the same thing as twelve months.

Although Einstein's main theory of relativity has been amply confirmed by observation, the cosmological part of it did not predict any special features such as permitted of a direct observational test. De Sitter's cosmology, on the other hand, predicted that the spectra of all distant objects must show a displacement towards the red, of amount depending on the distance of the object. The absolutely equal partnership of space and time is found to result in the vibrations of the light-waves emitted by any specified source being slower in distant than in near parts of the universe; the stream of time rolls more rapidly just where we happen to be than anywhere else. This sounds paradoxical at first, but examination shows that it is not; de Sitter was not asking us to return to a geocentric universe, because he showed that the inhabitant of a distant star would also find that terrestrial atoms were keeping slower time than his own. The paradox is completely resolved by the concept of the relativity of all measures of space and time.

This displacement to the red as a result of mere distance is peculiar to de Sitter's cosmology. It is additional to the displacement which, as all cosmologies agree, the spectrum of a moving body must show as the result of its motion, this latter being towards the red only if the body is receding from the earth (p. 34). On de Sitter's cosmology, the two displacements are not entirely independent, for it is an essential feature of this cosmology that near bodies should tend to move farther apart from one another. Just as bits of straw thrown together into a stream tend to get separated as they float down the stream, so objects in de Sitter's universe move farther apart as they float down the stream of time.

THE EXPANDING UNIVERSE. It was at first thought that the cosmologies of Einstein and de Sitter were antagonistic to one another, since obviously no one universe could be an Einstein universe and a de Sitter universe at the same time. But mathematical investigations by the Russian Friedmann (1922) and the Belgian Lemaître (1929) soon put a very different complexion on the matter. In brief, they showed that the cosmological theories of Einstein and de Sitter were not so much antithetical as complementary to one another. For they proved that no universe could stay permanently in the state considered by Einstein. A universe in this state is an unstable structure; immediately it came into being it would start to expand, and would not cease from expanding until it had become a de Sitter universe. Even after this the expansion would continue, but it would now become identical with the normal expansion of the de Sitter universe, such as we have already considered.

In the light of these results, the problem of cosmology assumed a new form. The question at issue was no longer whether the actual universe was an Einstein universe or a de Sitter universe, but rather how far it had travelled along the road which begins with an Einstein universe and ends with a de Sitter universe.

It is clearly to observation that we must look for an answer. The fundamental characteristic of an Einstein universe is that space is static; it stands still, so that the objects in it have no motion other than that which they have acquired from inter-action with other bodies. On the other hand, the fundamental characteristic of the de Sitter universe is best explained by picturing space as expanding, with the result that every pair of objects in it continually increase their distance apart. Objects may have motions of their own, but superposed on to this they have a general motion, each away from all its neigh-bours, resulting from the expansion of space; like straws floating in a stream, they show the way in which its currents are flowing. This motion would be such that every object would recede from every other object at a speed exactly proportional to its distance from that object.

Such a motion is characteristic not only of the de Sitter universe, but also of all the universes which are intermediate between those of Einstein and de Sitter. If then our actual universe occupies a position anywhere on this chain of theo-retically possible universes, we might hope to detect such motions of recession by observational means. We should naturally look first to the most distant of known objects, the great extra-galactic nebulae, because if the motion occurs at all, it is here that we ought to find the highest speeds of recession.

Now the type of motion demanded by theory is precisely that which, as we have seen, is exhibited by the extra-galactic nebulae. When the motion of the sun round the centre of the galaxy is duly taken into account, it is found that all known nebulae, except perhaps for a few insignificant exceptions, are receding from the centre of the galactic system with speeds which are almost exactly proportional to their distances from us, exactly as demanded by the theory of the expanding universe. The speed of recession is about 105 miles a second for each million light-years of distance.

Thus, observation clearly gives full support of the general theory of the expanding universe, and through this also to the general theory of relativity on which the more detailed theory is based. We find a general expansion which indicates that if the universe ever was in the stable Einstein configuration, it must have left it some time ago.

Yet observation cannot of itself tell us how far our universe has travelled along its path. Sir Arthur Eddington has recently tried to obtain a more definite answer to this problem by some brilliant, even if somewhat conjectural, theoretical researches, which we can best approach through a very simple analogy. When a grocer places a package of sugar on a spring balance, he will probably say he is weighing the sugar, but actually he is measuring the gravitational pull between the earth and the sugar—a pull in which the earth and the sugar enter in precisely similar capacities. If he were to fly around the solar system, taking his spring balance and package of sugar with him, he would find that the package had different weights on the different planets. On Jupiter it would weigh two-thirds as much as on the earth; on Mercury only a quarter as much, and so on. We could no longer say that the grocer was weighing the sugar; if we had to make a one-sided statement, it would be more accurate to say that he was weighing the planets. The full truth is that in any such measurement the weights of two bodies are always involved, and enter in a symmetrical way; if we know one weight, we can deduce the other, but if we know neither, it is a matter merely of our individual viewpoints whether we say we are weighing the one body or the other.

Certain well-known physical experiments are designed to weigh the smallest particles in the universe, namely the electrons, which enter into the composition of all matter (p. 112). Just as the measurement made with the spring balance involved the mass of the earth as well as that of the sugar, so Mach, Einstein and others have conjectured that the measurements made in experiments such as these involve both the mass of the particles and the mass of the whole universe. If so, it is a matter of choice whether the experimenter says he is measuring the one or the other, and it becomes possible to estimate the mass of the whole universe from these experiments, much as we can estimate the mass of the whole earth from the attraction the earth exerts on a pound of sugar. Eddington estimates it to be that of $1 \cdot 08 \times 10^{22}$ suns.

We have imagined the expanding universe to have started its existence as an Einstein universe in equilibrium, the whole of space being as full of matter as it could be. Calculation shows that an Einstein universe which contained the same amount of matter as $1 \cdot 08 \times 10^{22}$ suns would have a radius of 1068 million light-years. If, then, Eddington's theory is to be trusted, our universe must have started with this radius, and have been expanding ever since.

General mechanical theory shows that the speed of a falling object depends on the height from which the object has fallen. In a similar way, the speeds of the nebulae ought to depend on the extent to which the universe has expanded, or, more precisely, on the radius from which it started. Thus, if this universe had an original radius of 1068 million light-years, it ought to be possible to calculate the speeds of recession of the nebulae in terms of their distances. Eddington calculates velocities which are at least fairly close to those actually observed.

He accordingly supposes that the universe started as an Einstein universe, having a radius of 1068 million light-years, and that it contained an amount of matter equal to that of $1 \cdot 08 \times 10^{22}$ suns. If this matter were uniformly spread throughout the original universe, there would be about 2×10^{-27} grammes to the cubic centimetre, which is ten or twenty times what we have estimated to be the present average density of matter. Thus, the mean density of the matter in the universe must have decreased to a tenth or a twentieth since the universe started expanding. This is the same thing as saying that the linear dimensions of the universe have rather more than doubled, so that the present universe must have a radius of something more than 2000 million light years.

There are not, I think, many astronomers who have whole-heartedly accepted Eddington's theories on which this estimate is based, and many have formed very different estimates of the size of the present universe.

But on any estimate which is at all reasonably probable, the part of space through which our telescopes can range forms only a small fraction of the whole of space—something like one part in a thousand. There is plenty of space still awaiting exploration. It is perhaps not surprising. Mankind, who has been possessed of telescopes for only 300 years out of the 300,000 of his residence on earth, could hardly hope to discover the whole of space in so short a time. Our astronomer explorers are moving from island to island in the small archipelago which surrounds their home in space, but they are still far from circumnavigating the globe. And, just as the earliest geographers tried to estimate the size of the earth long before they thought of circumnavigating it, so astronomers are now trying to form estimates, which are necessarily vague, of the size of the whole universe from the properties of that part of it with which they are already acquainted. And we can well imagine that even the next generation will have completed the circumnavigation of space, and will think of a finite but unbounded space in the same way, and with the same ease, as we think of the finite but unbounded surface of the earth.

THE AGE OF THE UNIVERSE. Quite apart from all theory, we have seen that observation reveals an apparent expansion at the speed of about 105 miles a second for every million light-years of distance. To put the same datum in another way, the universe appears to increase its dimensions one per cent. in every 20 million years. Now the theories we have discussed all require that this rate of increase shall be approximately uniform, at least after the expansion has once got well under way. Thus, allowing for increase at "compound interest," the universe must double its dimensions every 1434 million years, and increase its dimensions eight-fold in 4300 million years. If, for instance, we have been right in estimating that the whole increase has been little more than one of doubling, then the main expansion must have taken place in the last 2000 million years or so.

To this we must add something for the time it took initially for the expansion to get under way, and it is exceedingly difficult to estimate how much to add. We have supposed that the original Einstein universe was unstable, just as a stick balanced on its point is unstable. Some small jar or irregularity starts the stick falling, and in the same way we must imagine that some small occurrence or disturbance started the universe expanding. We cannot calculate how long it takes for the fall of the stick to get well under way, until we know all the details of the disturbance which started the motion. In the same way, we cannot calculate how long it took for the expansion of the universe to get well under way until we have the corresponding information about the universe—and this we shall never know. Still, it is possible to calculate the time for various hypothetical disturbances. Calculations by Lemaître show that the time in question can hardly have been more than about another 30,000 million years.

OTHER POSSIBILITIES. The agreement between the foregoing theories, which suggest that the universe ought to be expanding, and observation, which indicates that it is, is so unexpected and so striking in its completeness that it is difficult to hold our enthusiasm in check. Yet we must be careful not to interpret the concepts underlying the theories in too literal or too concrete a sense.

Science used to imagine that the happenings of the world all occurred in a real continuum, existing independently of ourselves, which we called "space"; in this real space there moved a variety of real objects that we described as stars, nebulae, atoms and so forth. But there was no warrant for imagining this. We can know nothing of the universe beyond the effects that its happenings produce on our senses, either directly or through the intervention of instruments—telescopes, spectroscopes, etc. All that the science of any period can legitimately set out to do, then, is to devise a scheme or model that shall account for such of the effects as are known to the period in question. If two schemes *A* and *B* can be found, both of them accounting equally well for the effects in question, it will be impossible to decide between the two and neither will be able to claim any greater validity than the other unless or until some new phenomenon is brought to light which proves to be inconsistent with one scheme *A*. Then *A* can be ruled out, but we still cannot say that *B* must be true, for *C* may appear at any moment and show the same capacity of accounting for the phenomena as *B*. If, for instance, Einstein had lived in the time of Newton, and had produced his relativity scheme of a curved space, there would have been no means of deciding between the two schemes—the Newtonian scheme of gravitational force acting in a non-curved space, and the Einstein scheme of no force and a curved space—since both would have accounted for all the gravitational phenomena known in the period.

This being so, science has left trying to answer the question "What is the universe?" Indeed there are excellent reasons for thinking that if a higher intelligence came to us from another world, bringing with him a complete answer to this question, we should be totally unable to understand it. Science tries only to construct a picture of the universe, subject to two conditions—first, the picture must be intelligible to our minds, and second, it must account for some or all of the phenomena observed in one particular branch of science—the more, of course, the better.

Thus it is not surprising that other theories of the expansion, or apparent expansion, of the universe are in the field in addition to those already mentioned; other pictures have been drawn, some very different in character. It would be quite impossible to describe them all, even in the very briefest outline, so that we shall mention only two.

DIFFERENT KINDS OF SPACE

We have seen how Einstein interpreted astronomical orbits as straight paths through a curved space. The orbits are most curved in the neighbourhood of massive bodies, so that it is clear that the curvature of space must be greatest near big masses of matter, as Einstein's theory implied. Thus we may say that these masses themselves produce a curvature of space.

Now Einstein very soon found that if space possessed no curvature beyond this, the universe would be unstable unless extremely complicated conditions were satisfied. To avoid this difficulty, he supposed space to have a further curvature inherent in its structure. This curvature existed even when there were no massive bodies present, and was assumed to be uniform throughout space. Its amount—the same at every point of space and in every direction at each point—was measured by the "cosmical constant," which was thus a constant associated with the universe as a whole. If we again compare space to the earth's surface, the "cosmical constant" will give a measure of the quantity which corresponds to the radius of the earth, while the presence of massive bodies will produce minor local curvatures, like hills and valleys, mole-hills and rabbit-holes, on the earth's surface.

Einstein originally introduced this "cosmical constant" curvature because he saw no other means of obtaining a static universe; this was in the days before the apparent recessions of the nebulae had been noticed. As these now suggest that the universe is not static, Einstein's original reason for introducing the "cosmical constant" no longer exists. He and de Sitter accordingly examined whether any other reasons compelled the retention of this "cosmical constant" and its associated curvature. They found none. The observed recessions of the nebulae are, they considered, consistent with the cosmical constant having any value whatever within certain assigned limits, including the zero value which represents a space having no intrinsic curvature.

De Sitter subsequently examined the consequences of attributing various values, including zero, to this constant. He found that widening the possibilities in this way brings two new types of universe into the field beyond the expanding universe we have already described. There is a type of universe which begins life in an expanded form, contracts to a minimum and, after passing this mimimum, continually expands without limit. There is also a type of universe—the "oscillating universe"—in which expansions and contractions succeed one another in regular alternation. But still other types of universe are possible in which there is no curvature at all beyond the purely local curvature resulting from the proximity of gravitating masses, as well as universes in which the curvature is of a different and opposite kind from that of the original Einstein universe.* In both of these latter types of universe, space is infinite in extent.

So far as present observations inform us, the large-scale phenomena of astronomy can be represented equally well in any one of these various types of universe. Thus we have still no justification for saying that space is either finite or infinite in extent, and it is possible that astronomical happenings, no matter how accurately we observe them, will always be found capable of representation in either kind of space.

We have seen that in the Einstein-Lemaître universe, past time is limited to 30,000 million years or some such finite period. But there is no such limit for the other types of universe we have mentioned, so that it is impossible to say whether time had a beginning or not.

MILNE'S THEORY. In 1932 Professor E. A. Milne propounded a theory which has since, I think, been adequately proved to differ from those already discussed only in its mode of formulation. When a shell bursts on the field of battle, the various fragments travel at different rates, so that at any moment they are at different distances from the location of the original shell-burst. Those which are farthest away are of course travelling at the greatest speed, and in general the distance is exactly proportional to the speed of travel—which is exactly the law obeyed by the nebular velocities. Milne attempted to explain the nebular recessions in a somewhat similar manner, picturing the whole motion as taking place in an uncurved space which is precisely identical with the ordinary space of everyday experience.

His original investigation was based on a hypothesis which he described as the "cosmological principle." We look out into space from our own galaxy, and see other galaxies receding from us in every direction, their speeds of recession conforming to the simple law already explained. But there is

---

* In a space with no curvature the volume of space lying within a distance r of a fixed point increases as r^3; in a space having curvature of the Einstein kind it increases *less rapidly* than r^3; in a space having the opposite kind of curvature from that of the Einstein universe it increases *more rapidly* than r^3.

no obvious reason in the nature of things why this should be, so that, if we went to some other galaxy, we ought not to expect that the motions of the galaxies as seen from there would conform to the same simple law. If they did, we might conclude we were in a special position in the universe—why should it be from us in particular that the galaxies all run away?

The cosmological principle asserts that we are in no special position; the picture which an observer in our galaxy would draw of the largest-scale phenomena of astronomy would be equally applicable to any other galaxy—what we see from our galaxy (apart from detail), that he must also see from his.

By the use of this hypothetical principle, Milne succeeds in constructing a picture of the universe which at first appears to be essentially different from the picture of Einstein and Lemaître we have just explained. But there is no reason why the same picture should not be drawn in many different ways, just as a map may be drawn on many different projections. We have already compared Einstein's conception of space to the curved surface of the earth. Now the earth's surface can be mapped out on a spherical surface—for instance, the ordinary globe of the geographical class-room—but it can also be mapped out on a flat surface, such as the ordinary Mercator or stereographic projections we find in our atlases. Kermack and McCrea have shown, in brief, that Milne's description of the expanding universe bears much the same relation to the Einstein-Lemaître description as does a Mercator projection to a globular map. As a result Milne's theory provides us with no new territory to explore; the physical phenomena of his theory must necessarily be precisely identical with those of the earlier Einstein-Lemaître theory. We are given two equally valid pictures of the phenomena, and there can be no possible means of deciding observationally between them.

Milne claims nevertheless that his theory gives definite answers to questions which the relativity theory can only answer ambiguously, as, for instance,

(1) Is the universe expanding or non-expanding?
(2) Is it finite or infinite in spatial extent?

(3) Is the number of particles in it finite or infinite?

(4) Is the space appropriate to it curved or flat?

(5) Is its past history in time finite or infinite?

(6) Is the universe homogeneous or not?

He explains that the answers to these questions depend on the way in which we choose to measure time. For time can be measured in several ways, and the selection of a particular way represents an arbitrary act on our part. Milne assumes that the way chosen will be such that observers in different parts of the universe will be able to set up the same measure of time. We may, for instance, agree to measure time in the Newtonian way, taking the period of rotation of the earth on its axis, or of its revolution round the sun, as unit. When time is measured in this way, the laws of dynamics assume the familiar Newtonian form. In other parts of the universe also it will be possible to find regularly recurring astronomical phenomena, and these will again provide a unit by the use of which the laws of dynamics will again assume the Newtonian form. If we agree to measure time in this way, Milne finds that the universe is not expanding, its past history in time is of infinite duration, while its space is curved and extends to infinity.*

But our picture of the universe can also be drawn on another canvas, in which the unit of time is taken to be the period of an atomic, and not of an astronomical, orbit. In the year 1943 this is a definite fraction of our former astronomical unit, but according to Milne this fraction has not always been the same; the ratio of the two units of time continually varies with the passage of time. It has changed, for instance, while the light by which we see the distant nebulae has been travelling from them to us. This is why their spectra are all displaced to the red; atomic periods were slower, on the Newtonian scale of time-measures, when the light started out than they now are.

When the picture is drawn on this second canvas, we find that the universe is expanding uniformly, that it has a finite past history in time, and that its space is finite. On whichever canvas the picture is drawn, the number of particles in the

---

* It is the third of the spaces referred to in the footnote to p. 91.

universe is infinite, but a quantity which plays the part of "total mass" is finite.

We have already compared Milne's way of representing the universe to a flat map in an atlas, contrasting it with the Einstein-Lemaître representation which we compared to a spherical globe. The relation of Milne's two pictures to one another may perhaps be compared to that of a Mercator projection and an equal-area projection in an atlas. So long as we limit our attention to a single small part of the earth's surface, the two modes of projection give the same result, except that the maps that they provide will probably be on different scales. But, on passing to other parts of the earth's surface, we shall find that this difference of scale varies from place to place, and as we approach the poles the scale of the Mercator projection becomes enormously great compared with that of the other map. Because of this, actual Mercator maps are seldom carried beyond 75° or 80° latitude. To carry them up to 90° would require a piece of paper of infinite size, and we should then have two maps, one telling us that the surface of the earth was finite and the other telling us that it was infinite—in close analogy with Milne's two pictures of the universe.

We may feel tempted to say that the earth's surface is really of finite extent, so that one of these maps may be right but the other must be wrong. But if we say this, it can only be because we have already committed ourselves to a definite mode of measurement—e.g. by yardsticks. This is admirably suited to the measurement of distances on earth, but is not available for astronomical distances, since we cannot transport yardsticks about in the sky. If we had not been able to transport yardsticks about on earth, we might have readily agreed to take 1 sec. of longitude as our unit of length at any place, this being a unit which could easily be determined by astronomical measurements. In such units we should have found that the distance from equator to pole was literally infinite.

Milne's work and theories are still under discussion and criticism, especially as regards the assumptions which are introduced above and beyond the cosmological principle. McVittie has recently given a list of nine additional assumptions which he believes to be involved, either explicitly or implicitly, and which, he says, Milne and his co-workers have treated as axiomatic, and so as needing no justification.

The main value of Milne's work has perhaps proved to be something different from what he intended. It shows in how many ways the phenomena of nebular recession can be regarded, and leads us to reflect how little justification there can be for labelling any explanation as the "true" explanation. Incidentally we see how impossible it is to endow Einstein's curved space with any "physical reality" (whatever this may mean).

A MODEL OF THE UNIVERSE

We found it difficult enough to visualise the 4¼ light-years which constitute the distance to the nearest star, so we may be well advised not even to attempt to visualise the hundreds of millions of light-years which carry us to the farthest of visible nebulae. Yet we may try to see all these distances in proper proportion relative to one another by the help of a model drawn to scale. We can escape the effort of trying to imagine unimaginably great distances by keeping the scale very small.

The earth, travelling 1000 times faster than an express train, makes a journey of 600 million miles around the sun every year. Let us represent this journey by a pin-head $\frac{1}{16}$ of an inch in diameter. This fixes the scale of our model; the sun has shrunk to a minute speck of dust $\frac{1}{3400}$ of an inch in diameter, while the earth is a still more minute speck which is too small to be seen at all even in the most powerful of microscopes. On this scale the nearest star in the sky, Proxima Centauri, must be placed about 225 yards away, and to contain even the hundred stars nearest to our sun in space, the model must be a mile high, a mile long and a mile wide.

Let us go on building the model. We may think of stars indiscriminately as specks of dust, because their sizes vary about as much as the sizes of specks of dust. In the vicinity of the sun we must place specks of dust at average distances of about a quarter of a mile apart; in many other regions of space they are even farther apart. We go on building the model for hundreds of miles in every direction, and then, if we are building in a direction well away from the galactic plane, the specks of dust begin to thin out; we are approaching the confines of the galaxy. In the galactic plane itself we build out for perhaps 5000 miles before we come to the farthest globular cluster, and we are still inside the galactic system. With our earth's long yearly journey round the sun as a pin-head, the whole galactic system is considerably larger than the continent of Asia. It may be well to pause and try to visualise the relative sizes of a pin-head and a continent before we go on with our mental model-building.

After we have finished the galactic system, we must travel about 20,000 miles before we begin to set up the next bit of our model, at any rate if we are keeping it to scale. At this distance we place the next family of stars, a family which may be somewhat smaller and more compact than our own galactic family, but is comparable with it both in size and in numbers. So we go on building our model—a family of thousands of millions of stars every 30,000 miles or so—until we have two million such families. The model now stretches for about three million miles in every direction. This represents as far as we can see into space with our present telescopes. Beyond this we imagine the model going on in all directions, although perhaps not indefinitely; a journey of some hundreds of millions of miles in the model might bring us back to our starting point.

In this model, the sun is a very tiny speck of dust indeed—a speck less than a three-thousandth of an inch in diameter—while the other stars are other specks of dust, some larger, some smaller. The total number of specks of dust in our model is about comparable with the total number of specks of dust in the whole of London or New York—actually it is the number of dust particles in 3 cubic miles of air, with particles occurring at the rate of a million to the cubic inch. Think of the sun as something less than a single speck of dust in a vast city, of the earth as less than a millionth part of such a speck of dust, and we have perhaps as vivid a picture as the mind can really grasp of the relation of our home in space to the rest of the universe.

An alternative procedure would have been to construct our scale-model by taking all the specks of dust in London and spreading them out to the right distances to represent the various stars in space. The average actual distances between specks of dust in London is a quite small fraction of an inch; to get our model to correct scale, this distance must be increased to about a quarter of a mile, even when we are building the part which represents the crowded part of space round the sun. If we build our model in this way, we obtain a vivid picture of the emptiness of space. Empty Waterloo Station of everything except six specks of dust, and it is still far more crowded with dust than space is with stars. This is true even of the comparatively crowded region inside the galactic system: it takes no account of the immense empty stretches between one system of stars and the next. On averaging throughout the whole of the model, the mean distance of a speck of dust from its nearest neighbour proves to be something like 80 miles. The universe consists in the main not of stars but of desolate emptiness—inconceivably vast stretches of desert space in which the presence of a star is a rare and exceptional event.

Let us in imagination take up a position in space somewhere near the sun, and watch the stars moving past with speeds about 1000 times that of an express train. If space were really crowded with stars, our position would be as unenviable as if we sat down in the middle of Regent Street to watch the traffic go by—our life, though thrilling, would be brief. Yet, as exact calculation shows, the stellar traffic is so little crowded that we should have to wait about a million million million years before a star ran into us. Put in another form, the calculation shows that any one star may expect to move for something of the order of a million million million years before colliding with a second star. The stars move blindly through space, and the players in the stellar blind-man's-buff are so few and far between that the chance of encountering another star is almost negligible. This not only applies to direct collisions but also to near approaches; with things as they now are, a star would probably move through space for about a hundred million million years before it came to within ten diameters distance of another star. We shall see later that this concept is of the profoundest significance in our interpretation of the universe.

CHAPTER II

Exploring the Atom

So far our exploration of the universe has been in the direction from man to bigger things than man; we have been exploring ranges of space which dwarf man and his home in space into utter insignificance. Yet we have explored only about half the total range of the universe; an almost equal range awaits exploration in the direction of the infinitely small. We appreciate only half of the infinite richness of the world around us until we extend our survey down to the smallest units of matter. This survey has been first the task, and now the brilliant achievement, of modern physics.

It may perhaps be asked why a book which attempts primarily to give an account of modern astronomy should concern itself with this other end of the universe. The answer is that the stars are something more than huge inert masses; they are machines in action, generating and emitting the radiation by which we see them. To understand their mechanism, we must first study the ways in which radiation is generated and emitted on earth, and this takes us right into the heart of modern atomic physics. In the present book we naturally cannot attempt to cover the whole of this new field of knowledge; we shall concern ourselves only with those parts which are important for the interpretation of astronomical results.

ATOMIC THEORY

As far back as the fifth century before Christ, Greek philosophy was greatly exercised by the question of whether in the last resort the ultimate substance of the universe was continuous or discontinuous. We stand on the sea-shore, and all around us see stretches of sand which appear at first to be continuous in structure, but which a closer examination shows to consist of separate hard particles or grains. In front rolls the ocean, which also appears at first to be continuous in structure, and this we find we cannot divide into grains or particles, no matter how we try. We can divide it into drops, but then each drop can be subdivided into smaller drops, and there seems to be no reason, on the face of things, why this process of subdivision should not be continued for ever. The question which agitated the Greek philosophers was, in effect, whether the water of the ocean or the sand of the sea-shore gave the truer picture of the ultimate structure of the substance of the universe.

The "atomic" school, founded by Democritus, Leucippus and Lucretius, believed in the ultimate discontinuity of matter; they taught that any substance, after it had been subdivided a sufficient number of times, would be found to consist of hard discrete particles which did not admit of further subdivision. For them the sand gave a better picture of ultimate structure than the water, because they thought that sufficient subdivision would cause the water to display the granular properties of sand. And this intuitional conjecture is amply confirmed by modern science.

The question is, in effect, settled as soon as a thin layer of a substance is found to show qualities essentially different from those of a slightly thicker layer. A layer of yellow sand swept uniformly over a red floor will make the whole floor appear yellow if there is enough sand to make a layer at least one grain thick. If, however, there is only half this much sand, the redness of the floor inevitably shows through; it is impossible to spread sand in a uniform layer only half a grain thick. This abrupt change in the properties of a layer of sand is of course a consequence of the granular structure of sand.

Similar changes are found to occur in the properties of thin layers of liquid. A teaspoonful of soup will cover the bottom of a soup plate, but a single drop of soup will only make an untidy splash. It is sometimes possible to measure the exact thickness of layer at which the properties of liquids begin to change. In 1890 Lord Rayleigh found that thin films of olive oil floating on water changed their properties as soon as the thickness of the film was reduced to less than a millionth of a millimetre (or a 25,000,000th part of an inch). The obvious interpretation, which is confirmed in innumerable ways, is that olive oil consists of discrete particles—analogous to the "grains" in a pile of sand—each having a diameter somewhere in the neighbourhood of a 25,000,000th part of an inch.

Every substance consists of such "grains"; they are called molecules. The familiar properties of matter are those of layers many molecules thick; the properties of layers less than a single molecule thick are known only to the physicist in his laboratory.

MOLECULES

How are we to break up a piece of substance into its ultimate grains, or molecules? It is easy for the scientist to say that, by subdividing water for long enough, we shall come to grains which cannot be subdivided any farther; the plain man would like to see it done.

Fortunately the process is one of extreme simplicity. Take a glass of water, apply gentle heat underneath, and the water begins to evaporate. What does this mean? It means that the water is being broken up into its separate ultimate grains or molecules. If the glass of water could be placed on a sufficiently sensitive spring balance, we should see that the process of evaporation does not proceed continuously, layer after layer, but jerkily, molecule by molecule. We should find the weight of the water changing by jumps, and each jump would represent the weight of a single molecule. The glass may contain any integral number of molecules but never fractional numbers —if fractions of a molecule exist, at any rate they do not come into play in the evaporation of a glass of water.

THE GASEOUS STATE. The molecules which break loose from the surface of the water as it evaporates form a gas— water-vapour or steam. A gas consists of a vast number of molecules which fly about entirely independently of one another, except at the rare instants at which two collide and so interfere with each other's motion. The extent to which the molecules interfere with one another must obviously depend on their sizes; the larger they are, the more frequent their collisions will be, and the more they will interfere with one another's motion. Actually the extent of this interference provides the best means of estimating the sizes of molecules. They prove to be exceedingly small, being for the most part about a hundred-millionth of an inch in diameter, and, as a general rule, the simpler molecules have the smaller diameters, as we might perhaps have anticipated. The molecule of water has a diameter of 1·8 hundred-millionths of an inch ($4·6 \times 10^{-8}$ cm.), while that of the simpler hydrogen molecule is only just over a hundred-millionth of an inch ($2·7 \times 10^{-8}$ cm.). The fact that a number of different lines of investigation all assign the same diameters to these molecules provides an excellent proof of the reality of their existence.

As molecules are so exceedingly small, they must also be exceedingly numerous. A pint of water contains $1·89 \times 10^{25}$ molecules, each weighing $1·06 \times 10^{-24}$ ounce. If these molecules were placed end to end, they would form a chain capable of encircling the earth over 200 million times. If they were scattered over the whole land surface of the earth, there would be nearly 100 million molecules to every square inch of land. If we think of the molecules as tiny seeds, the total amount of seed needed to sow the whole earth at the rate of 100 million molecules to the square inch could be put into a pint pot.

These molecules move with very high speeds; those which constitute the ordinary air of an ordinary room move with an average speed of about 500 yards a second. This is roughly the speed of a rifle-bullet, and is rather more than the ordinary speed of sound. As we are familiar with this latter speed from everyday experience, it is easy to form some conception of molecular speeds in a gas. It is not a mere accident that molecular speeds are comparable with the speed of sound. Sound is a disturbance which one molecule passes on to another when it collides with it, rather like relays of messengers passing a message on to one another, or Greek torch-bearers handing on their lights. Between collisions the message is carried forward at exactly the speed at which the molecules travel. If these all travelled with precisely the same speed and in precisely the same direction, the sound would of course travel with just the speed of the molecules. But many of them travel on oblique courses, so that although the average speed of individual molecules in ordinary air is about 500 yards a second, the net forward velocity of the sound is only about 370 yards a second.

At high temperatures the molecules may have even greater speeds; the molecules of steam in a boiler may move at 1000 yards a second.

It is the high speed of molecular motion that is responsible for the great pressure exerted by a gas; any surface in contact with ordinary air is exposed to a hail of molecules each moving with the speed of a rifle-bullet. With each breath we take, swarms of millions of millions of millions of molecules enter our bodies, each moving at about 500 yards a second, and nothing but their incessant hammering on the walls of our lungs keeps our chests from collapsing under the hammering of the molecules of the air outside. To take another instance, the piston in a locomotive cylinder is bombarded by about 14×10^{28} molecules every second, each moving at about 800 yards a second. This incessant fusillade of innumerable tiny bullets urges the piston forward in the cylinder, and so propels the train.

Perhaps the best general mental picture we can form of a gas is that of an incessant hail of shot or rifle-bullets flying indiscriminately in all directions, and running into one another at frequent intervals. In ordinary air each molecule collides with some other molecule about 3000 million times every second, and travels an average distance of about $\frac{1}{160,000}$ inch between successive collisions. If we compress a gas to a greater density, so that more molecules are crowded into a given space, collisions become more frequent and the molecules travel shorter distances between collisions. If, on the contrary, we reduce the pressure of the gas, and so lessen its density, collisions become less frequent and the distance that a molecule travels between successive collisions—the "free-path" as it is called—is increased. In the lowest vacua which are at present obtainable in the laboratory, a molecule can travel hundreds of yards without colliding with any other molecule, although there are still 600,000 million molecules to the cubic inch.

Under astronomical conditions still lower vacua may occur. In interstellar space molecules of gas may travel millions of miles without a collision, so few are the molecules to a given volume of space.

It might be thought that the flying molecules would soon be brought to rest by their collisions; rifle-bullets undoubtedly would, but not the molecule-bullets of a gas, for reasons now to be explained.

ENERGY. The amount of the charge of powder used to fire a rifle-bullet gives a measure of the "energy of motion" which is imparted to the bullet. To fire a bullet of double weight at the same speed requires twice as much powder, because the energy of motion of a bullet, or indeed of any other moving object, is proportional to its weight. But to fire the same bullet with double speed does not merely require double the charge of powder. Four times as much powder is needed, because the energy of motion of a moving body is proportional to the *square* of its speed. The experienced motorist is familiar with this; if our brakes stop our car in 20 feet when we are travelling 20 miles an hour, they will not stop it in 40 feet when travelling at 40 miles an hour; we need 80 feet. Double speed requires four times the distance to pull up in, because double speed represents fourfold energy of motion. In general, the energy of motion of any moving body whatever is proportional both to the weight of the body and to the square of its speed.*

One of the great achievements of nineteenth-century physics was to establish the general principle known as the "conservation of energy." Energy can exist in a great variety of forms, and can change about almost endlessly from one form to another, but it can never be utterly destroyed. The energy of a moving body is not lost when the body is brought to rest; it merely takes some other form. When a bullet is brought to rest by hitting a target, part of its energy of motion goes into heating up the target, and part into heating up, or perhaps even melting, the bullet. In its new guise of heat, there is just

---

* This is expressed in the mathematical formula $\frac{1}{2}mv^2$ for the energy of motion of a body of weight m moving with a speed v. If m is measured in grammes, and v in centimetres per second, the energy of motion of the body is said to be $\frac{1}{2}mv^2$ "ergs." Thus an "erg" is the energy of motion of a body of 2 grammes weight (so that $\frac{1}{2}m=1$) moving with a speed of one centimetre a second. As an example, the energy of an express train of 300 tons' weight (3×10^8 gms.) moving at 60 miles an hour (2682 cms. a second) is 1079×10^{14} ergs; a cannon-ball or shell weighing a ton and moving at 1520 feet a second has precisely the same energy.

as much energy as there was in the original motion of the bullet.

In accordance with the same principle, energy cannot be created; all existing energy must have existed from all time, although possibly in some form entirely different from its present form. For instance, gunpowder contains a large amount of energy stored up in the form of chemical energy; we have to take precautions to prevent this bottled-up energy suddenly breaking free and doing damage, as, for instance, by exploding the vessel in which it is contained, kicking things up into the air, and so forth. A rifle is in effect a device for setting free the energy contained in a measured charge of gunpowder, and directing as much of it as possible into the form of energy of motion of a bullet. When we fire a bullet at a target, a specified amount of energy (determined by the charge of powder we have used) is transformed from chemical energy residing in the powder, first into energy of motion residing in the bullet (and to a minor degree in the recoil of the rifle), and then finally into heat-energy residing partly in the spent bullet and partly in the target. Here we have energy taking three different forms in rapid succession. All the life of the universe may be regarded as manifestations of energy masquerading in various forms, and all the changes in the universe as energy running about from one of these forms to the other, but always without altering its total amount. Such is the great law of conservation of energy.

Among the commoner forms of energy may be mentioned electric energy, as exemplified by the energy of a charged accumulator or of a thundercloud; mechanical energy, as exemplified in the coiled spring of a watch or the raised weight of a clock; chemical energy, as exemplified by the energy stored up in gunpowder or in coal, wood and oil; energy of motion, as exemplified by the motion of a bullet, and finally heat-energy, which, as we have seen, is exemplified by the heat which appears when the motion of a rifle-bullet is checked, and the energy of motion of the bullet is lessened.

HEAT. This last example expresses no mere isolated fact; it is a general law that heat can be increased only at the expense of some other form of energy. When, for instance, we want to heat up a room, we light a fire and set free some of the chemical energy which is stored up in coal or wood, or we turn on an electric heater and let the electric current transport to us some of the energy which is being set free by the burning of coal in a distant power-station. But what, in the last resort, is heat, and how does it come to be a form of energy?

Heat, whether of a gas, a liquid or a solid, is merely the energy of motion of individual molecules. When we heat up the air of a room we simply make its molecules move faster, and the total heat of the substance is the total energy of all the molecules of which it is composed. In pumping up a bicycle tyre, we drive the piston of the pump forward in opposition to the impact of innumerable millions of molecules of air inside the pump. In pushing the opposing molecules out of its way, the piston increases their speed of motion. The resulting increase in the energy of motion of the molecules is simply an increase of heat. We could verify this by inserting a thermometer, or, still more simply, by putting our hand on the pump; it feels hot.

MOLECULAR COLLISIONS. Let us now return to the problem we mentioned on p. 103, and examine what happens when two molecule-bullets collide in a gas. Two lead bullets colliding on a battlefield would probably change most of their energy of motion into heat-energy; they would become hotter, or perchance even melt. But how can the molecule-bullets of a gas transform their energy of motion into heat-energy? For them heat and energy of motion are not two different forms of energy, they are one and the same thing; their heat is their energy of motion. The total energy must be conserved, and there is no new disguise that it can assume. So it comes about that when two molecule-bullets collide, the most that can happen is that they may exchange a certain amount of energy of motion. If their energies of motion before collision were, say 7 and 5 respectively, their energies after collision may be 6 and 6, or 8 and 4, or 9 and 3, or any other combination which adds up to 12.

It is the same at every collision; energy can neither be lost nor transformed, and so the bullets on the molecular battlefield go on flying for ever, happily hitting only one another, and doing no harm to one another when they hit. Their energies of motion go up and down, down and up, according as they make lucky hits or the reverse, but the most they have to fear are fluctuations and never total loss of energy; their motion is perpetual, and the total energy of their motion is conserved.

EQUIPARTITION OF ENERGY. Into this random hail of bullets, let us imagine that we project a far heavier projectile, which we may call a cannon-ball, with a speed equal to about the average speed of the bullets. We have seen (p. 103) that the energies of the various projectiles are proportional jointly to their weights and to the squares of their speeds, so that in the present case, in which the speeds are all much the same, the big projectile has more energy than the bullets simply on account of its greater weight. If it weighs as much as a thousand bullets, it has a thousand times as much energy as each single bullet.

Yet the heavy projectile cannot for long continue swaggering through its lesser companions with a thousand times its fair share of energy. Its first experience is to encounter a hail of bullets on its chest. Very few bullets hit it in the back, for they are only moving at about its own speed, and so can hardly overtake it from behind. Moreover, even if they do, their blows on its back are very feeble because they are hardly moving faster than it. But the shower of blows on its chest is serious; every one of these tends to check its speed, and so to lessen its energy. And as the total energy of motion is conserved at every collision, it follows that, while the big projectile is losing energy all the time, the little ones must be gaining energy at its expense.

For how long will this interchange of energy go on? Will it, for instance, continue until the big projectile has lost all its energy, and been brought completely to rest? The problem is one for the mathematician, and it admits of a perfectly exact mathematical solution, which Maxwell gave as far back as 1859. The big projectile is not deprived of all its energy. As its speed gradually decreases, conditions change in all sorts of ways. When we allow for this change of conditions, we find that the energy of the big projectile goes on decreasing, not until it has lost all its energy, but until it has no more energy than the average bullet. When this stage is reached, the hits of the bullets are as likely on the average to increase the energy of the big projectile as to decrease it, so that this ends up by fluctuating around an amount equal to the average energy of the little projectiles.

Maxwell, and others after him, further showed that no matter how many kinds of molecules there may be mixed together in a gas, and no matter how widely their weights may differ from one another, their repeated collisions must ultimately establish a state of things in which big molecules and little, light and heavy, all have the same average energy. This is known as the law of "equipartition of energy".

For instance, air consists of a mixture of molecules of different kinds and of different weights—molecules of helium which are very light, molecules of nitrogen which are far heavier, each weighing as much as seven molecules of helium, and the still heavier molecules of oxygen, each with the weight of eight molecules of helium. The theorem tells us that at any instant the average energy of all the molecules of helium, in spite of their light weights, is exactly equal to the average energy of the molecules of nitrogen, and again each of these is exactly equal to the average energy of the molecules of oxygen. The lighter types of molecule make up for their small weights by their high speeds of motion. Similar statements are of course true for any other mixture of gases.

The truth of the theorem is confirmed observationally in a great variety of ways. As far back as 1846, Graham measured the relative speeds with which the molecules of different kinds of gas moved, by observing the rates at which they streamed through an orifice into a vacuum; these proved to be such that the average energies of the various types of molecules were precisely equal to one another. Thus, it may be accepted as a well-established law of nature that no molecule is allowed permanently to retain more energy than his fellows; in respect of their energies of motion, a gas forms a perfectly organised communistic state in which a law, which they cannot evade, compels the molecules to share their energies equally and fairly.

The average energy of motion of the molecules in a gas is proportional to the temperature of the gas—indeed, this is the way in which temperature is defined. The temperature must not, however, be measured on the Fahrenheit or Centigrade scale in ordinary use, but on what is called the "absolute" scale, which has its zero at $-273°$ Centigrade, or $-459°$ Fahrenheit. This "absolute" zero, being the temperature of a body which has no further heat to lose, is the lowest temperature possible. We can approach to within a small fraction of one degree of it in the laboratory, and find that it freezes air, hydrogen and even helium, the most refractory gas of all, solid. A thermometer placed out in interstellar space, far from any star, would probably show a temperature of only about four degrees above absolute zero, while still lower temperatures must be reached out beyond the limits of the galactic system.

Subject to certain slight modifications, the law of equipartition of energy applies also to liquids and solids.

In liquids and gases, it is possible to perform an experiment analogous to that of projecting our imaginary cannon-ball into the hail of molecule-bullets, and watch events. We may take a few grains of very fine powder, such as powdered gamboge or lycopodium seed, and let these play the part of super-molecules amongst the ordinary molecules of a gas or liquid. A powerful microscope shows that these super-molecules are not brought completely to rest, but retain a certain liveliness of movement, as they are repeatedly hit about by the smaller and quite invisible true molecules. It looks for all the world as though they were affected by a chronic St Vitus' dance, which shows no signs of diminishing as time goes on. These movements are called "Brownian movements," after Robert Brown, the botanist, who first observed them in the sap of plants. Brown at first interpreted them as evidence of real life in the small particles affected by them, an interpretation which he had to abandon when he found that particles of wax showed the same movements. In a series of experiments of amazing delicacy, Perrin not only observed, but also measured, the Brownian movements of small solid particles as they were hit about by the molecules of air and other gases, and deduced the weights of the molecules of these gases with great accuracy.

The molecules of a solid are not possessed of much energy, and so do not move very fast—so slowly indeed that they seldom change their relative positions, the neighbouring molecules gripping them so firmly that their feeble energy of motion cannot extricate them. If we warm the solid up, its molecules acquire more energy, and so begin to move faster. After a time they are moving with such speeds that they can laugh at the restraining pulls from their neighbours; each molecule has enough energy of motion to go where it pleases, and we have a crowd of molecules moving freely as independent units, jostling one another and pushing their way past one another; the substance has assumed the liquid state. To make the picture definite, ice has melted and become water; the frozen grip is relaxed, and the molecules flow freely past one another. Each still exerts forces on its neighbours, but these are no longer strong enough to preclude all motion. Heat the liquid further, thus further increasing the energy of motion of the molecules, and these begin to break loose entirely from their bonds and fly about freely in space, thus forming a gas or vapour. If we go on supplying heat, the whole substance will in time assume the gaseous state. Heating the gas still further now causes the molecule-bullets to fly still faster; it increases their energy of motion.

ATOMS

In the gaseous state, each separate molecule retains all the chemical properties of the solid or liquid substance from which it originated; molecules of steam, for instance, moisten salt or sugar, or combine with thirsty substances such as unslaked lime or potassium chloride, just as water does.

Is it possible to break up the molecules still further? Lucretius and his predecessors would, of course, have said "No." A simple experiment, which, however, was quite beyond their range, will speedily show that they were wrong.

On sliding the two wires of an ordinary electric bell circuit into a tumbler of water, down opposite sides, bubbles of gas will be found to collect on the wires, and chemical examination shows that the two lots of gas have entirely different properties. They cannot, then, both be water-vapour, and in point of fact neither of them is; one proves to be hydrogen and the other oxygen. There is found to be twice as much hydrogen as oxygen, whence we conclude that the electric current has broken up each molecule of water into two parts of hydrogen and one of oxygen. These smaller units into which a molecule is broken are called "atoms." Each molecule of water consists of two atoms of hydrogen (H) and one atom of oxygen (O); this is expressed in its chemical formula H_2O.

A substance which consists solely of atoms of one single kind is described as an element, while one which contains more than one kind of atom is described as a compound. For example, hydrogen and oxygen are elements but water, which is a chemical blend of the two, is a compound.

All the innumerable substances which occur on earth—shoes, ships, sealing-wax, cabbages, kings, carpenters, walruses, oysters, everything we can think of—can be analysed into their constituent atoms, either in this or in other ways. It might be thought that a quite incredible number of different kinds of atoms would emerge from the rich variety of substances we find on earth. Actually the number is quite small. The same atoms turn up again and again, and the great variety of substances we find on earth results, not from any great variety of atoms entering into their composition, but from the great variety of ways in which a few types of atoms can be combined —just as in a colour-print three colours can be combined so as to form almost all the colours we meet in nature, not to mention other weird hues such as never were on land or sea.

Analysis of all known terrestrial substances has, so far, revealed only 92 essentially different kinds of atoms. And even of these 92, the majority are exceedingly rare, most common substances being formed out of the combinations of only about 14 different atoms, say hydrogen (H), carbon (C), nitrogen (N), oxygen (O), sodium (Na), magnesium (Mg), aluminium (Al), silicon (Si), phosphorus (P), sulphur (S), chlorine (Cl), potassium (K), calcium (Ca), and iron (Fe).

In this way, the whole earth, with its endless diversity of substances, is found to be a building built of standard bricks—

the atoms. And of these only a few types, about 14, occur at all abundantly in the structure, the others appearing but rarely.

We have already seen (p. 34) how the spectrum of the light received from a star informs us as to the composition of the star's atmosphere. With a few quite unimportant exceptions, every line in the spectra of the stars can be identified as originating in some type of atom known on earth, so that the whole universe appears to be built of the same 92 kinds of atoms as are known on earth, although it must be remembered that we have no direct evidence as to the kinds of atoms existing in stellar interiors.

We shall see below (pp. 164, 165) that the various kinds of atoms occur in much the same relative proportions in the stars as on earth. Thus twelve of the fourteen elements which are abundant on earth are abundant also in the stars. This is not surprising if we consider that the earth probably came into being as a condensation of the gases in the atmosphere of one particular star—namely, the sun (p. 245). Hydrogen and helium are less abundant on earth than in stellar atmospheres, but there is a reason for this also. When the earth was still a diffuse ball of hot gas, its gravitational power would not be adequate to hold down the rapidly moving atoms of these substances (p. 212) so that these would rapidly diffuse away and be lost to the earth for ever. Thus very little helium remains on earth, while hydrogen is found only in combination with other atoms of other substances.

THE STRUCTURE OF THE ATOM. Until quite recently, atoms were regarded as the permanent bricks of which the whole universe was built. All the changes of the universe were supposed to amount to nothing more drastic than a re-arrangement of permanent indestructible atoms; like a child's box of bricks, these built many buildings in turn. The story of twentieth-century physics is primarily the story of the shattering of this concept.

It was towards the end of the last century that Crookes, Lenard and, above all, Sir J. J. Thomson first began to break up the atom. The structures which had been deemed the unbreakable bricks of the universe for more than 2000 years were suddenly shown to be very susceptible to having fragments chipped off. A mile-stone was reached in 1897, when Thomson showed that these fragments were identical, no matter what type of atom they came from; they were of equal weight and they carried equal charges of negative electricity. On account of this last property they were called "electrons." The atom cannot, however, be built up of electrons and nothing else, for as each electron carries a negative charge of electricity, a structure which consisted of nothing but electrons would also carry a negative charge. Two negative charges of electricity repel one another, as also do two positive charges, while two charges, one of positive and one of negative electricity, attract one another. This makes it easy to determine whether any body or structure carries a positive or a negative charge of electricity, or no charge at all. Observation shows that a complete atom carries no charge at all, so that somewhere in the atom there must be a positive charge of electricity, of amount just sufficient to neutralise the combined negative charges of all the electrons.

In 1911 experiments by Lord Rutherford and others revealed the architecture of the atom, in its main lines at least. We shall see below (p. 120) how nature herself provides an endless supply of small particles charged with positive electricity, and moving with very high speeds, in the α-particles shot off from radio-active substances. Rutherford's method was in brief to fire these into atoms and observe the result. And the surprising result he obtained was that the vast majority of these bullets passed straight through the atom as though it simply did not exist. It was like shooting at a ghost.

Yet the atom was not all ghostly. A tiny fraction—perhaps one in 10,000—of the bullets were deflected from their courses as if they had met something very substantial indeed. A mathematical calculation showed that these obstacles could only be the missing positive charges of the atoms.

A detailed study of the paths of these projectiles proved that the whole positive charge of an atom must be concentrated in a single very small space, having dimensions of the order of only a millionth of a millionth of an inch. In this way,

Rutherford was led to propound the view of atomic structure which is generally associated with his name. He supposed the chemical properties and nature of the atom to reside in a weighty, but excessively minute, central "nucleus" carrying a positive charge of electricity, around which a number of negatively charged electrons described orbits. He had to suppose that the electrons were in motion in the atom, otherwise the attraction of positive for negative electricity would immediately draw them into the central nucleus—just as gravitational attraction would cause the earth to fall into the sun, were it not for the earth's orbital motion. In brief, Rutherford supposed the atom to be constructed like the solar system, the heavy central nucleus playing the part of the sun and the electrons acting the parts of the planets.

We have already noticed that science cannot hope ever to discover the true nature of the ingredients of the material universe; from the nature of things, this lies for ever beyond our ken. The most we can aspire to is a model or picture which shall explain and account for some of the observed properties of matter; where this fails, we must supplement it with some other model or picture, which will in its turn fail with other properties of matter, and so on.

Rutherford's picture of the atom does not account for all of the observed properties of matter, but it accounts for a great number, and these happen to include those properties which are important for our present discussion. For this reason we shall continue to describe the atom in terms of Rutherford's picture, and its subsequent extension by Bohr and others.

According to this picture, the electrons are supposed to move round the nucleus with just such speeds as are necessary to save them from being drawn into it. These speeds prove to be terrific, the average electron revolving around its nucleus several thousand million million times every second, with a speed of hundreds of miles a second. Thus the smallness of their orbits does not prevent the electrons moving with higher orbital speeds than the planets, or even the stars themselves.

By clearing a space around the central nucleus, and so preventing other atoms from coming too near to it, these electronic orbits give size to the atom. The volume of space kept clear by the electrons is enormously greater than the total volume of the electrons; roughly, the ratio of volumes is that of the battlefield to the bullets. The atom, with a radius of about 2×10^{-8} cm., has about 100,000 times the diameter, and so about a thousand million million times the volume, of a single electron, which has a radius of only about 2×10^{-13} cm. The nucleus, although it generally weighs 3000 or 4000 times as much as all the electrons in the atom together, is at most comparable in size with, and may be even smaller than, a single electron.

We have already commented on the extreme emptiness of astronomical space. Choose a point in space at random, and the odds against its being occupied by a star are enormous. Even the solar system consists overwhelmingly of empty space; choose a spot inside the solar system at random, and there are still immense odds against its being occupied by a planet or even by a comet, meteorite or smaller body. And now we see that this emptiness extends also to the space of physics. Even inside the atom we choose a point at random, and the odds against there being anything there are immense; they are of the order of at least millions of millions to one. We saw how six specks of dust inside Waterloo Station represented—or rather over-represented—the extent to which space was crowded with stars. In the same way a few wasps—six for the atom of carbon—flying around in Waterloo Station will represent the extent to which the atom is crowded with electrons—all the rest is emptiness. As we pass the whole structure of the universe under review, from the giant nebulae and the vast interstellar and internebular spaces down to the tiny structure of the atom, little but vacant space passes before our mental gaze. We live in a gossamer universe; pattern, plan and design are there in abundance, but solid substance is rare.

ATOMIC NUMBERS. The different elements have acquired names—hydrogen, helium, argon, etc.—which are usually related to some property of the element or to the circumstances of its discovery. Thus hydrogen is so named because it is the prime constituent of water, helium because it was first detected in the sun, argon (a-$\epsilon\rho\gamma o\nu$) because it is an inert gas which refuses to combine with other elements, so that its only activity in the universe consists of a mere existence.

It would be far simpler, although less picturesque, if we could agree to designate the different elements by the numbers 1, 2, 3, 4, ... For the chemical properties of the elements and the structure of the atoms which compose them are intimately related to the integral numbers 1, 2, 3, 4, ... These are the numbers of electrons which fly round in orbits in the different atoms, and are known as the "atomic numbers" of the elements. Atoms of all atomic numbers from 1 to 92 have now been found, so that there are 92 "elements" whose atomic numbers occupy the whole range from 1 to 92 continuously.

The atom of atomic number unity is of course the simplest of all. It is the hydrogen atom, in which a solitary electron revolves around a nucleus whose charge of positive electricity is exactly equal in amount, although opposite in sign, to the charge on the negative electron. Experiment shows that the nucleus has about 1847 times the mass of the electron, so that, to a good approximation, we may suppose the whole mass of the atom to be concentrated in the nucleus. And this, as we shall soon see, is true for every kind of atom.

Next comes the helium atom of atomic number 2, in which two electrons revolve about a nucleus which has four times the weight of the hydrogen nucleus, although carrying only twice its electric charge. After this comes the lithium atom of atomic number 3, in which three electrons revolve around a nucleus having seven times the weight of the hydrogen nucleus and three times its charge. And so it goes on, until we reach uranium, the heaviest of all atoms known on earth, which has 92 electrons describing orbits about a nucleus of 238 times the weight of the hydrogen nucleus.

The chemical properties of an atom are determined by its atomic number. We shall see that a great variety of atoms may all have the same atomic number, but if so they all have the same chemical properties. Thus there are eleven kinds of atom all with the atomic number 50, but all have the chemical properties of simple tin.

ATOMIC WEIGHTS. From our picture of a gas as a collection of molecules flying about at random, it can be deduced that the number of molecules in any assigned volume of a gas does not depend on the chemical constitution of the gas at all, but only on the pressure, volume and temperature of the gas. We hardly realise how remarkable a law this is until we take a concrete example of it. Let us take two flasks of equal size, and stand them side by side so that both will be at the same temperature; let us leave small openings in the stoppers of each, so that the interiors of both will be at the same pressure, namely atmospheric pressure; let us now fill one with the lightest gas we know—hydrogen—and the other with a heavy gas such as oxygen. The law tells us that the two flasks will contain precisely the same number of molecules, notwithstanding that the molecules are so different in their properties.

If we weigh the two flasks, we shall find that the oxygen in one flask will weigh just about sixteen times as much as the hydrogen in the other. From this we conclude that each molecule of oxygen must weigh about sixteen times as much as a molecule of hydrogen. By this method it is possible to discover the relative weights of the molecules of different substances.

It has long been known that these weights stand in simple relations to one another; they can in fact usually be expressed as exact or nearly exact multiples of a definite unit weight. This unit is approximately the weight of the hydrogen atom, but is more conveniently defined as one-sixteenth of the weight of the oxygen atom, since this definition is found to bring the weights of the various atoms still nearer to integral multiples of the unit.

The weight of any type of molecule, measured in terms of this unit, is called the "molecular weight" of the molecule in question. The weight of any type of atom, measured in terms of the same unit, is called the "atomic weight" of the atom in question. In a general way, those atoms which have the higher atomic numbers have also the higher atomic weights: the two increase together. Except for hydrogen and the heaviest atoms of all, the atomic weight is usually about double the atomic number. We have, for instance:

Element			Atomic number	Atomic weight
Hydrogen	...	...	1	1
Helium	...	...	2	4
Carbon	...	...	6	12
Nitrogen	...	...	7	14
Oxygen	...	...	8	16
Tin	...	...	50	118·7
Mercury	...	...	80	200·6

ISOTOPES. It used to be thought that a pure sample of any element, such as mercury or chlorine, consisted of entirely similar atoms, every one of which had not only the same atomic number, but also the same atomic weight. We now know that atoms of the same chemical element can exist in a variety of different forms, known as "isotopes," which are distinguished by having different atomic weights.

When the existence of isotopes is recognised, the atomic weights of atoms are found to move still nearer to integral numbers. For example, the atomic weight of chlorine used to be given as 35·5, which was taken to mean that a sample of pure chlorine consisted of atoms every one of which was 35·5 times as massive as the atom of hydrogen. Aston now finds that it consists of a mixture of two different kinds of atoms of atomic weights 35 and 37, these being mixed in the proportion of 3 : 1, and so giving a mean atomic weight of 35·5. Actually the atomic weights of the two isotopes are 34·980 and 36·978. In the same way mercury of atomic weight 200·6 is found to be a mixture of nine isotopes of atomic weights 196, 197, 198, 199, 200, 201, 202, 203, and 204. Tin, of atomic weight 118·7, is a mixture of eleven isotopes of atomic weights 112, 114, 115, 116, 117, 118, 119, 120, 121, 122 and 124.

Even the simplest of substances now proves to be a mixture of isotopes. Hydrogen is a mixture of three of atomic weights 1, 2 and 3—or, more precisely, 1·0081, 2·0142, and 3·016. Helium again is a mixture of three of weights 3, 4 and 5—or, more precisely, 3·0172, 4·0034 and 5·01.

PROTONS AND NEUTRONS. The atomic number of an atom must be an exact integer, because the outer structure of the atom consists of an integral number of similar units—electrons. The facts just recorded about atomic weight have often led to the conjecture that the inner structure of the atom—the weight-carrying nucleus—must also consist of an integral number of similar units. If this were so, the unit in question could be only one thing, namely the nucleus of the hydrogen atom, which we call the proton. The atomic weights of all atoms would then be integral numbers, since the mass-carrying part of the atom would consist of an integral number of protons.

But such a conjecture leads to difficulties. The hydrogen atom, like all other atoms, is electrically uncharged—the total charge of its constituents is nil. As there are only two constituents, an electron and a proton, we see that the proton must carry a positive electric charge equal in amount to the negative charge of the electron.

This explains the normal hydrogen atom well enough, but not the normal helium atom. This has an atomic number 2, but an atomic weight 4, so that according to our conjecture its nucleus must consist of four protons, and, as there would be only two electrons circling round it, there would be an unbalanced electric charge equal to that of two electrons.

Element	Atomic number (no. of electrons)	Atomic weight (no. of neutrons)	No. of protons	No. of neutrons
Hydrogen	1	1, 2, 3	1	0, 1, 2
Helium	2	3, 4, 5	2	1, 2, 3
Carbon	6	12, 13	6	6, 7
Nitrogen	7	14, 15	7	7, 8
Oxygen	8	16, 17, 18	8	8, 9, 10
Tin	50	112 to 122; 124	50	62 to 72; 74
Mercury	80	196 to 204	80	116 to 124

We now picture the nucleus of every atom, except the simple hydrogen atom, as containing particles of two kinds—the proton already described, and a second kind of particle, known as a neutron (p. 123). The latter has about the same weight as the proton but carries no electric charge, either positive or negative. The nucleus of every atom contains just sufficient protons to neutralise the negative charge of the electrons outside, while neutrons provide the remainder of its mass. Thus the atomic number of the atom measures both the number of protons and of electrons. If the atomic weight is exactly twice the atomic number, it also measures the number of neutrons. Isotopes are of course formed by varying the number of neutrons, while keeping the number of protons fixed.

This is illustrated in the table above (p. 118), which exhibits the composition of all the elements and isotopes just mentioned.

RADIO-ACTIVITY

While physical science was still engaged in breaking up the atom into its component factors, it made the further discovery that the nuclei themselves were neither permanent nor indestructible. In 1896 Becquerel had found that various substances containing uranium possessed the remarkable property, as it then appeared, of spontaneously affecting photographic plates in their vicinity. This observation led to the discovery of a new property of matter, namely radio-activity. All the results obtained from the study of radio-activity in the few following years were co-ordinated in the hypothesis of "spontaneous disintegration" which Rutherford and Soddy advanced in 1903. According to this hypothesis in its present form, radio-activity indicates a spontaneous break-up of the nuclei of the atoms of radio-active substances. These atoms are so far from being permanent and indestructible that their very nuclei crumble away with the mere lapse of time, so that what was once the nucleus of a uranium atom is transformed after sufficient time into the nucleus of a lead atom.

The process of transformation is not instantaneous; it proceeds gradually and by distinct stages. During its progress, three types of product are emitted, which are designated α-rays, β-rays, and γ-rays.

These were originally described indiscriminately as "rays" because all three were found to have the power of penetrating through a certain thickness of air, metal, or other substance. It was not until later that their true nature was discovered. It is well known that magnetic forces, such as, for instance, occur in the space between the poles of a magnet, cause a moving particle charged with electricity to deviate from a straight course; the particle deviates in one direction or the other according as it is charged with positive or negative electricity. On passing the various rays emitted by radio-active substances through the space between the poles of a powerful magnet, the α-rays were found to consist of particles charged with positive electricity, and the β-rays to consist of particles charged with negative electricity. But the most powerful magnetic forces which could be employed failed to cause the slightest deviation in the paths of the γ-rays, from which it was concluded that either the γ-rays were not material particles at all, or that, if they were, they carried no electric charges. The former of these alternatives was subsequently proved to be the true one.

α-PARTICLES. The positively charged particles which constitute α-rays are generally described as α-particles. In 1909 Rutherford and Royds allowed α-particles to penetrate through a thin glass wall of less than a hundredth of a millimetre thickness into a chamber from which they could not escape—a sort of mouse-trap for α-particles. After the process had continued for a long time, the final result was not an accumulation of α-particles but an accumulation of the gas helium, the next simplest gas after hydrogen. In this way it was established that the positively charged α-particles are simply nuclei of helium atoms; the α-particles, being positively charged, had attracted negatively charged electrons to themselves out of the walls of the chamber and the result was a collection of complete helium atoms.

The α-particles move with enormous speeds, which depend upon the nature of the radio-active substance from which they have been shot out. The fastest particles of all, those emitted by Thorium C', move with a speed of 12,800 miles a second; even the slowest, those from Uranium 1, have a speed of 8800 miles a second, which is about 30,000 times the ordinary molecular velocity in air. Particles moving with such speeds as these knock all ordinary molecules out of their way; this explains the great penetrating power of the α-rays.

β-PARTICLES. By examining the extent to which their motion was influenced by magnetic forces, the β-rays were found to consist of negatively charged electrons, exactly similar to those which surround the nucleus in all atoms. As an α-particle carries a positive charge equal in amount to that of two electrons, an atom which has ejected an α-particle is left with a deficiency of positive charge, or, what comes to the same thing, with a negative charge, equal to that of two electrons. Consequently it is natural, and indeed almost inevitable, that the ejections of α-particles should alternate with ejections of negatively charged electrons, in the proportion of one α-particle to two electrons, so that the balance of positive and negative electricity in the atom may be maintained. The β-particles move with even greater speeds than the α-particles, many approaching to within a few per cent. of the velocity of light (186,000 miles a second).

We have described the nucleus of an atom as containing only protons and neutrons, so that the question arises as to the origin of these electrons. The simplest solution is to regard a neutron as a composite particle which consists of a proton and an electron in combination. In radio-active disintegration a neutron may break up into its two component particles; the electron is shot away, but the proton remains.

One of the most beautiful devices known to physical science, the invention of Professor C. T. R. Wilson, makes it possible to study the motions of the α- and β-particles as they thread their way through a gas, colliding with its molecules on their way. A chamber through which the particles can be made to travel is filled with water-vapour in such a condition that the passage of an electrically charged particle leaves behind it a trail of condensations which can be photographed. We cannot see the α- or β-particles themselves, but we see the condensation they produce, much as we can see the condensation trail of an aeroplane which is too high up in the sky to be itself seen.

In Plate XXV (p. 122), the trails of both α- and β-particles appear on the same photographic plate. The four straight thick lines are tracks of α-particles; the curved and much fainter lines are tracks of β-particles. As the α-particles weigh nearly 7400 times as much as the β-particles, they naturally create more disturbance in the gas, and so leave broader and more pronounced tracks; also they pursue a comparatively straight course while the lighter β-particles are deflected from their courses by many of the molecules they meet. The knobby-looking excrescences which may be seen emerging from both sides of the longest of the α-ray tracks are of interest; they represent the short paths of electrons knocked out of atoms by the passage of the α-particle.

γ-RAYS. As has already been mentioned, the γ-rays are not material particles at all; they prove to be merely radiation of a very special kind, which we shall discuss below (p. 130).

Thus the break-up of a radio-active atom may be compared to the discharge of a gun; the α-particle is the shot fired, the β-particles are the smoke, and the γ-rays are the flash. The atom of lead which finally remains is the unloaded gun, and the original radio-active atom, of uranium or what not, was the loaded gun. And the special peculiarity of radio-active guns is that they go off spontaneously and of their own accord. All attempts to pull the trigger have so far failed, or at least have led to inconclusive results; we can only wait and the gun will be found to fire itself in time, although it may take thousands of millions of years to do so.

ATOMIC NUCLEI

With unimportant exceptions the property of radio-activity occurs only in the most complex and massive of atoms, being indeed confined to those of atomic numbers above 83. Yet, although the lighter atoms are not liable to spontaneous disintegration in the same way as the heavy radio-active atoms, their nuclei can be broken up by artificial means. In 1920 Rutherford, using radio-active atoms as guns, fired α-particles at light atoms and found that direct hits broke up the nuclei of the atoms.

In the earliest experiments of all, the α-particles were shot at atoms of nitrogen; some of the projectiles penetrated their targets, the joint structure subsequently disintegrating into an oxygen nucleus (an isotope of atomic weight 17), and a hydrogen nucleus (or proton). Here then a transmutation of elements had at last been effected by man; the dream of the alchemists had come true.

This simple transmutation disclosed one typical difference between the spontaneous disintegration of the heavy radio-active atoms and the artificial disintegration of the light atoms; in the former case, apart from the ever-present β-rays and

PLATE XXV

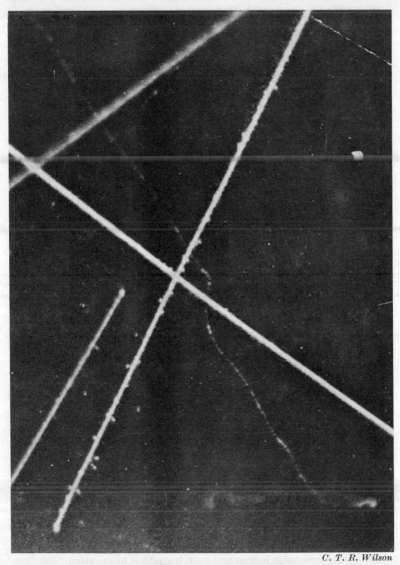

C. T. R. Wilson

The tracks of α- and β-particles

PLATE XXVI

P. M. S. Blackett

Fig. 2

Collisions of α-particles with Nitrogen Atoms

In fig. 1 the α-particle merely rebounds from a nitrogen atom. In fig. 2
it drives out a proton and then joins itself to the atom

γ-rays, only α-particles are ejected, while in the latter case α-particles were not ejected, but protons.

These sensational events in the atomic underworld could be photographed by Professor C. T. R. Wilson's condensation method already explained. Plate XXVI shows two collisions of an α-particle with a nitrogen atom photographed by P. M. S. Blackett. The straight lines are merely the quite uneventful tracks of ordinary α-particles similar to those already shown in Plate XXV. But one α-particle track in each photograph suddenly branches, so that the complete figure is of a Y-shape. There is little room for doubt that in fig. 1 the branch occurs because the α-particle has collided with a nitrogen atom; the stem of the Y is the track of the α-particle before the collision; the two upper branches are the tracks of the α-particle and the nitrogen atom after the collision, the latter now moving with enormous speed and hitting everything out of its way. By taking simultaneous photographs in two directions at right angles, as shown in the Plate, Blackett was able to reconstruct the whole collision, and the angles were found to agree exactly with those which dynamical theory would require on this interpretation of the photograph.

The occurrence photographed in fig. 2 is of a different type, for exact measurement shows that the angles are not those which dynamical theory would require if the upper branches of the Y were the tracks of the α-particles and the nitrogen atom as in fig. 1. The stem of the Y is still an ordinary α-particle track, but the long faint upper branch is the track of something less massive than an α-particle, namely a particle of only a quarter the weight of an α-particle which has been shot out of the nucleus, whilst the shorter and clearer branch is that of the nitrogen atom moving along in company with the α-particle, which it has captured. It would take too much space to describe in full the beautiful method by which Blackett has established this interpretation of his photographs, but there is little room for doubt that in fig. 2 he has succeeded in photographing the break-up of the nucleus of an atom of nitrogen.

It was by a very similar procedure that the existence of the neutron was established. In 1931, two German physicists,

Bothe and Becker, bombarded the light elements beryllium and boron with α-particles and obtained a new and very penetrating form of radiation, which Chadwick subsequently showed must consist of material particles having the same mass as the proton *but uncharged*. This was something new in a world which was supposed to contain only charged particles. But we have noticed that the neutron may be regarded as a proton and an electron in combination, and this interpretation restores the picture of a world consisting of only charged particles.

COSMIC RADIATION

At one time it seemed to be a piece of extraordinary good luck that in the α-particles nature had herself provided us with projectiles of sufficient shattering power to smash the nucleus of the atom and disclose its secrets to the observation of the physicist. More recently nature has been found to provide projectiles of even greater shattering power in the "cosmic radiation" which continually bombards the surface of the earth. The same radiation is found throughout the atmosphere and as its intensity increases as we move upwards, it is clear that it must originally come in from outside. It cannot, however, come from the sun or stars; if it did, the radiation received on earth would come mostly from the sun, and so would be more intense by day than by night. As this is found not to be the case, the radiation is generally supposed to originate in distant nebulae or cosmic masses other than stars—hence the name of "cosmic radiation."

The amount of this radiation is very great. Even at sealevel, where it is least intense, it breaks up about ten atoms in every cubic inch of air each second. It must break up millions of atoms in each of our bodies every second—and we do not know what its physiological effects may be. Regener has estimated that the total energy of the radiation that we receive on earth is very nearly equal to that of the total radiation, light and heat together, that we receive from all the stars. Yet our position well inside the galactic system secures for us a greater amount of stellar light and heat than is received by most parts of space, and this is only slightly above the cosmic radiation in total amount. On taking an average through the whole of space, including the vast stretches of internebular space, it seems likely that cosmic radiation is enormously more plentiful than stellar light and heat, and so is the most abundant form of radiation in the whole universe.

It is also the most penetrating form of radiation known. Ordinary light will hardly pass through metals or solid substances at all; only a tiny fraction emerges through the thinnest of gold-leaf. The X-radiation has far greater penetrating power, but will pass through only a few millimetres thickness of lead. The most highly penetrating γ-rays from radium B will pass through inches of lead. The radiation we have just been discussing varies in penetrating power; the most penetrating part of it will pass through many yards of lead.

Because of its immense powers of penetration, this radiation must pass through the sparse matter of interstellar space so freely that, when once it has been set free in space, it may fairly be regarded as indestructible. For, as we have already seen, the amount of matter in space, including the masses of the stars and nebulae, is probably only sufficient to give an average density in space of the order of 10^{-28} gramme to the cubic centimetre. This means that radiation must travel over an average path of 10^{28} centimetres before encountering as much matter as there is in a layer of water one centimetre in thickness. Radiation travelling with the speed of light requires ten thousand million years to traverse this length of path; corpuscles or charged particles must necessarily travel more slowly than light, and so would take an even longer time. In this length of time the decrease in the radiation is only that due to traversing a single centimetre of water, and so is quite inappreciable; the radiation must travel for millions of millions of years before experiencing any appreciable diminution in strength. In view of what we shall find later as to the probable age of the universe this means that the radiation is virtually inextinguishable; practically all that has ever been generated since time began is still wandering round and round space. The question of primary interest, however, is not when or where the radiation was generated, but how.

It might seem easy to test whether the radiation is a kind of γ-radiation, or consists of particles or corpuscles, by observing whether or not the radiation is bent in a magnetic field, but actually the problem is one of very great complexity. The one certain and outstanding property of the radiation is its capacity to shatter any molecules on which it falls. The *débris* of these shattered molecules then follows the original radiation on its course, so that by the time the radiation reaches the surface of the earth, it is likely in any event to consist of a mixture of particles of various kinds and of waves of varied wave-lengths, as is in fact found to be the case.

This being so, there is only one magnetic field which is of any use for testing the quality of the original radiation; it is the magnetic field of the earth, which the radiation has to traverse before it reaches the earth's atmosphere and becomes mixed up with atomic *débris* of its own creation. Measurements of the intensity of cosmic radiation have shown that it reaches different parts of the earth's surface in different strengths; the inference is that it has been bent by the earth's magnetic field, and so must consist, in part at least, of electrified particles. Millikan and Neher have recently found that more than 60 per cent of the energy of cosmic radiation entering the earth's atmosphere must be carried by electrically charged particles, each particle carrying energy which ranges from 2 to 15 times that acquired by an electron in falling through a thousand million volts. Thus the energy of motion of each incoming particle is comparable with that of a whole atom moving at a speed nearly equal to that of light. No wonder, then, that the radiation exhibits the high penetrating power already mentioned, or that it is so nearly indestructible.

THE POSITRON. Magnetic fields created in the laboratory can, however, be used to test the nature of the *débris* which results from the impact of the radiation on atomic nuclei. In 1932, C. D. Anderson showed in this way that this *débris* contained, amongst other ingredients, particles which had a positive charge equal to that of the proton, but a mass only comparable with, and probably equal to, the mass of the electron. These particles may properly be described as positively charged electrons, and are called "positrons." As they are believed to emerge from atomic nuclei, it would seem reasonable to suppose that they must be normal constituents of the nuclei. Anderson suggested that the proton may not be a fundamental indivisible particle, but may be a composite structure consisting of a positron and a neutron in combination.

But the *débris* of nuclei which have been shattered by cosmic radiation is found to contain electrons as well as positrons, the electrons emerging, so far as can be seen, from the same atomic nuclei as the positrons. This led Blackett and Occhialini to suggest that the electrons and positrons may be born in pairs as the result of the processes of bombardment and disintegration of atomic nuclei.

It seems fairly certain that the positron has at most but a temporary existence. For positrons do not appear to be associated with matter under normal conditions, and it seems likely that they disappear from existence, almost as soon as they are born, by combining with negative electrons. Just as a pair of electrons—one positively charged and one negatively charged—can be born out of nothing but energy, so they can die in one another's arms and leave nothing but energy behind.

Before the existence of the positron had been observed, or even suspected experimentally, Professor Dirac of Cambridge had propounded a mathematical theory which predicted not only the existence of the positron, but also the way in which it ought to behave. Dirac's theory is too abstrusely mathematical to be explained here, but it predicts that a shower of positrons ought gradually to fade away by spontaneous combination with negative electrons, following the same law of decay as radio-active substances. And the average life of a positron is predicted to be one of only a few millionths of a second, which amply explains why the positron can live long enough to be photographed in a condensation chamber, but not long enough to show its presence elsewhere in the universe.

THE MESON. The study of cosmic radiation has unearthed yet another type of particle—the meson, or heavy electron as it is sometimes called. This also is found in the *débris* which cosmic radiation leaves behind when it strikes matter. It has the same charge as an electron, but its mass is intermediate between those of the electron and the proton. Its existence seems to be necessitated by certain properties of cosmic radiation, especially the high penetrating power, but very little is known of its own properties. Different determinations of its mass have given values ranging from 40 to 500 times the mass of the electron—perhaps a mass of about 120 electron-masses seems the most likely, but it is not even certain that the meson always has the same mass. There is some evidence that it is liable to spontaneous decay of the radio-active type, its normal life being only a few millionths of a second. If so, mesons cannot, of course, form a constituent of the primary cosmic radiation, but must arise as secondary by-products after the primary radiation has become entangled in the earth's atmosphere.

There is also some evidence that both positively and negatively charged mesons exist, and that a free proton may dissociate into a neutron and a positively charged meson, while it has also been conjectured that a negative meson may dissociate into an ordinary electron and yet another new type of particle known as the *neutrino*. These and other similar conjectures are, however, somewhat unimportant for our present discussion.

RADIATION

We have so far discussed only the material constituents of matter, picturing the atom as built up of some or all of the particles which we have described as electrons, protons, neutrons and positrons. Yet this is not the whole story. If it were, every atom would consist of a certain number of protons and neutrons combined with just sufficient electrons and positrons to make the total electric charge equal to zero. Thus, apart from the insignificant weights of electrons and positrons, the weight of every atom would be an exact multiple of the weight of a hydrogen atom. Experiment shows this not to be the case.

ELECTROMAGNETIC ENERGY. To get at the whole truth, we have to recognise that, in addition to containing material electrons and protons, with possible neutrons and positrons, the atom contains yet a further ingredient which we may describe as electromagnetic energy. We may think of this, although with something short of absolute scientific accuracy, as bottled radiation.

If we disturb the surface of a pond with a stick, a series of ripples starts from the stick and travels, in a series of ever-expanding circles, over the surface of the pond. As the water resists the motion of the stick, we have to work to keep the pond in a state of agitation. The energy of this work is transformed, in part at least, into the energy of the ripples. We can see that the ripples carry energy about with them, because they cause a floating cork or a toy boat to rise up against the earth's gravitational pull. Thus the ripples provide a mechanism for distributing over the surface of the pond the energy that we put into the pond through the medium of the moving stick.

Light and all other forms of radiation are analogous to water-ripples or waves, in that they distribute energy from a central source. The sun's radiation distributes through space the vast amount of energy which is generated inside the sun.

We have noticed how we cannot hope to know the true nature of the universe; the most we can do is to draw pictures or models for ourselves to illustrate some or all of the properties of some or all of its parts. And to illustrate those properties of light with which we are now concerned, the best picture that we can draw consists of a succession of waves. Light and other types of radiation are propagated in such a form that they have many of the properties of a succession of waves.

We have seen how the different colours of light which in combination constitute sunlight can be separated out by passing the light through a prism, thus forming a rainbow or "spectrum" of colours. The separation can also be effected by an alternative instrument, the diffraction grating, which consists merely of a metal mirror with a large number of parallel lines scratched evenly across its surface. The theory of the action of this latter instrument is well understood; it shows that actually the light is separated into waves of different wave-lengths.* This proves that different colours of light are produced by waves of different lengths, and at the

---

* The wave-length in a system of ripples is the distance from the crest of one ripple to that of the next, and the term may be applied to all phenomena of an undulatory nature.

same time enables us to measure the lengths of the waves which correspond to the different colours of light.

These prove to be very minute. The reddest light we can see, which is that of longest wave-length, has a wave-length of only $\frac{3}{100,000}$ inch ($7 \cdot 5 \times 10^{-5}$ cm.); the most violet light we can see has a wave-length only half of this, or $0 \cdot 000015$ inch. Light of all colours travels with the same uniform speed of 186,000 miles, or 3×10^{10} centimetres, a second. The number of waves of red light which pass any fixed point in a second is accordingly no fewer than four hundred million million. This number is called the "frequency" of the light. Violet light has the still higher frequency of eight hundred million million; when we see a violet object, eight hundred million million waves of light enter our eyes each second.

The spectrum of analysed sunlight appears to the eye to stretch from red light at one end to violet light at the other, but these are not its true limits. When certain chemical salts are placed beyond the violet end of the visible spectrum, they are found to shine vividly, showing that even out here energy is being transported, although in invisible form. And other methods make it clear that the same is true out beyond the red end of the spectrum. A thermometer, or other heat-measuring instrument, placed here will show that energy is being received in the form of heat.

In this way we find that regions of invisible radiation stretch indefinitely from both ends of the visible spectrum. From one end—the red—we can pass continuously to waves of the type used for wireless transmission, which have wave-lengths of the order of hundreds, or even thousands, of yards. From the violet end, we pass through waves of shorter and ever shorter wave-length—all the various forms of ultra-violet radiation. At wave-lengths of from about a hundredth to a thousandth of the wave-length of visible light, we come to the familiar X-rays, which penetrate through inches of our flesh, so that we can photograph the bones inside. Far out even beyond these, we come to the type of radiation which constitutes the γ-rays, its wave-length being of the order of $\frac{1}{10,000,000,000}$ inch, or only about a hundred-thousandth part of the wave-length of visible light. Thus the γ-rays may be regarded as invisible radiation of extremely short wave-length. We shall discuss the exact function they serve later. For the moment let us merely remark that in the first instance they served the extremely useful function of fogging Becquerel's photographic plates, thus leading to the detection of the radio-active property of matter.

It is a commonplace of modern electromagnetic theory that energy of every kind carries weight about with it, weight which is in every sense as real as the weight of a ton of coal. A ray of light causes an impact on any surface on which it falls, just as a jet of water does, or a blast of wind, or the fall of a ton of coal; with a sufficiently strong light one could knock a man down just as surely as with the jet of water from a fire-hose. This is not a mere theoretical speculation. The pressure of light on a surface has been both detected and measured by direct experiment. The experiments are extraordinarily difficult because, judged by all ordinary standards, the weight carried by radiation is exceedingly small; all the radiation emitted from a 50 horse-power searchlight working continuously for a century weighs only about a twentieth of an ounce.

It follows that any substance which is emitting radiation must at the same time be losing weight. In particular, the disintegration of any radio-active substance must involve a decrease of weight, since it is accompanied by the emission of radiation in the form of γ-rays. The ultimate fate of an ounce of uranium may be expressed by the equation:

$$1 \text{ ounce uranium} = \begin{cases} 0 \cdot 8653 \text{ ounce lead,} \\ 0 \cdot 1345 \quad ,, \quad \text{helium,} \\ 0 \cdot 0002 \quad ,, \quad \text{radiation.} \end{cases}$$

The lead and helium together contain just as many electrons and just as many protons as did the original ounce of uranium, but their combined weight is short of the weight of the original uranium by about one part in 4000. Where 4000 ounces of matter originally existed, only 3999 now remain; the missing ounce has gone off in the form of radiation.

This makes it clear that we could in no case expect the

weights of the various atoms to be exact multiples of the weight of the hydrogen atom; any such expectation would ignore the weight of the bottled-up electromagnetic energy which is capable of being set free and going off into space in the form of radiation as the atom changes its make-up. The weight of this energy is relatively small, so that the weights of the atoms must be expected to be approximately, although not exactly, integral multiples of that of the hydrogen atom, and this expectation is confirmed. The exact weight of our atomic building is not simply the total weight of all its bricks; something must be added for the weight of the mortar—the electromagnetic energy—which keeps the bricks bound together.

Thus the normal atom consists of its material constituents—protons, electrons, neutrons and positrons, or some at least of these—and also of energy, which also contributes something to its weight. When the atom re-arranges itself, either spontaneously or under bombardment, protons and electrons, or other fragments of its material structure, may be shot off in the form of α- and β-particles, and energy may also be set free in the form of γ-rays. The final weight of the atom will be obtained by deducting from its original weight not only the weight of all the ejected electrons and protons, but also the weight of all the energy which has been set free as radiation.

There is also a possibility of two or more atoms re-arranging their constituents so as to form some new and more complex atom, or combination of atoms. For instance, the hydrogen isotope of mass 2 contains precisely the same constituents as two normal hydrogen atoms, but its mass is not double that of the two normal atoms. Taking the mass of the oxygen atom to be 16, that of the normal hydrogen atom is 1·0081, while that of the isotope is 2·0142, which is 0·0020 units less than that of two normal atoms. If, then, the two normal atoms should ever combine to form an atom of the isotope, energy would be set free of mass 0·0020 units.

Again the normal helium of mass 4 contains the same ingredients as four normal hydrogen atoms, but contains 0·0280 units less of mass. Thus if four normal hydrogen atoms should combine and form an atom of helium, energy would be set free of amount equal to 0·0280 units of mass.

Atoms may also break up into something simpler, and set energy free in so doing. Lauritsen and Fowler have found in the laboratory that an atom may transform itself into a pair of simple oppositely-charged particles, while the greater part of its mass becomes energy of motion. Millikan believes that the energy of cosmic radiation is of this kind. The particles of cosmic radiation mentioned on p. 126 move with energies ranging from $3\cdot6 \times 10^{-24}$ to 27×10^{-24} grammes, which are comparable with the masses of complete atoms. Millikan suggests that this energy originates in the almost complete annihilation of atoms; with Neher and Pickering he is finding (1943) that this supposition gives a highly satisfactory account of the way in which cosmic radiation is found to be distributed over the earth's surface after deflection by the earth's magnetic field. The atoms which must be broken up are those of helium, carbon, nitrogen, oxygen and silicon. The list is significant. It is no random selection of atoms, for Bowen and Wise have found that, apart from hydrogen (which could not reveal its presence in cosmic radiation) these are the only elements which are abundant in the planetary nebulae, and so presumably in outer interstellar space also.

If this interpretation of cosmic radiation is finally established, we shall have evidence that the annihilation of matter, and its transformation into energy, forms one of the fundamental processes of nature. Some years ago many astronomers thought that a similar process might well provide the energy required for the radiation of the stars, but, as we shall soon see, a different source now seems more probable.

QUANTUM THEORY

The series of concepts which we now approach are difficult to grasp and still more difficult to explain—largely, no doubt, because our minds receive no assistance from our everyday experience of nature.* Once again we must remember that it is useless to try to comprehend the true nature of reality; we can only speak in terms of pictures and models which can make no claim to represent ultimate reality, and shall again depict our atom as a nucleus with electrons revolving round it.

* The reader whose interest is limited to astronomy may prefer to proceed at once to Chapter III.

The laws of electricity which were in vogue up to about the end of the nineteenth century—the famous laws of Maxwell and Faraday—would require that the energy of such an atom should continually decrease, through the electrons scattering energy abroad in the form of radiation. These same laws predict that all energy set free in space would rapidly transform itself into radiation of almost infinitesimal wave-length. Yet these things simply do not happen, making it obvious that the laws in question must be discarded.

CAVITY-RADIATION. A crucial case of failure is provided by what is known as "cavity-radiation." A body with a cavity in its interior is heated up to incandescence; no notice is taken of the light and heat emitted by its outer surface, but the light imprisoned in the internal cavity is let out through a small window and analysed into its constituent colours by a spectroscope or diffraction grating. This is the radiation that is known as "cavity-radiation." It represents the most complete form of radiation possible, radiation from which no colour is missing, and in which every colour figures at its full strength. No known substance ever emits quite such complete radiation from its surface, although many approximate to doing so. We speak of such bodies as "full radiators."

The nineteenth-century laws of electromagnetism predicted that the whole of the radiation emitted by a full radiator or from a cavity ought to be found out beyond the extreme violet end of the spectrum, independently of the precise temperature to which the body had been heated. In actual fact the radiation is usually found piled up at exactly the opposite end of the spectrum, and in no case does it ever conform to the predictions of the nineteenth-century laws, or even approximate to doing so.

In the year 1899 Professor Planck of Berlin discovered experimentally the law by which cavity-radiation is distributed among the different colours of the spectrum. He further showed how his newly discovered law could be deduced theoretically from a system of electromagnetic laws which differed very sensationally from those then in vogue.

Planck imagined all kinds of radiation to be emitted by systems of vibrators which emitted light when excited, much as tuning forks emit sound when they are struck. The old electrodynamical laws predicted that each vibration should gradually come to rest and then stop, as the vibrations of a tuning fork do, until the vibrator was in some way excited again. Rejecting all this, Planck supposed that a vibrator could change its energy by sudden jerks, and in no other way; it might possess one, two, three, four or any other integral number of units of energy, but not intermediate fractional numbers, so that gradual changes of energy were rendered impossible. The vibrator, so to speak, kept no small change, and could only pay out its energy a shilling at a time until it had none left. Not only so, but it refused to receive small change, although it was prepared to accept complete shillings. This concept, sensational, revolutionary and even ridiculous, as many thought it at the time, was found to lead exactly to the distribution of colours actually observed in cavity-radiation.

In 1913 Professor Niels Bohr of Copenhagen applied similar ideas to atomic structures. He supposed that an atomic or molecular structure does not change its configuration, or dissipate away its energy, by gradual stages; on the contrary, the changes are so abrupt that it is almost permissible to regard them as a series of sudden jumps or jerks. Bohr supposed that an atomic structure has a number of possible states or configurations which are entirely distinct and detached one from another, just as a particle placed on a staircase has only a possible number of positions; it may be 3 stairs up, or 4 or 5, but cannot be $3\frac{1}{4}$ or $3\frac{3}{4}$ stairs up. The change from one position to another is generally effected through the medium of radiation. The system can be pushed upstairs by absorbing energy from radiation which falls on it, or may move downstairs to a state of lower energy and emit energy in the form of radiation in so doing. Only radiation of a certain definite colour, and so of a certain precise wave-length, is of any account for effecting a particular change of state. The problem of shifting an atomic system is like that of extracting a box of matches from a penny-in-the-slot machine; it can only be done by a special implement, to wit a penny, which must be of precisely the right size and weight—a coin which is either too small *or too large*, too light *or too heavy*, is doomed to fail.

If we pour radiation of the wrong wave-length on to an atom, we may reproduce the comedy of the millionaire whose total wealth will not procure him a box of matches because he has not a loose penny, or we may reproduce the tragedy of the child who cannot obtain a slab of chocolate because its hoarded wealth consists of farthings and half-pence—but we shall not disturb the atom. When mixed radiation is poured on to a collection of atoms, these absorb the radiation of just those wave-lengths which are needed to change their internal states, and none other; radiation of all other wave-lengths passes by unaffected.

This selective action of the atom on radiation is put in evidence in a variety of ways; it is perhaps most simply shown in the spectra of the sun and stars. Dark lines similar to those which Fraunhofer observed in the solar spectrum are observed in the spectra of practically all stars (see Plate XV, p. 32), and we can now understand why this must be. Light of every possible wave-length streams out from the hot interior of a star, and bombards the atoms which form its atmosphere. Each atom drinks up that radiation which is of precisely the right wave-length for it, but has no interaction of any kind with the rest, so that the radiation which is finally emitted from the star is deficient in just the particular wave-lengths which suit the atoms. Thus the star shows an *absorption spectrum* of fine lines. The positions of these lines in the spectrum show what types of radiation the stellar atoms have swallowed, and so enable us to identify the atoms from our laboratory knowledge of the tastes of different kinds of atoms for radiation. But what ultimately decides which types of radiation an atom will swallow, and which it will reject?

It had been part of Planck's theory that radiation of each wave-length has associated with it a certain amount of energy, which he called the "quantum," and this depends on the wave-length of the radiation and on nothing else. The quantum is supposed to be proportional to the "frequency" (p. 130), or number of vibrations of the radiation per second,* and so is

* To be precise, if ν is the frequency of the radiation, its quantum of energy is $h\nu$, where h is a universal constant of nature, known as Planck's constant. This constant is of the physical nature of energy multiplied by time; its numerical value is:

$$6.55 \times 10^{-27} \text{ erg} \times \text{second}.$$

inversely proportional to the wave-length of the radiation—the shorter the wave-length, the greater the energy of the quantum, and conversely. Red light has feeble quanta, violet light has energetic quanta, and so on. In many physical problems, we may properly picture radiation as travelling through space in the form of detached packets of energy, each packet containing just one quantum of energy. These packets are usually described as "photons." The photons of high-frequency radiation will of course carry more energy than those of low-frequency radiation, and so will usually penetrate into matter more readily. This explains the high penetrating power of the X- and γ-rays (p. 130).

Einstein now supposed that radiation of a given type could effect an atomic or molecular change, only if the energy needed for the change was precisely equal to that of a single quantum of the radiation. This is commonly known as Einstein's law; it determines the precise type of radiation needed to work any atomic or molecular penny-in-the-slot mechanism.*

We notice that work which demands one powerful quantum cannot be performed by two, or indeed by any number whatever, of feeble quanta. A small amount of violet (high-frequency) light can accomplish what no amount of red (low-frequency) light can effect.

The law prohibits the killing of two birds with one stone, as well as the killing of one bird with two stones; the whole quantum is used up in effecting the change, so that no energy from this particular quantum is left over to contribute to any further change. This aspect of the matter is illustrated by Einstein's photochemical law: "in any chemical reaction which is produced by the incidence of light, the number of molecules which are affected is equal to the number of quanta of light which are absorbed." Those who manage penny-in-the-slot machines are familiar with a similar law: "the number of articles sold is exactly equal to the number of coins in the machine."

* In the form of an equation:
$$E_1 - E_2 = h\nu,$$
where E_1, E_2 are the energies of the material system before and after the change, ν is the frequency of the radiation, and h is Planck's constant already specified.

If we think of energy in terms of its capacity for doing damage, we see that radiation of short wave-length can work more destruction in atomic structures than radiation of long wave-length—a circumstance with which every photographer is painfully familiar; we can admit as much red light as we please without any damage being done, but even the tiniest gleam of violet light spoils our plates. Radiation of sufficiently short wave-length may not only rearrange molecules or atoms; it may break up any atom on which it happens to fall, by shooting out one of its electrons. These activities are described as photo-electric action. Again there is a definite limit of frequency, such that light whose frequency is below this limit does not produce any effect at all, no matter how intense it may be; whereas as soon as we pass to frequencies above this limit, light of even the feeblest intensity starts photo-electric action at once. Again the absorption of one quantum affects only one atom, and can at most eject only one electron from the atom. If the radiation has a frequency so high that its quantum has more energy than the minimum necessary to remove a single electron from the atom, the whole quantum is still absorbed, the excess energy now being used in endowing the ejected electron with motion.

ELECTRON ORBITS. These concepts are based upon Bohr's supposition that only a limited number of orbits are open to the electrons in an atom, all others being prohibited for reasons which Bohr's theory did not fully explain, and that an electron is free to move from one permitted orbit to another under the stimulus of radiation. Subject to these suppositions, Bohr himself investigated the way in which the various permitted orbits would be arranged.

Following Rutherford, Bohr pictured the hydrogen atom as consisting of a single proton with a single electron revolving around it. The proton, with about 1847 times the weight of the electron, stands practically at rest unagitated by the motion of the electron, just as the sun remains practically undisturbed by the motion of the earth round it. The proton and electron carry charges of positive and negative electricity, and therefore attract one another; this is why the electron describes an orbit instead of flying off in a straight line, again like the earth and sun. Furthermore, the attraction between electric charges of opposite sign, positive and negative, follows, as it happens, precisely the same law as gravitation, the attraction falling off as the inverse square of the distance between the two charges. Thus the proton-electron system is similar in all respects to a sun-planet system, and the orbits which an electron can describe around a central proton are precisely identical with those which a planet can describe about a central sun; they consist of a system of ellipses each having the nucleus in one focus (p. 43)

Yet the general concepts of quantum-dynamics prohibit the electron from moving in all these orbits indiscriminately. Bohr's original theory supposed that the electron in the hydrogen atom could move only in certain circular orbits whose diameters were proportional to the squares of the natural numbers, and so to 1, 4, 9, 16, 25, ... Bohr subsequently modified this very simple hypothesis, and the theory of wave-mechanics has recently modified it much further.

Yet it still remains true that the hydrogen atom has always very approximately the same energy as it would have if the electron were describing one or another of these simple orbits of Bohr. Thus, when its energy changes, it changes as though the electron jumped over from one to another of these orbits. For this reason it is easy to calculate what changes of energy a hydrogen atom can experience—they are precisely those which correspond to the passage from one Bohr orbit to another. For example, the two orbits of smallest diameters in the hydrogen atom differ in energy by 16×10^{-12} erg. If we pour radiation of the appropriate wave-length on to an atom in which the electron is describing the smallest orbit of all, it crosses over to the next orbit, absorbing 16×10^{-12} erg of energy in the process, and so becoming temporarily a reservoir of energy holding 16×10^{-12} erg. If the atom is in any way disturbed from outside, it may of course discharge the energy at any time, or it may absorb still more energy and so increase its store.

If we know all the orbits which are possible for an atom of any type, it is easy to calculate the changes of energy involved in the various transitions between them. As each transition absorbs or releases exactly one quantum of energy, we can immediately deduce the frequencies of the light emitted or absorbed in these transitions. In brief, given the arrangement of atomic orbits, we can calculate the spectrum of the atom. In practice the problem of course takes the converse form: given the spectrum, to find the structure of the atom which emits it. Bohr's model of the hydrogen atom is a good model at least to this extent—that the spectrum it would emit reproduces the hydrogen spectrum almost exactly. Yet the agreement which is not quite perfect even for hydrogen fails completely for more complex spectra, so that it is now generally accepted that Bohr's scheme of orbits is inadequate to account for actual spectra. We continue to discuss Bohr's scheme, not because the atom is actually built that way, but because it provides a working model which is good enough for our present purpose.

An essential, although at first sight somewhat unexpected, feature of the whole theory is that even if the hydrogen atom charged with its 16×10^{-12} erg of energy is left entirely undisturbed, the electron must, after a certain time, lapse back spontaneously to its original smaller orbit, ejecting its 16×10^{-12} erg of energy in the form of radiation in so doing. Einstein showed that, if this were not so, then Planck's well-established "cavity-radiation" law could not be true. Thus, a collection of hydrogen atoms in which the electrons describe orbits larger than the smallest possible orbit is similar to a collection of uranium or other radio-active atoms, in that the atoms spontaneously fall back to their states of lower energy as the result merely of the passage of time.

The electron orbits in more complicated atoms have much the same general arrangement as in the hydrogen atom, but are different in size. In the hydrogen atom the electron normally falls, after sufficient time, to the orbit of lowest energy and stays there. It might be thought by analogy that in more complicated atoms in which several electrons are describing orbits, all the electrons would in time fall into the orbit of lowest energy and stay there. Such does not prove to be the case. There is never room for more than one electron in the same orbit. This is a special aspect of a general principle which appears to dominate the whole of physics. It has a name—"the exclusion-principle"—but this is about all as yet; we have hardly begun to understand it. In another of its special aspects it becomes identical with the old familiar corner-stone of science which asserts that two different pieces of matter cannot occupy the same space at the same time. Without understanding the underlying principle, we can accept the fact that two electrons not only cannot occupy the same space, but cannot even occupy the same orbit. It is as though in some way the electron spread itself out so as to occupy the whole of its orbit, thus leaving room for no other. No doubt this must not be accepted as a literal picture of things, and yet the modern theory of wave-mechanics suggests that in some sense (which we cannot yet specify with much precision) the orbits of lowest energy in the hydrogen atom are possible orbits just because the electron can completely fill them, and that adjacent orbits are impossible because the electron would fill them $\frac{3}{4}$ or $1\frac{1}{2}$ times over, and similarly for more complicated atoms. In this connection it is perhaps significant that no single known phenomenon of physics makes it possible to say that at a given instant an electron is at such or such a point in an orbit of lowest energy; such a statement appears to be quite meaningless and the condition of an atom is apparently specified with all possible precision by saying that at a given instant an electron is in such an orbit, as it would be, for instance, if the electron had spread itself out into a ring. We cannot say the same of other orbits. As we pass to orbits of higher energy, and so of greater diameter, the indeterminateness gradually assumes a different form, and finally becomes of but little importance. Whatever form the electron may assume while it is describing a little orbit near the nucleus, by the time it is describing a very big orbit far out it has become a plain material particle charged with electricity.

Thus, whatever the reason may be, electrons which are describing orbits in the same atom must all be in different orbits. The electrons in their orbits are like men on a ladder; just as no two men can stand on the same rung, so no two electrons can ever follow one another round in the same orbit.

The neon atom, for instance, with 10 electrons is in its normal state of lowest energy when its 10 electrons each occupy one of the 10 orbits whose energy is lowest. For reasons which the quantum theory has at last succeeded in elucidating, there are, in every atom, two orbits in which the energy is equal and lower than in any other orbit. After this come eight orbits of equal but substantially higher energy, then 18 orbits of equal but still higher energy, and so on. As the electrons in each of these various groups of orbits all have equal energy, they are commonly spoken of, in a graphic but misleading phraseology, as rings of electrons. They are designated the *K*-ring, the *L*-ring, the *M*-ring and so on. The *K*-ring, which is nearest to the nucleus, has room for two electrons only. Any further electrons are pushed out into the *L*-ring, which has room for eight electrons, all describing orbits which are different but of equal energy. If still more electrons remain to be accommodated, they must go into the *M*-ring and so on.

In its normal state, the hydrogen atom has one electron in its *K*-ring, while the helium atom has two, the *L*, *M*, and higher rings being unoccupied. The atom of next higher complexity, the lithium atom, has three electrons, and as only two can be accommodated in its *K*-ring, one has to wander round in the outer spaces of the *L*-ring. In beryllium with four electrons, two are driven out into the *L*-ring. And so it goes on, until we reach neon with 10 electrons, by which time the *L*-ring as well as the inner *K*-ring is full up. In the next atom, sodium, one of the 11 electrons is driven out into the still more remote *M*-ring, and so on. Provided the electrons are not being excited by radiation or other stimulus, each atom sinks in time to a state in which its electrons are occupying its orbits of lowest energy, one in each.

So far as our experience goes, an atom, as soon as it reaches this state, becomes a true perpetual motion machine, the electrons continuing to move in their orbits (at any rate on Bohr's theory) without any of the energy of their motion being dissipated away, either in the form of radiation or otherwise. It seems astonishing and quite incomprehensible that an atom in such a state should not be able to yield up its energy still further, but, so far as our experience goes, it cannot.

And this property, little though we understand it, is, in the last resort, responsible for keeping the universe in being. If no restriction of this kind intervened, the whole material energy of the universe would disappear in the form of radiation in a few thousand-millionth parts of a second. If the normal hydrogen atom were capable of emitting radiation in the way demanded by the nineteenth-century laws of physics, it would, as a direct consequence of this emission of radiation, begin to shrink at the rate of over a metre a second, the electron continually falling to orbits of lower and lower energy. After about a thousand-millionth part of a second the nucleus and the electron would run into one another, and the whole atom would probably disappear in a flash of radiation. By prohibiting any emission of radiation except by complete quanta, and by prohibiting any emission at all when there are no quanta available for dissipation, the quantum theory succeeds in keeping the universe in existence as a going concern.

THE MECHANICAL EFFECTS OF RADIATION

The more compact an electrical structure is, the greater the amount of energy necessary to disturb it; and, as this energy must be supplied in the form of a single quantum, the greater the energy of the quantum must be, and so the shorter the wave-length of the radiation. A very compact structure can only be disturbed by radiation of very short wave-length.

A ship heading into a rough sea runs most risk of damage, and its passengers most risk of discomfort, when its length is about equal to the length of the waves. Short waves disturb a short ship and long waves a long ship, but a long swell does little harm to either. But this provides no real analogy with the effects of radiation, since the wave-length of radiation which breaks up an electrical structure is hundreds of times the size of the structure. The nautical analogy to such radiation is a very long swell indeed. As a rough working guide we may say that an electrical structure will only be disturbed by radiation whose wave-length is about equal to 860 times the dimensions of the structure, and will only be broken up by radiation whose wave-length is below this limit.* In brief, the reason why blue light affects photographic plates, while red light does not, is that the wave-length of blue light is less, and that of red light is greater, than 860 times the diameter of the molecule of silver bromide; we must get below the "860-limit" before anything begins to happen.

When an atom discharges its reservoir of stored energy, the light it emits has necessarily the same wave-length as the light which it absorbed in originally storing up this energy; the two quanta of energy being equal, their wave-lengths are the same. It follows that the light emitted by any electrical structure will also have a wave-length of about 860 times the dimensions of the structure. Ordinary visible light is emitted mainly by atoms, and so has a wave-length equal to about 860 atomic diameters. Indeed, it is just because it has this wave-length that visible light acts on the atoms of our retina, and so can be seen by us.

Radiation of this wave-length disturbs only the outermost electrons in an atom, but radiation of much shorter wave-length may have much more devastating effects; X-radiation, for instance, may break up the far more compact inner rings of electrons, the K-ring, L-ring, etc., of the atomic structure. Radiation of still shorter wave-length may even disturb the protons and electrons of the nucleus. For the nuclei, like the atoms themselves, are structures of positive and negative electrical charges, and so must behave similarly with respect to the radiation falling upon them, except for the wide difference in the wave-length of the radiation. Ellis and others have found that the γ-radiation emitted during the disintegration of the atoms of the radio-active element radium B has wave-lengths of 3·52, 4·20, 4·80, 5·13, and 23×10^{-10} cm. These wave-lengths are only about a hundred-thousandth part of

* The mathematician will readily see the reason for this rule, which is, in brief, as follows: the energy needed to separate two electric charges $+e$ and $-e$, at a distance r apart, is e^2/r, and the energy needed to re-arrange or break up a structure of electrons and protons of linear dimensions r will generally be comparable with this. If λ is the wave-length of the requisite radiation, the energy made available by the absorption of this radiation is the quantum hC/λ. Combining this with the circumstance that the value of h is very approximately $860 \, e^2/C$, we find that the requisite wave-length of radiation is about 860 times the dimensions of the structure to be broken up.

those of visible light, the reason being that the atomic nucleus has only about a hundred-thousandth part the dimensions of the complete atom. Radiation of such wave-lengths would be just as effective in disturbing the nucleus of radium B as that of 100,000 times longer wave-length is effective in disturbing the hydrogen atom.

Since the wave-length of the radiation absorbed or emitted by an atom is inversely proportional to the quantum of energy, the quantum needed to "work" the atomic nucleus must have something like 100,000 times the energy of that needed to "work" the atom. If the hydrogen atom is a penny-in-the-slot machine, nothing less than five-hundred-pound notes will work the nuclei of the radio-active atoms.

Matter at the high temperatures which occur within the stars contains an abundant supply both of quanta of high energy, and of particles moving with high speeds. But before we can discuss the effects of these quanta and particles, we must consider how their energy depends on the temperature.

TEMPERATURE-RADIATION. We speak in ordinary life of a red-heat or a white-heat, meaning the heat to which a substance must be raised to emit red or white light respectively. The filament in a carbon-filament lamp is said to be raised to a red-heat, that in a gas-filled lamp to a yellow-heat. It is not necessary to specify the substance we are dealing with; if carbon emits a red light at a temperature of 3000°, then tungsten or any other substance, raised to this same temperature, will emit exactly the same red light as the carbon, and the same is true for other colours of radiation. Thus each colour, and so also each wave-length of radiation, has a definite temperature associated with it, this being the temperature at which this particular colour is most abundant in the spectroscopic analysis of the light emitted by a hot body. As soon as this particular temperature begins to be approached, but not before, radiation of the wave-length in question becomes plentiful; at temperatures well below this it is quite inappreciable.*

* The wave-length λ of the radiation and the associated temperature T (measured in Centigrade degrees absolute) are connected through the well-known relation:

$$\lambda T = 0.2885 \text{ cm. degree.}$$

Just as we speak of a red-heat or a white-heat, we might, although we do not do so, quite legitimately speak of an X-ray heat or a γ-ray heat. The shorter the wave-length of the radiation, the higher the temperature with which it is specially associated. Thus, as we make a substance hotter and hotter, it emits light of ever shorter wave-length, and runs in succession through the whole rainbow of colours—red, orange, yellow, green, blue, violet—and after this proceeds to emit ultra-violet radiation, X-radiation, and so on in turn. We cannot command a sufficient range of temperature to perform the complete experiment in the laboratory, but nature performs it for us in the stars.

THE EFFECTS OF HEAT. We have already seen that radiation of short wave-length is needed to break up an electric structure of small dimensions. As short wave-lengths are associated with high temperatures, it now appears that the smaller an electrical structure is, the greater the heat needed to break it up. And we can calculate the temperature at which an electric structure of given dimensions will first begin to break up under the influence of heat.*

For instance, an ordinary atom with a diameter of about 4×10^{-8} cm. will first be broken up at temperatures of the order of thousands of degrees. To take a definite example, yellow light of wave-length 0·00006 cm. is specially associated with the temperature 4800 degrees; this temperature represents an average "yellow-heat." At temperatures well below this, yellow light only occurs when it is artificially created. But stars, and all other bodies, at a temperature of 4800 degrees emit yellow light naturally, and show lines in the yellow region of their spectrum, because yellow light removes the outermost electron from the atoms of calcium and similar elements. The electrons in the calcium atom begin to be disturbed when a temperature of 4800 degrees begins to be approached, but not before. This temperature is not approached on earth (except in the electric arc and other

---

* On combining the relation just given between T and λ with that implied in the rough law of the "860-limit," we find that a structure whose dimensions are r cm. will begin to be broken up by temperature-radiation when the temperature first approaches $1/3000r$ degrees.

artificial conditions), so that terrestrial calcium atoms are generally at rest in their states of lowest energy.

The Mechanical Effects of Radiation

Wave-lengths (cm.)	Nature of Radiation	Effect on Atom	Temperature (degrees abs.)	Where found
7500×10^{-8} to 3750×10^{-8}	Visible light	Disturbs outer-most electrons	3,850° to 7,700°	Stellar at-mospheres
250×10^{-8} to 10^{-8}	X-rays	Disturbs inner electrons	115,000° to 29,000,000°	Stellar in-teriors
5×10^{-9} to 10^{-9}	Soft γ-rays	Strips off all or nearly all elec-trons	58,000,000° to 290,000,000°	Centres of dense stars?
4×10^{-10}	γ-rays of radium B	Disturbs nu-clear arrange-ment	720,000,000°	?
5×10^{-11}	Shortest γ-rays	—	5,800,000,000°	?

At the other end of the scale, we have seen that the shortest wave-length of the γ-radiation emitted during the disintegration of radium B is $3 \cdot 52 \times 10^{-10}$ cm.; this corresponds to a temperature of 820,000,000 degrees. The shortest wave-length for uranium is $0 \cdot 5 \times 10^{-10}$ cm., which corresponds to the enormously high temperature of 5,800,000,000 degrees. When such terrific temperatures as these begin to be approached, but not before, the constituents of the radio-active nuclei ought to begin to re-arrange themselves, just as the constituents of the calcium atom do when a temperature of 4800 degrees is approached. And if we suppose that re-arrangements of an electric structure can also be effected by bombarding it with material particles, the temperature at which bombardment by electrons, nuclei, or molecules first becomes effective is about the same as that at which radiation of the effective wave-length would first begin to be appreciable; the two processes begin at approximately the same temperature. This of course explains why no temperature we can command on earth has any appreciable effect in expediting or inhibiting radio-active disintegration. And the same is true in the stars; calculation shows that these contain no temperatures high enough to affect radio-active processes.

The table on p. 147 shows the wave-lengths of the radiation necessary to effect various atomic transformations. The last two columns show the corresponding temperatures, and the kind of place, so far as we know, where this temperature is to be found, these latter entries anticipating certain results which will be given in detail in Chapter v below (p. 196 ff.). In places where the temperature is far below that mentioned in the last column but one, the transformation in question cannot be effected by heat, and so can only occur spontaneously. Thus it is entirely a one-way process. The available radiation not being of sufficiently short wave-length to work the atomic slot-machine, the atoms absorb no energy from the surrounding radiation and so are continually slipping back into states of lower energy, if such exist.

THERMO-NUCLEAR REACTIONS

To complete the discussion, we must not only consider the interaction of matter and radiation, but also that of matter and other matter. We must especially consider the reactions which will occur under astronomical conditions, and in particular in the hot interiors of the stars. Here the temperatures are entirely beyond any attainable in the laboratory, so that in many respects we have little but theory to guide us.

Nevertheless we can build on the sure foundation of a number of well established experimental facts. In 1920, Rutherford bombarded light atoms with swiftly-moving α-particles (p. 120), and found that direct hits could change the nuclei of the atoms, transmuting a nucleus for instance of nitrogen into one of oxygen. In these experiments the α-particles were obtained from ordinary radio-active disintegration, but under suitable conditions such particles can also exist in their own right. For they are simply the nuclei of helium atoms, and at the high temperatures of stellar interiors the heat effects we have just been considering will break up every helium atom into two electrons and an α-particle. At temperatures such as prevail in the interiors of the stars, these α-particles will be moving at speeds comparable with those used by Rutherford, and so may be expected to produce the same results when they impinge on other nuclei. Thus nature herself must not only perform Rutherford's experiment but also many others in the hot interiors of the stars, which thus become veritable alchemists' laboratories in which the chemical elements are continually changing, the one into the other, as the nuclei of their atoms are bombarded by a variety of swiftly moving projectiles—protons, neutrons, deuterons, α-particles and more complex nuclei. Reactions of this type are known as "thermo-nuclear" and the laws controlling them have been studied by a number of investigators—Atkinson and Houtermanns, Gamow and Teller and others. In many cases a reaction is found to be so sensitive to changes of temperature that it may be associated with one definite critical temperature, and we do not go far wrong if we assume that below this temperature the reaction occurs only in negligible amounts, at and near this temperature in moderate amounts, and above this temperature in torrential amounts.

For any specified reaction the critical temperature depends primarily on the charges on the reacting nuclei, and so on the atomic numbers of the substances involved. It is lowest for protons and the simplest nuclei and increases rapidly as the nuclei increase in complexity, varying approximately as the square of the atomic numbers. For instance, it is about four times as high for a reaction in which an α-particle is involved as for the similar reaction in which only a proton takes part.

The reaction which occurs at the lowest temperatures is the simple reaction of one proton with another. The two protons combine to form a "deuteron"—the nucleus of the hydrogen isotope of mass 2 (p. 117)—and, as there is then an excess of positive electricity, a positron (p. 126) is ejected. After this, the deuteron may capture two more protons and form a helium nucleus.

Next, at temperatures of from 3 to 7 million degrees, come reactions of a proton with light nuclei such as those of lithium, beryllium and boron.

Then, at temperatures of the order of 20 million degrees, comes the reaction of a proton with a carbon nucleus. These combine to form a nitrogen nucleus of mass 13, but this is only the beginning of a long series of processes. The nitrogen nucleus may capture another proton, and thus become an ordinary nitrogen nucleus of mass 14, and then a third proton, becoming a nitrogen nucleus of mass 15. This may capture yet a fourth proton, but the combination cannot form a nitrogen nucleus of mass 16, for none such exists. In all except a very few cases, the combination re-arranges itself into a carbon nucleus of mass 12, and a helium nucleus, or α-particle, of mass 4.

In brief, the capture of successive protons pushes what was originally a carbon nucleus along the sequence of nitrogen isotopes until this road comes to an end. The structure then resumes the form of the carbon nucleus from which it started, all the protons it has swallowed then being disgorged in the form of a helium nucleus.

Actually our description has over-simplified the sequence of processes at two points. The nitrogen nucleus of mass 13 does not capture the second proton directly, but must first disintegrate spontaneously into a carbon nucleus of mass 13 and a positron. The carbon nucleus then captures the proton, and is thereby transformed into the nitrogen nucleus of mass 14. In the same way, the capture of the third proton does not result in the immediate formation of a nitrogen nucleus of mass 15; the first product is an oxygen nucleus of mass 15, but this immediately disintegrates into a nitrogen nucleus of mass 15 and a positron.

The net result is that four protons are bound together to form a helium nucleus. And, as we have seen above (p. 133), energy carrying with it 0·0280 units of atomic weight must have been liberated in the process. We shall see below that a continual repetition of this process, at the rate of unthinkable millions of millions of times a second, probably provides the energy for most of the radiation of the sun and stars.

CHAPTER III

Exploring in Time

We have explored space to the farthest depths to which our
telescopes can probe; we have explored into the intricacies
of the minute structures we call atoms, of which the whole
material universe is built; we now wish to go exploring in
time. Man's individual span of life, and indeed the whole
span of time covered by our historical records—some few
thousands of years at most—are both far too short to be of
any service for our purpose. We need far longer measuring
rods, both to sound the depths of past time and to probe
forward into the future.

Our general method will be one which the study of geology
has already made familiar. Undeterred by the absence of
direct historical evidence, the geologist insists that life has
existed on earth for millions of years, because fossil remains
of life are found to occur under deposits which, he estimates,
must have taken millions of years to accumulate. As he digs
down through different strata in succession, he is exploring
in time just as truly as the geographer who travels over the
surface of the earth is exploring in space. A similar method
can be used by the astronomer. We find some astronomical
effect, quality, or property, which exhibits a continual accumulation or decrease, like the sand in the bottom or top half
of the hour-glass; we estimate the rate at which it is changing
at the present moment, and also, if we can, the rate at which
it must have changed under the different conditions prevailing
in the past. It then becomes a question, perhaps of mere
arithmetic, although possibly of more complicated mathematics, to estimate the time which has elapsed since the process
first started.

THE AGE OF THE EARTH

The method is well exemplified in the comparatively simple
problem of the age of the earth.

The first scientific attempt to fix the age of the earth was
made by Halley, the astronomer, in the year 1715. Each day
the rivers carry a certain amount of water down to the sea,
and this contains small amounts of salt in solution. The water

evaporates and in due course returns to the rivers; the salt does not. As a consequence the amount of salt in the oceans goes on increasing; each day they contain a little more salt than they did on the preceding day, and the present salinity of the oceans gives an indication of the length of time during which the salt has been accumulating. "We are thus furnished with an argument," said Halley, somewhat optimistically, "for estimating the duration of all things."

We cannot make any very precise estimates of the earth's age in this way, but calculations based on modern data suggest that it must be many hundreds of millions of years.

THE GEOLOGICAL HOUR-GLASS. More valuable information can be obtained from the accumulation of sediment washed down by the rain. Every year that passes witnesses a levelling of the earth's surface. Soil which was high up on the slopes of hills and mountains last year has by now been washed down to the bottoms of muddy rivers by the rain and is continually being carried out to sea. The Thames alone carries between one and two million tons of soil out to sea every year. For how long will England last at this rate, and for how long can it have already lasted? In our own lifetimes we have seen large masses of land round our coasts form landslides, and either fall wholly into the sea or slip down nearer to sea-level. Such conspicuous land-marks as the Needles, and indeed a large part of the southern coast of the Isle of Wight, are disappearing before our eyes. The geologist can form an estimate of the rapidity with which these and similar processes are happening, and so can estimate how long sedimentation has been in progress to produce the observed thickness of geological layers.

These thicknesses are very great; Professor Arthur Holmes gives the observed maximum thicknesses as follows:

Cainozoic Era (modern life)	73,000 feet
Mesozoic Era (mediaeval life)	91,000 „
Palaeozoic Era (ancient life)	185,000 „
Pre-cambrian Eras (still earlier life, primaeval life, and dawn of life)	at least 180,000 „
Total—at least	529,000 feet

We can form a general idea of the rate at which these sediments have been deposited. Since Rameses II reigned in

Egypt over 3000 years ago, sediment has been deposited at Memphis at the rate of a foot every 400 or 500 years; the excavator must dig down 6 or 7 feet to reach the surface of Egypt as it stood when Rameses II was king. Yet a foot of this material ultimately forms only a few inches of rock; to deposit a single foot of rock is a matter of thousands of years.

With geological strata deposited at an average rate of one foot per 1000 years, the total 529,000 feet of strata listed above would require over 500 million years for their deposition. At a rate of one foot per 4000 years, the time would be about 2100 million years. Estimates from the rates of denudation suggest similar figures.

This method of estimating geological time has been described as the "Geological hour-glass." We see how much sand has already run, we notice how fast it is running now, and a calculation tells us how long it is since it first started to run. The method suffers from the usual defect of hour-glasses, that there is no guarantee that the sand has always run at a uniform rate. Geological methods suffice to show that the earth must be hundreds of millions of years old, but to obtain more definite estimates of its age the more precise methods of physics and astronomy must be called in. Fortunately the radio-active atoms discussed in the previous chapter provide a more perfect system of hour-glasses, or perhaps we may say of clocks, since their rate, so far as we know, does not vary by a hair's breadth from one age to another.

THE RADIO-ACTIVE CLOCK. We have seen how, with the lapse of sufficient time, an ounce of uranium disintegrates into 0·865 ounce of lead and 0·135 ounce of helium. The process of disintegration is absolutely spontaneous; no physical agency known in the whole universe can either inhibit or expedite it to an appreciable degree. The following table shows the rate at which it progresses:

History of One Ounce of Uranium

Initially:		1 oz. uranium		No lead	
After 100	million years	0·985 oz. uranium		0·013 oz. lead	
„ 1000	„	0·865	„	0·116	„
„ 2000	„	0·747	„	0·219	„
„ 3000	„	0·646	„	0·306	„

and so on. Thus, a small amount of uranium provides a perfect clock, provided we are able to measure the amount of lead it has formed, and also the amount of uranium still surviving, at any time we please. When the earth first solidified, many fragments of uranium were imprisoned in its rocks; these may now be used to disclose the age of the earth. We are not entitled to assume that all the lead which is found associated with uranium has been formed by radio-active disintegration. But, by a fortunate chance, lead which has been formed by the disintegration of uranium is just a bit different from ordinary lead; the latter has an atomic weight of 207·2, while the former is of atomic weight only 206·0. Thus, a chemical analysis of any sample of radio-active rock shows exactly how much of the lead present is ordinary lead, and how much has been formed by radio-active disintegration. The proportion of the amount of lead of this latter kind to the amount of uranium still surviving tells us exactly for how long the process of disintegration has been going on.

In general all samples of rock which are drawn from the same geological strata tell the same story, and so enable us to fix the age since the deposition of the strata in question. On combining this evidence with that of the fossils found in particular strata, we can construct a conjectural time-table, somewhat as follows:

	Duration	Total
	Millions of years	
Cainozoic or modern life (mammals, toothless birds, flowers)	60	60
Mesozoic or mediaeval life (enormous reptiles, toothed birds)	140	200
Palaeozoic or ancient life (fishes in sea, vegetation on land)	400 (?)	600 (?)
Pre-cambrian (primitive life)	400 (?)	1000 (?)

In this way we can fix the duration of life on earth at something between 300 million and 1000 million years. It is less easy to fix the age of the earth itself. The oldest rocks so far examined show an age of 1750 million years, so that this is the minimum time which can have elapsed since the earth solidified. But the radio-active clock cannot tell us for how long before this the earth had existed in a plastic or fluid state, since in this earlier state the products of disintegration were liable to become separated from one another, so that we must look to other sources for this information.

Uranium has an isotope (see p. 117) called actino-uranium. As uranium and the isotope have different periods of decay, the relative abundance of the two is continually changing. From the ratio of the amounts of these substances now surviving on earth, Rutherford has calculated that terrestrial matter cannot be more than 3400 million years old, and is probably substantially less.

Other estimates are somewhat higher. Lead has eight isotopes of atomic weights ranging from 203 to 210, some of which are produced by the radio-active disintegration of uranium and actinium. From a study of the relative abundance of the different isotopes, S. Meyer has estimated the age of terrestrial matter to be about 4600 million years, a figure which Kocky, using more recent data, has amended to 5300 million years. The age of the earth as a planet must of course be less than this.

Again, it is estimated that a million grammes of average igneous rock contain 7·5 grammes of lead, 6 grammes of uranium, and 15 grammes of thorium. From this, Russell has calculated that even if all the lead were of radio-active origin, the age of the earth could not be greater than 3000 million years. Actually it must be less—partly because some of the lead in question may not be of radio-active origin at all, partly because some even of the radio-active lead may have been produced in the sun before the earth became detached from it (see p. 245 ff. below).

These various physical estimates of the time which has elapsed since the earth solidified stand as follows:

Age of the Earth by the Radio-active Clock

1. From the lead-uranium ratio in radio-active rocks } More than 1750 million years.

2. From the relative abundance of uranium and actino-uranium } Less than 3400 million years.

3. From the relative abundance of the isotopes of lead } Less than 5300 million years.

4. From the lead content of igneous rocks } Less than 3000 million years.

Various astronomical methods are also available for determining the time since the solar system came into being. Here "clocks" are provided by the shapes of the orbits of various planets and satellites. The orbits do not change at uniform rates, but their changes are determined by known laws, so that the mathematician can calculate the rates at which change occurred under past conditions, and hence, by totalling up, can deduce the time needed to establish present conditions. The following two estimates are both due to H. Jeffreys:

Age of the Solar System by the Astronomical Clock

1. From the orbit of Mercury   From 1000 to 10,000 million years.
2.   „   „   the Moon   Roughly about 4000 million years.

A further clock is provided by the radio-activity of meteoric stones (p. 254). Paneth and various co-workers have analysed the chemical and radio-active composition of a great number of these, and have deduced ages ranging from less than 110 million years to about 7000 million years. If we could be certain that the meteorites of this last class had originated within the solar system, we should be compelled to assign an age of at least 7000 million years to the matter of which the solar system is composed.

While these various figures do not lead to any very exact estimate of the ages of the earth as a planet and of terrestrial matter they all indicate that these must be measured in thousands of millions of years. If we wish to fix our thoughts on a round number, probably 3000 million years is the best to select for the age of the earth; terrestrial matter would of course have existed for a further period before the earth was formed.

THE SUN'S RADIATION

A geological study extending down to those rocks which were laid down some 300 million years ago indicates that, throughout the whole period between then and now, the sun has been pouring out radiation at about the same rate as now. Furthermore, general astronomical considerations to which we shall shortly come make it highly probable that the sun has been radiating at about its present rate during the greater part of the 3000 million years or so that have elapsed since the earth was born.

If our ancestors thought about the matter at all, they probably saw nothing remarkable in this profuse outpouring of light and heat; they had no clear-cut ideas about the conservation of energy, and no conception of the stupendous length of time during which it had lasted. It was only in the middle of last century, when the principle of conservation of energy first began to be clearly understood, that the source of the sun's energy was seen to constitute a scientific puzzle of really first-class difficulty. The sun's radiation obviously represented a loss of energy to the sun, and, as the principle of conservation showed that energy could not originate out of nothing, this energy necessarily came from some source or store adequate to supply vast outpourings of energy over a very long period of time. Where was such a store to be found?

The sun's present output of radiation is such that if the necessary energy were generated in a power-station outside the sun, this station would have to burn coal at the rate of many thousands of millions of millions of tons a second. There is of course no such power-station. The sun is dependent on its own resources; it is a ship on an empty ocean. And if, like such a ship, the sun carried its own store of coal, or if its whole substance were a store of coal, so that its light and heat came from its own combustion, the whole would be burnt into ashes and cinders in a few thousand years at most.

The history of science records one solitary attempt to explain the sun's energy as coming in from outside. We have seen how the energy of motion of a bullet is transformed into heat when the speed of the bullet is checked. An astronomical example of the same effect is provided by the familiar phenomenon of shooting-stars. These are bullet-like bodies which fall into the earth's atmosphere from outer space. So long as such a body is travelling through empty space, its fall towards the earth continually increases its speed, but, as it enters the earth's atmosphere, its speed is checked by air-resistance, and the energy of its motion is gradually transformed into heat. The shooting-star becomes first hot and then incandescent, emitting the bright light by which we recognise it. Finally, it is completely vaporised by its own heat, and disappears from sight, leaving only a momentary trail of luminous gas behind. The original energy of motion of the shooting-star has been transformed into light and heat—the light by which we see it, and the heat by which it is ultimately vaporised.

In 1849 Robert Mayer suggested that the energy which the sun emitted as radiation might accrue to it from a continuous fall of shooting-stars or similar bodies into the solar atmosphere. As these entered the atmosphere, their speed would be checked and the energy of their motion transformed into heat. There can of course be no doubt that shooting-stars and similar bodies are continually falling into the sun, but their contribution to the sun's output of energy must be quite negligible; a simple calculation shows that a mass of such bodies equal to the weight of the whole earth would hardly maintain the sun's radiation for a century, and that the infall needed to maintain the sun's radiation for 30 million years would double its weight. As it is quite impossible to admit that the sun's weight can be increasing at any such rate, Mayer's hypothesis has to be abandoned.

In 1853 Helmholtz put forward a very similar theory, the famous "contraction-hypothesis" according to which the sun's own shrinkage sets free the energy which ultimately appears as radiation. If the sun's radius shrinks by a mile, its outer atmosphere falls through a height of a mile and sets free as much energy in so doing as would be yielded up by an equal weight of shooting-stars falling through a mile and having their motion checked. On Helmholtz's theory, the different parts of the sun's own body performed the *rôles* which Mayer had allotted to shooting-stars falling in from outside; they performed these same parts again and again, until ultimately the sun had shrunk so far that it could shrink no farther. This theory also failed to survive the test of numerical computation. In 1862 Lord Kelvin calculated that the shrinkage of the sun to its present size could hardly have provided energy for more than about 50 million years of radiation in the past, whereas the geological evidence just mentioned (p. 153) shows that the sun must have been shining for a period enormously longer than this. As before, there can be no doubt that contraction has supplied the energy for some part of the sun's radiation in the past, but the present contribution from this source must be quite negligible.

To track down the actual source of the sun's energy with any hope of success, we must give up guessing, and approach the problem from a new angle. We have seen (p. 131) how radiation carries mass about with it, so that any body which is emitting radiation is necessarily losing weight; the radiation emitted by a searchlight of 50 horse-power would, we saw, carry away mass at the rate of about a twentieth of an ounce a century. Now each square inch of the sun's surface is in effect a searchlight of just about 50 horse-power, whence we conclude that mass is streaming away from every square inch of the sun's surface at the rate of about a twentieth of an ounce a century. Such a loss of weight seems small enough, until we multiply it by the total number of square inches which constitute the whole surface of the sun. We then find that the sun as a whole is losing weight at the rate of rather over 4 million tons a second, or about 250 million tons a minute something like 650 times the rate at which water is streaming over Niagara. If it has radiated at this rate for the whole 3000 million years or so since the earth came into existence, its total loss of mass since that time would be 400,000 million million million tons, which is about one part in 5000 of its total mass.

In the preceding chapter we considered the transformation of substance into radiation which accompanies the spontaneous disintegration of radio-active atoms. The most energetic instance of this phenomenon which we know on earth is the transformation of uranium into lead, in which about one part in 4000 of the total mass is transformed into radiation. Thus, if the sun were originally formed of pure uranium, it would be able to discharge this fraction of its substance as radiation, and this would maintain the sun's radiation at its present strength for rather less than four thousand million years. Although spontaneous radio-active disintegration could provide an adequate supply of energy for the sun, there is no reason to think that it is the actual source of the sun's energy. Indeed, if it were, the greater part of the substance of the present sun would consist of the products of the disintegration of uranium, and we are pretty sure that it does not. Moreover, the problem of the sun's radiation is not an isolated problem, but forms a small fraction of the wider problem of the radiation of the stars in general. Many of these radiate far more energetically than the sun, and a source which provides sufficient energy for the sun may well fail to provide adequately for these other stars. We shall soon see that radio-activity does not provide a sufficient solution for the stars as a whole.

We have also considered a second loss of mass, namely that accompanying a transmutation of elements, such as we saw might occur in the hot interior of a star. We saw that the combination of four atoms of hydrogen into one of helium would set free 0·0280 units of mass to be discharged as radiation. This is 0·0070 units of mass per hydrogen atom, or one part in 144 of the total mass involved. If the sun consisted originally of pure hydrogen, the transmutation of all of this hydrogen into helium would give the sun energy enough to radiate at the present rate for more than 100,000 million years.

Other transmutations of hydrogen will provide radiation for very similar periods. Looking at the problem in a very broad way, we may suppose, to an approximation, that all atomic weights are integers except that for hydrogen which is 1·0081. If so, the mass set free by any transmutation whatever will be 0·81 per cent. of the total mass of hydrogen which is transmuted, and this is one part in 124. Such transmutations, then, can obviously provide adequate energy for the sun's radiation, and we shall find that they probably form the main source of energy both for the sun and for the other stars as well. But to discuss this latter question we need a fuller knowledge of the stars, both in detail and in general. The quest for such knowledge will occupy the next chapter.

CHAPTER IV

Stars

In the preceding chapter we were led to think of the sun as a store of energy, and of its radiation as an outpouring of energy; and similarly for the other stars. If we could acquire a complete knowledge of the structure of a star, of its store of energy, and of the mode of outpouring of this energy, we should be able to follow out the changes which would occur year after year, and thus to trace the complete evolutionary history of the star. Each known stellar configuration would then be expanded into a whole series of possible stellar configurations, and we might, for instance, be able to say: "This star is as our sun was a thousand million years ago, and this as our sun will be a thousand million years hence." We should be able to picture the stars as a vast army marching along well-defined paths, and could describe the original state, and also the age, of each star. We might be able to announce that the stars had been created throughout the whole of time, or that they had all come into existence at one definite epoch.

Such are the problems to which we now turn, but we must first describe the physical states of the various types of stars observed in the sky, and explain how the observations of the astronomer are translated into a form which gives us direct information as to the condition of a star.

STELLAR OBSERVATIONS

SURFACE-TEMPERATURE. In Chapter II (p. 145) we saw how each colour of light or wave-length of radiation has a special temperature associated with it, light of this colour predominating when a body is heated up to the temperature in question. For instance, a body raised to what we call a red heat emits more red light than light of any other colour, and so looks red to the eye.

Thus if a star looks red, it is legitimate to infer that its surface is at the temperature we describe as a red heat. If another star has the colour of the carbon of an arc-light, we may conclude that its surface is at about the same temperature as the arc. In this way we can estimate the temperatures of the surfaces of the stars.

In practice the procedure is not so crude as the foregoing description might seem to imply. The astronomer passes the light from a star through a spectroscope, thus analysing it into its different colours. By a process of exact measurement, he then determines the proportions in which the different colours of light occur. This shows at once which colour of

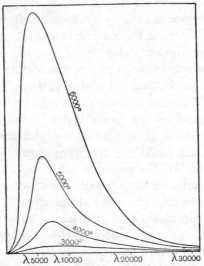

Fig. 11. Distribution of radiation of different wave-lengths at various temperatures.

light is most plentiful in the spectrum of the star. Either from this or from the general distribution of colours, he can deduce the temperature of the star's surface.

We have already seen (p. 134) how Planck discovered the law according to which the radiation emitted by a "full radiator" is distributed amongst the different colours or wave-lengths of the spectrum. The four curves shewn in fig. 11 represent the theoretical distribution for the radiation emitted by surfaces at the four temperatures 3000, 4000, 5000 and 6000 degrees absolute. The different wave-lengths of light are repre-sented by points on the horizontal axis, the marked wave-lengths being measured in the unit of a hundred-millionth part of a centimetre, which is usually called an Angstrom. The height of the curve above such a point represents the abundance of radiation of the wave-length in question.

The two methods of determining stellar temperature will be easily understood by reference to these curves. The 6000 degrees curve reaches its greatest height at a wave-length of 4800 Angstroms, so that if light of wave-length 4800 Angstroms proves to be most abundant in the spectrum of any star, we know that the star's surface has a temperature of 6000 degrees. The second method consists merely in examining to which of the theoretical curves shown in fig. 11 the observed curve can be fitted most closely.

Either of these methods indicates that the temperature of the sun's surface is about 6000 degrees absolute, or somewhat below, but is still 2000 degrees hotter than the hottest part of the electric arc. The total amount of light and heat received on earth from the sun shows that the sun's radiation must be very nearly, although not quite, that of a full radiator at this temperature. This is also shown by the sun's radiation being distributed among the various colours in a way which conforms very closely to the theoretical curve for a full radiator at 6000 degrees shown in fig. 11.

CHEMICAL COMPOSITION. From a study of the spectrum of a star we can tell (p. 33) what chemical substances are present in its atmosphere. We can also tell in what proportions they occur. For, knowing that the atmosphere of a star is at such or such a temperature, it is possible to calculate what the spectrum would look like if the substances were all present in equal strength. A comparison of this hypothetical spectrum with that actually observed shows at once which elements are present in the star's atmosphere in strength and which only in small amounts, while a detailed comparison will disclose the relative amounts of the various elements.

In this way Russell has calculated a table, part of which is given below, which shows the relative strengths of the various elements in the sun's atmosphere. The relative *numbers* of atoms of the different elements are given in the second column. A query means that the estimate is uncertain, and a double query that it is very uncertain, while a blank means that no specific evidence of the presence of either the element or its compounds has been found in the sun.

Element	Relative no. of atoms	Element	Relative no. of atoms
Hydrogen	1,000,000,000	Sulphur	16,000?
Helium	30,000,000??	Chlorine	—
Lithium	3	Argon	—
Beryllium	2?	Potassium	200,000?
Boron	3,000	Calcium	160,000
Carbon	1,000,000	Scandium	130
Nitrogen	3,000,000?	Titanium	5,000
Oxygen	30,000,000	Vanadium	3,000
Fluorine	30,000?	Chromium	16,000
Neon	—	Manganese	25,000
Sodium	500,000	Iron	500,000
Magnesium	600,000	Cobalt	13,000
Aluminium	80,000	Nickel	30,000
Silicon	1,000,000	Copper	3,000
Phosphorus	300?	Zinc	2,500

Of the elements not mentioned above, some are present in only minute quantities, while others cannot be detected at all. But there are a number of elements for which the spectroscopic test is quite insensitive, so that these elements could not be expected to show themselves unless they were very abundant. Thus Russell concludes that there is no reason to suppose that any element is really absent from the sun.

We have noticed (p. 110) that only about fourteen kinds of atoms are really common on earth. Russell's table shows that these same fourteen are also commonest in the sun, apart from phosphorus and chlorine. But these elements do not occur in the same proportions in the two places; hydrogen and helium are enormously more abundant in the sun's atmosphere than in those parts of the earth which are accessible to our observation, and the other lighter elements, up to nitrogen or oxygen, are all somewhat more abundant. We have already found a reason for this (p. 111).

We notice that, in a general way, the heavier elements are far less plentiful than the lighter in the sun's atmosphere. We are tempted to explain this by the natural tendency of the heavier substances to sink down to layers in which they are inaccessible to observation, but it is becoming increasingly clear that this is not the whole of the explanation, and it may not even be the explanation at all. It is remarkable, for instance, that elements of even atomic number (see p. 114) are more abundant than considerably lighter elements whose atomic numbers are odd, magnesium being more abundant than the lighter sodium, and silicon more abundant than the lighter aluminium. A similar phenomenon is observable in the composition of the earth's crust. The heaviest elements do not appear to have sunk entirely to the earth's interior, and again there is a general tendency for elements of even atomic number to occur more plentifully than those whose atomic numbers are odd.

It is significant that practically all the chemical substances which are at all common on earth have been identified in the atmosphere of the sun. Of the 92 elements known on earth, 58 have been detected in the sun definitely and certainly, four more have been detected but not with absolute certainty, eighteen appear to be missing and the spectra of the remaining twelve are so little known that detection would hardly be possible even if these elements were present.

Similar studies by Miss Payne at Harvard and Adams and Russell at Mount Wilson suggest that the chemical composition of all stars is much the same. Although the stars show very varied spectra, these variations are believed to indicate differences of temperature (and to a lesser degree of pressure) rather than of chemical constitution. For instance, when stellar atmospheres are at one special temperature, the spectrum of hydrogen is very strong; at a lower temperature it becomes far weaker, while that of iron becomes stronger. The older spectroscopists made the error of supposing that the former star contained more hydrogen and less iron than the latter; the explanation is merely that the atmosphere of the former star is hot enough to give the hydrogen the needed chance to proclaim its presence, while that of the latter is not.

SPECTRAL TYPES. Knowing that a star's spectrum depends primarily upon the temperature of its surface, it follows that stellar spectra can, in the main, be arranged in a single continuous sequence. Their usual classification is by a sequence of letters, *O, B, A, F, G, K, M* with decimal subdivisions, the temperature falling as we pass along the sequence, so that *O*-type stars have the highest surface temperatures and *M*-type stars the lowest. Examples of stellar spectra have already been shown in Plate XV (p. 32); the spectral types of the various spectra are indicated on the left.

Also, as the spectral type of a star is determined mainly by the surface-temperature of the star, it follows that the surface-temperature of a star can be estimated from its spectral type. Many of the lines in stellar spectra are emitted by atoms from which one or more electrons have been torn off by the heat of the star's atmosphere. We know the temperatures at which the electrons in question are first stripped off their atoms, and so can deduce the star's temperature.

The temperatures which correspond to the different types of stellar spectra, as shown in Plate XV, are approximately as follows:

Spectral type	Temperature
B	20,000
A	10,000
F	7,000
G	6,000
K	5,100
M	3,400

The last three entries in the table refer only to normal stars having diameters comparable with that of the sun. We shall find (p. 184) that a second class of stars (giants) exist, with diameters enormously greater than that of the sun. These have the substantially lower temperatures shown below:

Spectral type	Temperature
G	5600
K	4200
M	3200

The surface temperatures of stars of type *O* are known with less accuracy, but are certainly higher than any of those just given, and appear to cover the whole range from

20,000 degrees to about 100,000 degrees. Novae when at their brightest (p. 57) belong to this spectral type, as do also the nuclei of the planetary nebulae (p. 23). Zanstra, who made a special study of the latter, found that the average surface-temperature of 18 nuclei is 42,000 degrees. Beals found that the temperature of Nova Aquilae when at its highest must have been about 65,000 degrees, and considers that the majority of novae probably attain to temperatures of this order at some time during their outbursts.

In studying stellar structure and mechanism, the temperature of a star's surface is less immediately important than the amount of radiation it pours out per square inch.

This of course depends on the temperature; the hotter a surface, the more radiation it emits. But the temperature does not measure the quantity of radiation emitted. If we double the temperature of a surface it emits 16 times, not twice, its previous amount of radiation; the radiation from each square inch of surface varies as the fourth power of the temperature. As a consequence, a star with a surface-temperature of 3000 degrees, or half that of the sun, emits only a sixteenth part as much radiation per square inch as the sun.* The radiation of each star is a compound of light, heat and ultra-violet radiation, and the proportions of these are not the same in different stars; the cooler a star's surface the greater the fraction of its radiation which is emitted as heat. Thus the star at 3000 degrees will emit nothing like as much as a sixteenth of the sun's light per square inch, but will emit more than a sixteenth of the sun's heat.

This shows that the total emission of radiation of a star cannot be estimated from its visual brightness alone; a substantial allowance must always be made for invisible radiations, both for the invisible heat at the red end of the spectrum and for the invisible ultra-violet radiation at the other end. The importance of these corrections is shown in fig. 12. The four curves are identical with those already given in fig. 11, and show how the radiation from a star of given surface-temperature is distributed over the different wave-lengths. The total

* This is shown in fig. 11, the area of the 3000 degree curve being only a sixteenth of the area of the 6000 degree curve.

radiation emitted at any temperature is of course represented by the whole area enclosed between the corresponding curve and the horizontal axis. The eye is only sensitive to radiation of wave-lengths lying between 3750 and 7500 Angstroms, so that of all this radiation only that part in the shaded strip is visible, all the rest representing invisible radiation.

We see at once that a fair proportion of the radiation emitted by a star at 6000 degrees comes within the range of visibility,

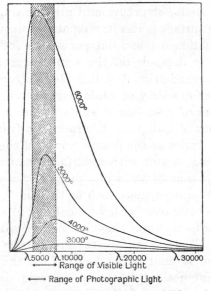

Fig. 12. Distribution of radiation into visible and invisible.

but only a small fraction of that emitted by a star at 3000 degrees, the main part of this latter radiation being heat-radiation, with a wave-length greater than that of visible light. It is impossible to insert a curve in fig. 12 to show the distribution of radiation from a star with a surface temperature of 60,000 degrees, because such a curve would be four miles in height, but if such a curve were drawn, we should see that practically all the radiation was ultra-violet radiation with a wave-length shorter than that of visible light. Taking the stars as a whole, it is fair to say that star-light forms only a small part of the radiation of the stars.

Allowances for invisible radiation have been made in all the calculations referred to in the present book, although it has not been thought necessary continually to re-state this.

COLOURS. The visible radiation from the stars consists of light of different pure (i.e. spectral) colours, blended in varying proportions, the exact proportion of course depending on the temperature of the star. To a rough approximation we may suppose that in the light from any single star never more than three adjacent spectral colours are really prominent, the other colours occurring only in small amounts; the average of the colours which are prominent will of course determine the colour which the star appears to the eye. Taking the six spectral colours in adjacent groups and averaging, we obtain the sequence of colours shown in the second column of the following table:

Spectral colours	Average colour (colour of star, as seen)
Violet, blue Violet, blue, green }	Blue
Blue, green, yellow	White
Green, yellow, orange	Yellow
Yellow, orange, red	Orange
Orange, red Red }	Red

It is often convenient to refer to the stars by their colours, instead of by the more exact measures provided by their temperatures, which may not be accurately known.

If our eyes were suddenly to become sensitive to all kinds of radiation, and not to visual light alone, the appearance of the sky would undergo a strange metamorphosis. The red stars Betelgeux and Antares, which are at present only 12th and 16th in order of brightness, would flash out as the two brightest stars in the sky, while Sirius, at present the brightest of all, would sink to third place. A star in the very undistinguished constellation of Hercules would be seen as the sixth brightest star in the sky. It is the star α Herculis, at present outshone by about 250 stars. As a consequence of its extremely low temperature of 2650 degrees, this star emits its radiation almost entirely in the form of invisible heat. For instance it emits 60 times as much heat as the blue star η Aurigae, whose temperature is about 20,000 degrees, but only four-fifths as much light.

STELLAR DIAMETERS. It is easy to measure the diameter of most of the planets; with the exception of Pluto these all appear in the telescope as discs of appreciable size. But the stars are too remote for their diameters to be measured in the same way. No star appears larger in the sky than a pinhead held at a distance of four miles, and no telescope yet built can show an object of this size as a disc. All stars, even the nearest and largest, appear as mere points of light,* so that their diameters can only be measured by roundabout methods.

When a star's distance is known, we can tell its luminosity from its apparent brightness. From this, after allowing for invisible radiation, we can deduce the star's total outpouring of energy—so many million million million million horsepower. We also know its outpouring of energy per square inch of surface, because this depends only on its surface temperature, which we deduce directly from spectroscopic observation. Knowing these two data, it is a mere matter of simple division to calculate the number of square inches which make up the star's surface, and this immediately tells us the diameter of the star.

The diameters of exceptionally large stars may be measured more directly by an instrument known as the interferometer. When we focus a telescope on a star we do not, strictly speaking, see only a point of light, but a point of light surrounded by a rather elaborate system of rings of alternating light and darkness, called a diffraction pattern. It might be thought that the size of these rings would tell us the size of the star, but the two have nothing to do with one another. The rings represent a mere instrumental defect, their size depending solely on the size and optical arrangement of the telescope. Following a method suggested by Fizeau in 1868, Professor Michelson

---

* The large round images of stars which are often seen in astronomical photographs, as for instance, that shown in Plate I (p. 16), result merely from over-exposure, and have nothing to do with the sizes of the stars.

showed how even this defect could be turned to useful ends, and by its aid produced what is perhaps the most ingenious and sensational instrument in the service of modern astronomy—the interferometer. In effect, this instrument superposes two separate diffraction patterns of the same star, and sets one off against the other in such a way as to disclose the size of star producing them. The diameters of a few of the largest stars have been measured in this way, so that we may say that we know their sizes from direct observation. In every case the directly measured diameter agrees fairly well, although not perfectly, with that calculated indirectly in the way already explained. The discrepancies, which are not serious, appear to result from red stars not being accurate "full radiators" in the sense explained on p. 134.

The interferometer method is only available for the largest stars, but at the extreme other end of the scale the theory of relativity has come to the rescue. Einstein showed it to be a necessary consequence of his theory of relativity that the spectrum of a star should be shifted towards the red end by an amount depending on both the mass and the diameter of the star. If, then, a star's mass is known, the observed spectral shift ought immediately to tell us its diameter. This spectral shift has recently been observed in the light received from the companion of Sirius, and measurements of its amount lead to a value for the star's diameter which agrees tolerably well with that calculated from its luminosity. Thus at both ends of the scale, for the very largest as well as for the very smallest of stars, direct observation confirms the values calculated for the diameters of the stars.

We may accordingly feel every confidence in the calculated diameters of all stars, even when these cannot be checked by direct measurement. The diameters are calculated on the assumption that the stars emit their full temperature-radiation. If the stars had not been approximately full-radiators, we should have found discordances between their calculated and measured diameters. The fact that no large discordances appear suggests that the stars emit nearly full temperature-radiation throughout the whole range of size from the largest to the smallest.

THE VARIETY OF STARS

Observation shows that the physical characteristics of the stars vary enormously, so that it is easy, as we shall soon see, to tell a sensational story by contrasting extremes, setting the brightest against the dimmest, the biggest against the smallest, and so on. This would, however, give a very unfair impression of the inhabitants of the sky; it would be like judging a nation from the giants and dwarfs, the strong men and the fasting men, seen inside the showman's tent.

We shall obtain a more balanced impression of the actual degree of diversity shown by the stars as a whole if we consider the physical states of those stars which are nearest the sun. By taking these precisely in the order in which they come, we avoid any suspicion of going out of our way to introduce stars merely because they are bizarre or exceptional. The small group of stars obtained in this way may be expected to form a fair sample of the stars in the sky, although of course it will not be a large enough sample to include extremes. We need not discuss the sun itself in detail because it will figure as our standard star, with reference to which all comparisons are made.

The System of α Centauri. This system consists of three constituent stars, which are believed to be our three nearest neighbours in space.

The brightest, α Centauri *A*, is very similar to the sun. It is of the same colour and spectral type, but weighs 10 per cent. more and is about 14 per cent. more luminous. Being of approximately the same colour as the sun, it emits the same amount of radiation per square inch. Thus its 14 per cent. greater luminosity shows that it must have a surface 14 per cent. greater, and therefore a diameter 7 per cent. greater, than the sun.

The second constituent, α Centauri *B*, is considerably redder than the sun, its surface-temperature being only about 4400 degrees against the sun's 6000 degrees or so. It has 89 per cent. of the sun's mass, but only about a third of its luminosity. Yet, as a consequence of its low temperature, it needs 50 per cent. more area than the sun to discharge a third of the sun's radiation; this makes its diameter 22 per cent. greater than that of the sun. α Centauri *A* and α Centauri *B* together form a visual binary, the two components revolving about one another in a period of 80 years.

Neither of these two constituents is very dissimilar from the sun, but the third star of the system, Proxima Centauri, is of an altogether different type. It is red in colour, with a surface-temperature of only about 3000 degrees. It is exceedingly dim, emitting only a twenty-thousandth part as much light as the sun, and so has only about a twentieth part of the sun's diameter. Its mass is unknown.

The sizes of the three stars of this system, with that of the sun for comparison, are shown in fig. 13.

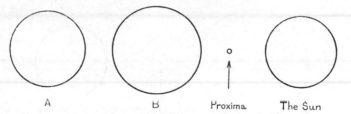

A   B   Proxima   The Sun

Fig. 13. The System of α Centauri, with the Sun for comparison.

Munich 15040. This is a single faint star about which little is known. Its surface is red, with a temperature probably little above 2500 degrees, and it emits only a two-thousandth part of the light of the sun.

Wolf 359. This is one of the three faintest stars so far discovered, but beyond this very little is known about it. It is red in colour and emits only about a fifty-thousandth part of the light of the sun.

Lalande 21185. Another faint red star, emitting a 160th part of the light of the sun.

The System of Sirius. This consists of two very dissimilar stars, there being some suspicion that a third also may exist.

The principal star, Sirius *A*, which appears as the brightest star in the sky (the Dog-star), is white in colour and has a surface-temperature of about 11,000 degrees. As this is nearly twice the sun's temperature, Sirius *A* emits nearly 16 times as much radiation per square inch as the sun. Its luminosity is about 24 times that of the sun, and this requires the star's diameter to be 50 per cent. greater than that of the sun. It has about three and a half times the sun's volume, but is only 2·35 times as massive, so that matter is not as closely packed in Sirius *A* as in the sun. An average cubic metre contains 1·42 tons in the sun, but only about a ton in Sirius *A*.

The faint companion Sirius *B* is one of the most interesting stars in the sky. It is of nearly the same colour and spectral type as Sirius *A*, but emits only a ten-thousandth part as much light. After allowing for the slight difference in surface-temperature, we find that its surface is only one three-thousandth, and its diameter a fifty-fifth of that of Sirius *A*. It has 0·98 times the mass of the sun, so that Sirius *A* weighs

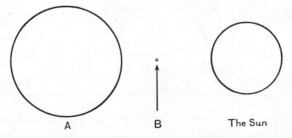

Fig. 14. The System of Sirius, with the Sun for comparison.

only 2·4 times as much as Sirius *B*, although having more than 160,000 times its volume. It is not Sirius *A* but Sirius *B* that is remarkable; the average density of matter in the latter is more than 80,000 times that of water, the average cubic inch containing more than a ton of matter. Fig. 14 shows the sizes of the two components of Sirius drawn to the same scale as fig. 13. These components revolve round one another in a period of about 50 years, so that their arrangement in space may be roughly compared to that of the sun and Uranus.

Proceeding outwards into space we come next to six very undistinguished stars, as follows:

Ross 248, *L* 789–6 and *Ross* 154. These are three of the reddest and so of the coolest stars known. Little is known of their physical state except that they emit a 9000th, a 10,000th and a 2000th part of the sun's light respectively.

ϵ *Eridani* and τ *Ceti.* Two brighter stars, but still both substantially redder and cooler than the sun, each emitting about a third of the light of the sun.

61 *Cygni.* A binary, both components being redder and cooler than the sun, one emitting a fourteenth and the other a sixteenth of the sun's light. The two components probably have a combined mass of about $1\frac{1}{8}$ times that of the sun, and revolve around one another in a period of about 720 years, so that they must be further apart than the sun and Pluto. Irregularities in the orbital motion (p. 45) point to the existence of a third dark body, having only a sixtieth of the mass of the sun, and revolving around one of the two components in a period of about 4·9 years. Thus in all probability 61 Cygni is a triple system. Next we come to

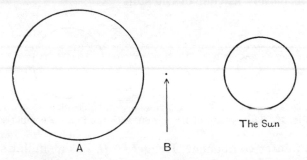

A   B

The Sun

Fig. 15. The System of Procyon, with the Sun for comparison.

The System of Procyon. This is a binary system, similar in many respects to Sirius. The main star, Procyon *A*, is of the same general type as the sun, but weighs 48 per cent. more, and emits $6\frac{1}{2}$ times as much light. Its surface-temperature is about 7000 degrees, and its diameter is nearly double that of the sun.

The faint companion, Procyon *B*, is so faint that nothing is known as to its physical condition except that it emits only a two-thousandth part of the light of the sun. It has 46 per cent. of the sun's mass.

Fig. 15 shows the sizes of the two components of Procyon on the same scale as before. These components revolve around one another in a period of slightly over 40 years.

Next in order, as we recede from the sun, comes a faint red star ε Indi, emitting one-seventh of the light of the sun. This is followed by seven very undistinguished stars, all of spectral type *M*, so that every one of them is redder and fainter than the sun, and none of them has a surface-temperature higher than 3400 degrees. None of them emits more than three per cent., and five of the seven emit less than a 160th of the sun's light. After these we come to

The System of Kruger 60. This is a binary system in which both components are small, red and dim.

The brighter component, Kruger 60 *A*, has a surface-temperature of 3200 degrees, and emits a 660th part of the light of the sun. Its diameter is a fifth, and its weight a quarter of the sun's, so that its substance must be packed about 30 times as closely as that of the sun.

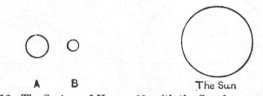

A   B   The Sun

Fig. 16. The System of Kruger 60, with the Sun for comparison.

The fainter component, Kruger 60 *B*, has a similar surface-temperature but emits only a 2400th part of the sun's light. Its diameter is an eighth, and its weight a seventh of the sun's, so that its substance must be packed about 70 times as closely as that of the sun. The system is illustrated in fig. 16. The two components revolve around one another in a period of about 44 years.

After passing another undistinguished red star, emitting a 600th of the light of the sun, we come to

van Maanen's star. Another very faint star, which has the high surface-temperature of 7000 degrees. Notwithstanding this, it only emits a six-thousandth part of the sun's light. Consequently its diameter is only about a hundred-and-tenth part of the sun's, the star being if anything smaller than the earth. Its weight is unknown, but its substance is in all probability packed even more closely than in Sirius *B*.

Next after this comes a binary system consisting of two extraordinarily red and extraordinarily faint components, each of which emits a 7000th part of the sun's light. This is followed by four more faint red stars, the brightest emitting a 150th of the sun's light, after which we come to

α *Aquilae*. This emits nine times as much light as the sun. It is a star of the same general type and of the same spectral class as Sirius, but, so far as is known, is not a binary.

After two more faint undistinguished red stars, we are at a distance of 16 light-years from the sun. We may suitably stop here; the stars we have already enumerated probably provide a fair sample of our part of the sky, but if we go farther we come to regions in which the bright stars are known, while the faint, in part at least, are still unknown.

The principal impression conveyed by this small sample of stars is that the majority of stars in space are smaller, cooler and fainter than the sun. Stars exist which are far brighter than the sun, but they are exceptional, the average star in the sky being a small, dull, dim affair in comparison with our sun.

Much the same is true of stellar masses. We know the masses of all the more important and more massive of these stars except α Aquilae, and the masses which are unknown can be estimated with fair accuracy by equating them to the known masses of similar stars. A rough calculation on these lines shows that the 40 stars (including the sun) which lie within a distance of 16 light-years, have a combined mass equal to that of about 20·8 suns. Thus, in this sample, the mass of the average star is just over half that of the sun.

These 40 stars lie within a sphere which has a radius of 16 light-years, and therefore a volume of 17,200 cubic light-years. Thus there is one star to every 430 cubic light-years— i.e. one star to every cube of edge $7\frac{1}{2}$ light-years—while every 800 cubic light-years contains stellar mass about equal to that of the sun. We do not know how much should be added to this last mass to allow for cosmical dust or gas and for dark stars, but the following calculation is of interest in this connexion. If we assume the galaxy to be shaped like an oblate spheroid, with a radius of 60,000 light-years in the galactic plane, and one of a twelfth of this (p. 25) in the direction perpendicular to the galactic plane, then the whole volume of the galaxy is about 7.5×10^{13} cubic light-years. As the whole mass of the galactic system is known to be about 1.5×10^{11} times the mass of the sun, there is one sun's mass to every 500 cubic light-years. Thus the average mass of all kinds throughout the system is a good deal larger than the average mass comprised within stars in the immediate neighbourhood of the sun; in fact it is 60 per cent. greater. This can be explained either by supposing that there is a great concentration of stars, and of matter in general, in the central regions of the galaxy, or by supposing that a large part of the mass of the galaxy is contributed by matter other than that of stars.

With this sample of the average population of the sky before us, we may proceed to discuss the various characteristics of stars in a systematic way, without fearing to mention extremes. Let us begin with their masses.

STELLAR MASSES. The two stars of smallest known mass in the whole sky are the faint constituent of Kruger 60, just discussed, with one-seventh of the sun's mass, and the faintest constituent of the triple system o_2 Eridani, which has a fifth of the sun's mass. But the masses of so few stars are known that there can be no justification for supposing these to be the smallest masses which occur in the whole universe of stars. Indeed we have just mentioned the third component of 61 Cygni, which appears to have only a sixtieth of the mass of the sun, although whether this should be regarded as a star or as a planet is very much an open question. A general survey of the situation suggests that there may be many stars of still smaller mass, but that very few are likely to have masses which are enormously smaller. Probably very few stars have as little as a tenth of the sun's mass.

The vast majority of stars have masses intermediate between this and ten times the sun's mass. Stars which have even three times as much mass as the sun are rare—we found not a single one in our sample of 39 stars near the earth—while those with ten times as much are very rare, probably only about one star in 100,000 having ten times the mass of the sun. Even higher masses undoubtedly occur—we have already mentioned Plaskett's star, whose two constituents certainly have more than 75 and 63 times the sun's mass respectively, and the Trumpler stars with masses of the order of one hundred suns—but such instances are very, very unusual. We may say that as a general rule the masses of the stars lie within the range of from a tenth to ten times that of the sun, and we shall find that stars differ less in their masses than in most of their other physical characteristics.

LUMINOSITY. A far greater range is shown, for instance, in the luminosities of the stars—in their candle-powers measured in terms of the sun's candle-power as unity. Of the stars of which the luminosity is accurately known, the faintest is Wolf 359 (p. 173) which emits only a 50,000th part of the sun's light, although preliminary measurements suggest that a star L 789–6 may have only a 300,000th of the luminosity of the sun.

At the other end of the scale, the most luminous stars of all are the "supernovae" already mentioned (p. 57)—apparitions which blaze furiously for a period of a few months and then fade into insignificance. The brightest supernova so far recorded was observed in the nebula *IC* 4182 in August 1937, its maximum luminosity being that of about 350 million suns. There is some uncertainty as to the distance of this nebula, so that this may be an overestimate, but there can be no doubt that some supernovae shine with a brilliance of the order of 100 million suns. Disregarding these and all other temporary outbursts of brilliance, the brightest of permanent stars is perhaps *S* Doradus, a variable star of which the average luminosity is at least 300,000 suns, and may be several times this. Thus the range of stellar luminosities, as of stellar masses, extends about equally on the two sides of the sun, and the sun is rather a medium star in both respects. It is medium in the sense of being about half-way between extremes, but we have seen that there are many more stars below than above it, and we can form no idea as to the numbers of stars which, through excessive faintness, escape observation entirely.

In comparison with the moderate range of stellar weights, the range of luminosity is enormous; *S* Doradus is more than 90,000,000,000 times as luminous as *L* 789–6. If the sun is represented by an ordinary candle, Wolf 359 and *L* 789–6 are both something less than fireflies, while *S* Doradus is a lighthouse—and the supernovae are cities on fire. If the sun suddenly started to emit as much light and heat as *S* Doradus, the temperature of the earth and everything on it would run up to about 7000 degrees, so that both we and the solid earth would disappear into a cloud of vapour. On the other hand, if the sun's emission of light and heat were suddenly to sink to that of Wolf 359, people at the earth's equator would find that their new sun only gave as much light and heat at mid-day as a coal fire two hundred yards away; we should all be frozen solid, even the earth's atmosphere being frozen solid around us. So far as we know, there is no possibility of the sun suddenly beginning to behave like *S* Doradus, but we shall see later that the possibility of its behaving like Wolf 359 is not altogether a visionary dream.

SURFACE-TEMPERATURE AND RADIATION. Sirius has the highest surface-temperature of all the stars near the sun, namely about 11,000 degrees, or nearly double that of the sun. Going farther afield, we find many stars with far higher surface-temperatures. For instance, Plaskett's star is credited with a temperature of 28,000 degrees, three *O*-type stars of the Wolf-Rayet class* with temperatures of the order of 110,000 and 95,000 (2) degrees, and Nova Aquilae with a maximum temperature of 65,000 degrees. It must, however, be admitted that a substantial element of uncertainty enters into all estimates of very high stellar temperatures.

At the other extreme, stellar temperatures ranging down to about 2500 degrees are comparatively common. The lowest temperatures of all are confined to red giant stars which are also long-period variables (p. 53), in which the light-variation is accompanied by, and indeed mainly arises from, a variation in the temperature of the star's surface. The temperature of these stars when at the lowest, ranges down to 1650 degrees, which is but little above the temperature of an ordinary coal fire. In many of them, the temperature varies through a large range, but it never sinks so low that the star becomes completely invisible. Thus there is a range of temperature below about 2500 degrees which no star is known to occupy, except

* These are *O*-type stars which show bright lines in their spectra in place of the more usual dark absorption lines.

for the long-period variables which only enter it at intervals. This would seem to suggest that the number of absolutely dark stars in the sky may be relatively small.

Thus, so far as our present knowledge goes, the temperature of stellar surfaces ranges, in the main, from about 60,000 degrees down to about 2500, the lower limit being extended to about 1650 for long-period variables at their lowest temperatures.

Apart from the long-period variables, this is only a 24 to 1 range, so that the temperatures of the stars are more uniform than either their luminosities or their weights. We must, however, remember that a star's radiation per square inch is far more fundamental than its surface-temperature, and that a 24 to 1 range in the latter involves a range of over 330,000 to 1 in the former. If we include the long-period variables, there is a range of about 1,750,000 to 1 in the emission of radiation per square inch.

In terms of horse-power, the sun emits energy at the rate of 50 horse-power per square inch, a star with a surface-temperature of 1650 degrees emits only a third of a horse-power per square inch, while Plaskett's star, with a surface-temperature of 28,000 degrees, emits about 28,000 horse-power per square inch. In plain English, each square inch of this last star pours out enough energy to keep a good-sized liner going at full speed, hour after hour and century after century. And the energy emitted per square inch by the surface of a star at a temperature of 70,000 degrees is forty times the foregoing—well above a million horse-power per square inch.

SIZE. The four stars of largest known diameter are the following:

Star	Diameter in terms of sun	Diameter in miles
Antares	450	390,000,000
α Herculis	about 400	346,000,000
o Ceti (at max.) ...	300	260,000,000
Betelgeux (maximum)	355	306,000,000
,, (minimum)	210	182,000,000

All these diameters have been measured directly by the interferometer. On the scale used in figs. 13 to 16, in which the sun is about the size of a sixpence, the circle necessary to represent o Ceti would be as large as the floor of a good-sized room, while the second star of the system (for o Ceti is binary) would be the size of a grain of sand. We may obtain some idea of the immense size of these stars by noticing that every one of their diameters is larger than the diameter of the earth's orbit, so that if the sun were to expand to the size of any one of them we should find ourselves inside it.

These stars must be exceedingly tenuous. Antares, for instance, occupies 90,000,000 times as much space as the sun, so that if its substance were as closely packed, it would weigh 90,000,000 times as much as the sun. In actual fact it probably has only about 40 or 50 times the sun's weight, the difference between this number and 90,000,000 arising from the difference between the densities of Antares and the sun. On the average a ton of matter in the sun occupies somewhat less than a cubic yard; in Antares it occupies considerably more space than the interior of Saint Paul's Cathedral. Yet a detailed study of stellar interiors shows that we can attach but little meaning to an average of this sort. It is quite likely that matter at the centre of Antares is packed nearly, although perhaps not quite, as closely as matter at the centre of the sun (p. 197), so that Antares owes its huge size mainly to an enormous atmosphere of very tenuous gas.

Possibly S Doradus is even larger. Goposchkin finds that it is an eclipsing binary (p. 49), and calculates that its components have at least 1400 and 1200 times the diameter of the un. The larger component of another eclipsing binary, ε Aurigae, is suspected of having a diameter 3000 times that of the sun, or 2600 million miles.

The planetary nebulae ought perhaps to be regarded as stars of still larger diameter. Surrounding the nucleus—a comparatively faint star with an extremely high surface-temperature—is the nebulosity from which these objects derive the second half of their unfortunate name. This is in all probability merely an atmosphere of even greater extent than that surrounding the six stars just mentioned. Van Maanen has estimated the diameter of the nebulosity of the Ring Nebula in Lyra (fig. 2 of Plate VI, p. 23) to be about four million million miles, while 21 nebulae which he studied had an average diameter of about a light-year, or nearly six million million miles. This nebulosity, however, differs from the atmosphere of an ordinary star in being very nearly transparent; we can see through millions of millions of miles of the Ring Nebula, but can only see a few tens or hundreds of miles into an ordinary star.

At the other extreme of size, the smallest known star, van Maanen's star (p. 176), is just about as large as the earth; over a million such stars could be packed inside the sun and still leave room to spare. And yet its mass is in all probability comparable, not with that of the earth, but with that of the sun; at a guess it may have about a fifth of the sun's mass. To pack a fifth of the sun's substance inside a globe of the size of the earth, the average ton of matter must be packed into a space of about the size of a small cherry—six tons or so to the cubic inch. The solidity of the earth suggests that its atoms must be packed pretty closely together, but the atoms in van Maanen's star must be packed 66,000 times more closely.

How is it done? As we shall shortly see (p. 199), there is only one possible answer. The atom consists mostly of emptiness—we compared the carbon atom to six wasps buzzing about in Waterloo Station. Let us break the atom up into its constituent parts, pack these together as closely as they will go, and we see the way in which matter is packed in van Maanen's star. Six wasps which can roam throughout the whole of Waterloo Station can nevertheless be packed inside a very small box.

GIANTS AND DWARFS. There is a continuous series of stars between the limits of weight we have mentioned, and the same is true of the limits of temperature (and so also of colour) and of size.

Within these specified limits I can find you a star of any weight or of any colour or of any size you like. But this does not mean that you may specify the weight *and* colour *and* size of the star you want, and that I will undertake to find it for you; if the weight is right the colour may be wrong, and so on. For instance, if you ask for a red star I can find you a very heavy one or a very light one, but it is no good your asking for one of intermediate mass. So far as we know, red stars of intermediate mass simply do not exist. The same is true as regards size—there are no red stars of intermediate size. As far back as 1905, Professor Hertzsprung of Leiden noticed that the red stars could be divided perfectly sharply into two distinct classes characterised by large and small size—he called them "giants" and "dwarfs". Russell, studying the question further in 1913, confirmed Hertzsprung's earlier conclusions, and showed that the giant-dwarf division extended to stars of other colours than red.

Imagine that we have a series of coloured ladders, one for each colour of star—red, orange, etc. Take all the red stars and stand them (in imagination) on the different rungs of the red ladder. Do not merely place them on at random; arrange them in order of their luminosities, placing those of highest luminosity uppermost. Further, if several stars are of about the same luminosity, let them all stand on the same rung of the ladder. To make the arrangement definite, let each rung represent five times higher luminosity than the rung immediately below it, so that each rung has a definite luminosity associated with it.*

With this agreement we are now ready to proceed. We take our red stars and place each on the appropriate rung of the red ladder, and so on for each other colour. The kind of result we obtain is shown diagrammatically in fig. 17, the different stars being represented by crosses. The red stars will be found to lie as on the right of the diagram, Hertzsprung's division into giants and dwarfs being very clearly marked. The orange stars lie as on the next ladder to the left; as Russell found, the division again appears, but is less marked.

THE RUSSELL DIAGRAM. Let us make ladder diagrams of this kind for each colour of star, and put them side by side in their proper order, so as to represent stars of all possible colours. We obtain a diagram of the kind shown in fig. 18 (p. 186). This type of diagram was introduced by Russell in 1913, and is now generally known as a Russell diagram.

---

* For purely practical reasons the height is not taken proportional to the luminosity but to its logarithm; without some such device as this it would be impossible to represent the range of more than 1,000,000 to 1 in the observed luminosities of red stars.

The letters at the top of the diagram represent spectral types of stars, because these provide a better and more exact working classification than the names of colours. The colours which approximately correspond to the various spectral types are indicated at the bottom of the diagram. The luminosities (in terms of that of the sun) are given by the figures at the right-hand edge of the diagram. The figures at the left-hand edge show the corresponding absolute magnitudes. This is the

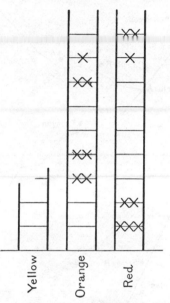

Fig. 17. Stars of different colours arranged in order of luminosity.

astronomer's technical way of measuring luminosity; each step of $2\frac{1}{2}$ magnitudes represents a ratio of 10 to 1 in luminosity.

Only a very few sample stars are shown, but all known stars are found to be concentrated around the positions of these few typical stars. Broadly speaking, there are two distinct and disconnected regions which are occupied by stars. First, and most important, is a region shaped rather like a reversed γ: the central line of this region is marked in by a continuous thick line, following a determination of its position by Redman. Second, there is a smaller region near the left-hand bottom corner of the diagram. The stars which occupy this region are very faint, and have far higher surface-temperatures than other stars of similar luminosity.

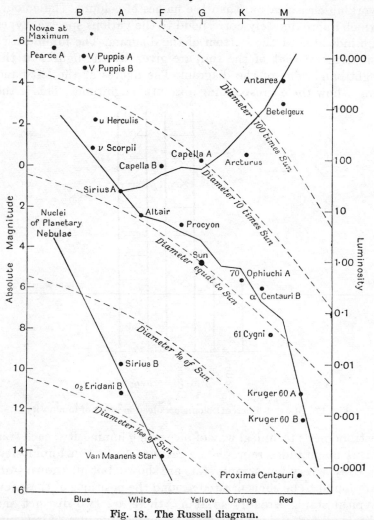

Fig. 18. The Russell diagram.

We have already seen how a star's diameter can be calculated from its surface-temperature and luminosity. This amounts to the same thing as saying that two stars which occupy the same position in the Russell diagram must have the same diameter. Thus there is a definite diameter associated with each point in the diagram, and we can map out stellar diameters in the diagram, just as we can map out heights above sea-level on a geographical map, by a system of "contour lines." In the present case the "contour lines" prove to be a system of almost parallel curves. These lie roughly as shown by the broken lines in fig. 18, all stars lying on any one line having the same diameter.

This diagram throws a flood of light on the general question of stellar diameters. We see at once that stars of the biggest diameters—100 times the sun's diameter or more—must necessarily be red stars of high luminosity. And in actual fact the stars of large diameter shown in the table on p. 181 all are red and have very high luminosities; they are red giants.

The majority of the stars in the sky lie in the belt which runs across the diagram from top left-hand to bottom right-hand. This is known as the "main sequence." The position of this band with reference to the "contour lines" of diameters shows that main-sequence stars are of moderate diameters. The brightest of all may have twenty times the diameter of the sun, while the faintest may have only about a twentieth of the sun's diameter, but they all have diameters which are at least comparable with that of the sun. The sample of stars from near the sun, which we have already discussed, provides many instances of main-sequence stars; we have, in order of decreasing luminosity:

Star	Luminosity	Diameter (in terms of sun)
Sirius *A*	24	1·50
Procyon *A*	6·6	1·80
α Centauri *A*	1·14	1·07
Sun	1·00	1·00
α Centauri *B*	0·32	1·22
τ Ceti	0·32	0·95
ε Indi	0·14	0·82
Kruger 60 *A*	0·0015	0·20
„ *B*	0·0004	0·12
Wolf 359	0·00002	0·03

This table shows clearly how stellar luminosity and diameter decrease together as we pass down the main sequence.

The remaining group of stars in fig. 18, those in the bottom left-hand corner, are generally known as "white dwarfs." Their position in the diagram shows that their diameters must be excessively small.

In addition to the three stars shown in the diagram, the faint companion of o Ceti is certainly a white dwarf. Beyond these only a very few other stars are either known or suspected to be white dwarfs, but the extreme faintness of these stars makes them very difficult of detection, so that it is quite likely that they are fairly frequent objects in space.

It seems clear, however, that the nuclei of the planetary nebulae must also be classified as white dwarfs. We have already mentioned the extraordinarily high temperatures of the surfaces of these nuclei. If stars with temperatures such as these lay on the main sequence, we should expect their luminosities to be many thousands of times that of the sun—a rough calculation suggests that they might well be about a million times as luminous—in which case their apparent faintness would compel us to suppose them to be very distant objects indeed.

Van Maanen has, however, studied the motions of the planetary nebulae across the face of the sky, and concludes, from the rapidity of their apparent motions, that they must be comparatively near objects of comparatively low luminosity. He estimates the average distance of the twenty-one nebulae he studied at about 4500 light-years, and concludes that they are not enormously more luminous than the sun. When the luminosity is studied visually, the average is found to be ten times that of the sun, but when it is studied photographically, the average is found to be fifteen times that of the sun; the nebular light, being much bluer in colour than ordinary sunlight, affects the photographic plate more vividly —hence the difference in the two estimates of luminosity.

Combining this average luminosity with the known surface-temperature, it is easy to calculate that the average nucleus of a planetary nebula has a diameter which is only about a fifth of that of the sun. The combination of low luminosity and small diameter labels these nuclei as unmistakable white dwarfs.

The following table shows the luminosity and diameter of representative stars of this class:

Star	Luminosity	Diameter (in terms of sun)
Nucleus of planetary nebula	10	0·2
Sirius *B*	0·0024	0·03
o₂ Eridani *B*	0·003	0·02
van Maanen's star	0·00016	0·009

In the table on p. 187, the main-sequence stars were intended to be arranged in the order of luminosity, but this happens also to be the order of mass. The masses of three of the stars are unknown; those of the remainder are as follows:

Star	Luminosity	Mass (in terms of sun)
Sirius *A*	24	2·35
Procyon *A*	6·5	1·48
α Centauri *A*	1·14	1·10
Sun	1·00	1·00
α Centauri *B*	0·32	0·89
Kruger 60 *A*	0·0015	0·27
„ *B*	0·0004	0·14

Like the luminosities, the masses fall off steadily as we pass down the main sequence, although mass falls very much less rapidly than luminosity.

Almost the only stars whose masses can be measured directly are the components of binary systems, and these are relatively few in number. Seares found, however, that the masses of binary systems conformed to the law of equipartition of energy already explained in Chapter III, so that it is highly probable that other stars which are not binary also conform, for it is difficult to imagine any reason why binary systems should attain to a state of equipartition if other stars do not. It will be remembered that this state is defined by a purely statistical law connecting the masses of stars with the speeds of motion, so that the fact that a system of stars has attained this state can give no information as to the weight of an individual star whose speed is known, but makes it possible to determine the average mass of any group of stars in terms of their average speeds of motion. In 1922 Seares used this method to estimate the average masses of stars of different assigned luminosities and spectral types—in other words, the average masses of the stars represented at the various points in the diagram of fig. 18. The results he obtained are shown by the continuous curved lines in fig. 19. The arrangement of these curves confirms the inference we have drawn from a few selected stars; the masses

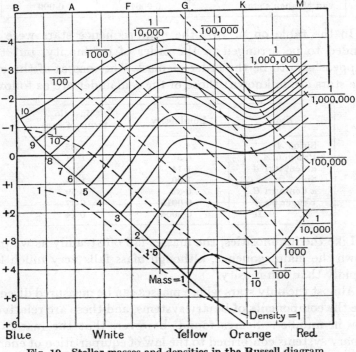

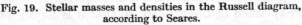

Fig. 19. Stellar masses and densities in the Russell diagram, according to Seares.

of main-sequence stars fall off steadily as we pass down the sequence from high luminosity to low.

The curved lines in fig. 19 specify the average mass of the stars represented at each point in the Russell diagram and the diameters are already known from fig. 18. From these two data the mean density of the star can of course be calculated. The mean densities as calculated by Seares are shown by the broken lines in fig. 19.

THE PHYSICAL CONDITION OF THE STARS

This completes our collection of observational material. We have gone as far as we can with the direct data which can be obtained from a study of the exteriors of the stars, and we now call on mathematical theory to conduct us inside the stars.

We have seen how a tremendous torrent of radiant energy is continually pouring from every point of the surface of a star. Let us imagine that we follow up each river of energy to its source in the star's interior. We may find that the various sources are all at or close to the centre of the star, or they may be spread about throughout the interior of the star. In either case the general principle prevails that the energy can only flow from a place of higher to a place of lower temperature, so that as we follow any torrent of energy upstream, we are necessarily passing to ever higher and yet higher temperatures. A vigorous flow of heat at the surface of a star is evidence of a steep temperature gradient inside the star. Thus the vigorous flow of energy from the sun shows that the temperature must rise sharply as we pass from the sun's surface into its interior, and this rise, continued along the whole 433,000 miles to the sun's centre, must result in a very high temperature being reached there.

There is a simple mathematical theorem, known as Poincaré's theorem, which proves to be of the utmost service in discussing the state of a star's interior, especially in the matter of temperature. The theorem is only true on the supposition that the star is gaseous throughout. We shall provisionally accept this supposition for the moment, for the purely opportunist reason that it provides the most convenient line of approach to an excessively difficult problem.

We have seen how Helmholtz thought that the energy of the sun's radiation might come from the sun's contraction, each layer falling in upon the next inner layer as the latter shrank, and transforming the energy set free by its fall into heat and light. It is easy to estimate how much energy would be set free by a contraction of this kind. For instance, Lord Kelvin calculated that the contraction of the sun, as it shrank from infinite size to its present diameter of 865,000 miles, would liberate about as much energy as the sun now radiates in 50 million years. In terms of ergs, the sun's shrinkage would liberate 6×10^{48} ergs of energy.

Poincaré's theorem states that the total energy of motion of all the molecules, or other independently-moving units of which a gaseous star is composed, must be equal to half of the total energy which the star would have liberated in shrinking from a state of infinite size, and so of infinite tenuity, down to its present size. The theorem is true quite independently of whether the star has actually so shrunk or not: nothing is involved but the present state of the star.

One consequence of the theorem is that the farther a gaseous star shrinks, the hotter it becomes; if a star shrinks to half its present size, the total energy set free by its shrinkage from infinite size is doubled, so that the total energy of motion of its molecules or other units is doubled, and therefore its average temperature is doubled—so long at least as the units remain the same. This is a special case of what is generally known as Lane's law.

Let us concentrate, for the moment, on the special case of the sun. Poincaré's theorem tells us that, if the sun is gaseous, the total energy of motion of all its molecules or other units is 3×10^{48} ergs. The next thing we want to know is how many units there are in the sun. The sun's mass is 2×10^{33} grammes, but how many units are there to a gramme? The answer of course depends on the type of unit concerned; there are for instance 3×10^{23} molecules of hydrogen in a gramme, 2×10^{22} molecules of air and only $2 \cdot 5 \times 10^{21}$ molecules of uranium.

TEMPERATURE. If we suppose the sun to be made of molecules of air, it must consist of 4×10^{55} such molecules, and as the total energy of motion of all these molecules is 3×10^{48} ergs, it follows that their average energy of motion must be $7 \cdot 5 \times 10^{-8}$ erg. Now this energy is only attained at a temperature of 375 million degrees, so that this ought to be the *average temperature of the interior* of the sun, if it were made of molecules of air. In 1907 Emden, by a different calculation, found that if the sun were made of molecules of air, the *temperature at its centre* would be 455 million degrees.

Apart from details, it is clear that the interior of a sun made of molecules of air would be at a temperature of hundreds of millions of degrees.

Yet this result proves conclusively that the sun cannot be made of molecules of air. A simple calculation of the type already explained on p. 144 shows that the quanta of radiation which fly about at such temperatures as we have just had under consideration would be energetic enough not merely to break up the molecules of air into atoms, but also to strip all, or nearly all, of the electrons from the atoms. At such temperatures each molecule of air would break up into its constituent nuclei and electrons just as surely as, on a hot day, a lump of ice breaks up into its constituent molecules. The electric forces which, in quieter surroundings, would bind the electrons and nuclei, first into atoms and then into complete molecules, find themselves powerless against the incessant hail of rapidly moving projectiles and the shattering blows of quanta of high energy; it would be like trying to build a house of cards in a hurricane. A sun consisting of molecules of air proves to be an inconsistency, a contradiction; our hypothesis has defeated itself, and we must start again from the beginning.

IONISATION. We have already noticed how the different types of stellar spectra correspond in the main to different temperatures; differences of pressure, density and chemical composition must also produce differences in stellar spectra, but these are small in comparison with those produced by differences of temperature. Now as we pass downwards—i.e. away from the surface—in a star, we are in effect passing through layers at different temperatures. Samples of matter taken from these layers would show different spectra, and these would agree pretty closely with the different types of stellar spectra.

Thus the different types of stellar spectra ought to give a graphical representation of the different layers of one and the same star—the sun's surface at a temperature of 6000 degrees shows a spectrum of *G* type, but those slightly deeper layers at which the temperature is 7500 degrees ought to show a spectrum of *F* type, and yet lower layers should show spectra of types *A*, *B* and *O* in succession. Now as we pass through these different types of spectra, from the coolest to the hottest in succession, we find evidence of an ever increasing break-up of the atoms. In M-type spectra, which correspond to the lowest temperatures of all, we find evidence of complete molecules, as for example titanium oxide and magnesium hydride. At higher temperatures, the complete molecules disappear and we come in turn to complete atoms, then to "singly-ionised" atoms from which one electron has been torn off, and finally to "doubly-ionised" atoms from which two electrons have been torn off. In the hottest of ordinary stars the atoms of silicon and oxygen are found to be doubly ionised; in the still hotter nuclei of planetary nebulae, neon is also doubly ionised. And there is little doubt that the spectra of matter at still higher temperatures would show even higher degrees of ionisation.

This suggests that as we pass inwards in either the sun or any other star, we come to ever increasing degrees of ionisation. A rough calculation shows that as an adequate preliminary approximation (to be amended as needed), the heat at the centre of the stars breaks up all the molecules and atoms, either completely or nearly so, into their constituent nuclei and electrons. The same is true for all other stars, and this introduces an extreme simplification into the problem of the interior constitution of the stars. We cannot say how many complete molecules there are to a gramme without knowing the nature of the molecules, but once let these molecules be broken up into their constituent nuclei and electrons, and we can state the total number of these constituent parts with fair accuracy without knowing the composition of the stellar matter. This is made possible by the circumstance that the atomic weights of most elements except hydrogen are approximately double their atomic numbers (p. 117).

For, in all except the lightest substances such as hydrogen and helium, the number of nuclei in the broken-up matter will be small in comparison with the number of electrons. Let us then neglect it. We then find that the number of particles to each atom is equal to the atomic number of the atom, and so is equal to half the atomic weight of the substance. This means that the average mass of all the particles is about 2, which is the mass of the hydrogen molecule; we see that the number of particles in any mass is approximately the same as it would be if the mass consisted of hydrogen molecules.

For instance, the atomic number of oxygen is 8 and the atomic weight is 16. Thus a completely broken-up atom of oxygen will consist of 9 independently moving parts—a nucleus and 8 electrons—and the effective molecular weight of the matter will be $\frac{16}{9}$, which is nearly 2. As we shall see later, it may be better to suppose the inner, or K-, ring of two electrons to remain attached to the nucleus; in this case the number of parts will only be seven, and the effective molecular weight $\frac{16}{7}$, which again is nearly two.

It is the same, to varying degrees of accuracy, for other elements. Hydrogen and helium provide exceptions, since their effective molecular weights, when completely broken up, are only $\frac{1}{2}$ and $\frac{4}{3}$; here of course the number of nuclei is not small in comparison with the number of electrons. Apart from hydrogen and helium, the lightest atom which occurs in any abundance in the stars is carbon, with atomic number 6 and atomic weight 12. Thus the effective molecular weight of completely broken-up carbon is 1·71, or, if the K-ring is retained, 2·4; both numbers are near to 2. The heaviest atom which occurs abundantly in the stars is iron of atomic number 26 and atomic weight 56; for this the corresponding numbers are 2·08 and 2·24. We reach the paradoxical conclusion that if stellar matter is hydrogen, it behaves very differently from terrestrial hydrogen, whereas if it is not hydrogen it behaves like terrestrial hydrogen—i.e. like hydrogen in complete molecules.

Thus, returning to the calculation already given, we see that if a star does not contain a great amount of hydrogen or helium, the number of constituent parts in a gramme of fully broken-up stellar matter must be about 3×10^{23}, regardless of the type of molecule from which these parts originate. And when we know the total number of such parts in any star, it becomes easy to calculate the temperature of the star's interior, either from the theorem of Poincaré just mentioned or otherwise. The temperature will be the same as though the star were made of unbroken molecules of hydrogen. Emden calculated in 1907 that the central temperature of a sun of this kind would be about 31,500,000 degrees. Later and more refined calculations by Eddington and others led to an almost identical temperature.

On the other hand, we have seen that the atmospheres of the sun and stars consist mainly of hydrogen, so that it is at least possible that their interiors may also consist largely of hydrogen. In the extreme case in which the sun is supposed to consist entirely, or almost entirely, of hydrogen throughout its whole volume, the foregoing estimates must all be divided by four, and we are left with a central temperature of the order of 8,000,000 degrees.

Taking all the relevant considerations into account, this temperature seems most likely to be about 20,000,000 degrees. Such a temperature so far transcends our experience that it is difficult to realise what it means. To keep a piece of ordinary matter of the size of an ordinary pin-head at a temperature of 20,000,000 degrees—i.e. merely to replenish the energy it loses by radiation from its surface—would need all the energy generated by an engine of one hundred million million horse power; the pin-head of matter would emit enough heat to kill any one who ventured within a hundred miles of it.

High though this temperature is, calculations show that it would not suffice to break up the stellar molecules completely. It would strip the atoms of all their electrons down to the K-rings (p. 142), but these would remain intact. It needs temperatures even higher than those we are now considering to strip the K-ring electrons from the nucleus of an atom. This result is true for the whole range within which the temperature of the sun's centre is most likely to lie, and it is true almost independently of the atomic weight or atomic number of the atoms of which we suppose the sun to be built.

Thus we may think of the central parts of the sun as consisting of a collection of atoms stripped down to their K-rings, but not beyond, flying about independently, more or less like the molecules of a gas, and with them, also flying about like the molecules of a gas, all the stripped-off electrons which originally formed the L-ring, the M-ring, etc., of the atoms, the whole being at a temperature of somewhere about 20,000,000 degrees. As we pass outwards towards the sun's surface we come to lower temperatures, at which the atoms are less completely broken up. Finally, close to the sun's surface, we may meet atoms which are completely formed except perhaps for one or two of their outermost electrons and even complete molecules, many of these being of substances which are unfamiliar on earth, such as CN, CH, NH, OH, TiO, AlH and AlO, BO and SiF.

When the internal constitution of other stars is investigated in the same way, we come upon a very interesting and significant result—*all main-sequence stars have about the same central temperatures as the sun.* Actually they range from about 20,000,000 degrees for the sun and the stars which are near to it on the main sequence to about 30,000,000 degrees for the brightest known stars of the main sequence. Thus a range of hundreds of thousands in luminosity is associated with a range of only about 1·5 in central temperature.

This is not the only property which the stars of the main sequence have in common. Fig. 19 (p. 190), which exhibits Seares' calculations of mean stellar densities, shows that the main-sequence stars are all of approximately the same mean density, except for comparatively small deviations at the two extremities. The mean density of the sun is 1·4, which means that the average cubic metre in the sun contains 1·4 ton of matter. At the sun's centre, the density may perhaps be 70 times this, so that a cubic metre there contains about 100 tons of matter. For comparison, a cubic metre of lead contains only about 11 tons. If all stars were built on the same model as the sun, any two stars which had the same mean density would also have equal densities at their centres. But in stars which are several times as massive as the sun, a new factor comes into play, namely pressure of radiation—the pressure which radiation exerts in virtue of the mass it carries about with it. In most stars this pressure is insignificant in comparison with the pressure produced by the impact of material atoms and electrons, but in very massive stars it is large enough to influence the structure of the star. It is to this that the very massive stars whose diameters are tabulated on p. 181 owe their abnormally large size. It is a general consequence of the disturbing effects of radiation-pressure, that the weight of a very massive star is far more concentrated in its central regions than that of a lighter star, so that if a light and a massive star have the same average density, the latter will have by far the higher density at its centre. When this disturbing factor is allowed for, all stars in the upper part of the main sequence are found to have approximately the same densities in their central regions, a density about equal to that at the centre of the sun, which is of the order of 100 tons to the cubic metre. And we have already seen that the central regions of these stars have also approximately the same temperatures as the centre of the sun, whence it follows that their physical conditions are all substantially the same. Thus, the atoms in the central regions of all these stars must be broken down to the same extent as the atoms in the central regions of the sun. The K-rings of electrons survive intact, but the outer rings are transformed into a hail of electrons flying about like independent molecules.

With sufficient accuracy for our present purpose, the central regions of all the stars on the main sequence, except perhaps of those at its extreme lower end, may be supposed to be in the same physical condition. On account of this property, the main sequence forms an admirable base-line from which to carry out a survey of the Russell diagram in respect of the physical conditions of stellar interiors.

We notice from fig. 18 that a star to the right of the main sequence in the Russell diagram has a greater diameter than a main-sequence star of the same weight. Consequently the energy it would emit in shrinking to its present diameter is less, and hence its molecular energy of motion is less (by Poincaré's theorem). It follows that its internal temperatures are lower, and its atoms are less completely broken up. Calculation shows that red giants such as Antares can only have central temperatures of from one to five million degrees, so that their atoms probably retain intact not only their K-rings of electrons, but also their L-rings and perhaps part also of their M-rings.

To the left of the main sequence we come to a region in which stars, if they occurred at all and could still be supposed to be gaseous, would have shrunk still further; such stars would have higher temperatures and more thoroughly broken atoms. Actually no stars are encountered until we come to the white dwarfs, and here it is reasonably certain that the stellar matter must no longer be treated as gaseous, even to an approximation. The mean density of Sirius *B* is about 80,000 times that of water, while that of van Maanen's star is probably over 300,000. There is no way in which matter can be packed as closely as this, except by stripping the atoms of electrons right down to their bare nuclei. Except for a small number of atoms which may have escaped this general fate, the stellar matter must consist of nuclei stripped absolutely bare, and of free electrons, all moving independently through the star.

STELLAR STRUCTURE

A star, like a house or a pile of sand, is a structure which would collapse under its own weight were it not that each layer is held up against gravity by the pressure which the next inner layer of the star exerts upon it. This pressure is not, like ordinary gas-pressure, the result of the impacts of complete molecules. It is produced in part by the impact of a certain number of atoms which have been stripped of electrons almost or quite down to their nuclei, but to a far greater extent by the impact of a hail of free electrons. We have seen how a still further pressure is produced by the impact of radiation which carries mass about with it, and so exerts pressure on any obstacle it encounters; in the more massive stars, this forms an appreciable fraction of the whole pressure, contributing more than half the total pressure in the most massive stars of all. The combined impacts of free electrons, of atoms (or bare nuclei), and of radiation prevent the star from falling in under its own gravitational attraction.

This gives a reasonably good snapshot picture of a star's structure. The corresponding picture of its mechanism is obtained by thinking of the nuclei as α-ray particles, of the free electrons as β-ray particles, and of the radiation as γ-rays (although in most stars the main bulk of the radiation has the wave-length of X-rays). All these thread their way through the star, and, precisely as in laboratory work, the β-rays are more penetrating than the α-rays, and the γ-rays are more penetrating than either.

THE TRANSPORT OF ENERGY IN A STAR. We have seen how the heat of a gas is merely the energy of its molecular motion. Conduction of heat in a gas is usually studied by regarding each molecule as a carrier of energy; when it collides with a second molecule the energy of the two colliding molecules is redistributed between them, and in this way heat is transported from hotter to cooler regions. Each molecule has a power of transport which is jointly proportional to its energy of motion, its speed of motion, and its "free-path"—the distance it travels between successive collisions.

In the interior of a star, there are three distinct types of carrier in action—atoms (or bare nuclei), free electrons and radiation. We can compare their relative capacities as carriers by multiplying up the energy, speeds and free-paths of each. For this purpose the "free-path" of radiation may be taken to be the distance the radiation travels before 63 per cent. of it has been absorbed, since it can be shown that this is the average distance it carries its energy. On performing the calculation, the carrying capacity of both nuclei and electrons is found to be insignificant in comparison with that of the radiation. The nuclei and electrons may possess the greater amount of energy, but, owing to their feebler penetrating powers, the distance over which they carry it, their free-path, is far less than that of the radiation. Their speed of transport is also less, since radiation transports its energy with the velocity of light. In this way it comes about that practically the whole transport of energy from the interior of a star to its surface is by the vehicle of radiation.

There are two exceptions to these general statements. In the first place, Kothari has shown that electrons are the most efficient carriers of energy in stars of very high density, such as white dwarfs. In the second place, Cowling has given reasons for thinking that there is a small central region in most stars in which the energy is transferred mainly by convection—i.e. by currents of stellar matter which ascend and descend, and so keep the stellar matter thoroughly mixed up within the region in question, as the winds keep the earth's atmosphere mixed up in its convective layers.

Apart from these exceptional cases, radiation completely outstrips atoms and electrons in carrying energy from a star's interior to its surface; it follows that the build of a star must be determined by the opacity of the matter in its interior. If this is altered, the carrying power of the radiation is altered, and this affects the whole structure of the star. A star whose interior was entirely transparent could not retain any heat at all; its whole interior would be at a very low temperature and the star would be of enormous extent. On the other hand, in a very opaque star, all energy would remain accumulated at the spot at which it was generated, so that the interior temperature would become very high and the star's diameter would be correspondingly small. It is, of course, the intermediate cases which are of practical interest, but the extreme instances just mentioned show how a star's build depends on its opacity.

Unfortunately it is impossible to obtain any sort of direct measurement of the opacity of stellar matter. We cannot even measure the opacity of terrestrial matter under stellar conditions, since the interiors of the stars are at incomparably higher temperatures than any available in the laboratory. However, we know that the opacity of stellar matter is due to the atoms, nuclei and free electrons of which it is composed checking the onward journey of radiation, and although we cannot obtain a sample of stellar matter, we know fairly definitely how many atoms, nuclei and electrons such a sample would contain. Thus it becomes a matter of theoretical calculation to determine its opacity.

Such a calculation was carried through by Kramers of Copenhagen in 1923, and, subject to minor modifications, his results have gained general acceptance. They are applicable under both stellar and terrestrial conditions, and in so far as they can be tested in the laboratory, they agree well with observation. And, although there is a big gap between laboratory conditions and stellar conditions, it is difficult to see how Kramers' formula could fail in the stars.

From this formula we can determine the build of the stars

completely, or, if the build of the star is supposed to be known, Kramers' formula tells us the rate at which energy will flow to its surface (this depending entirely on the opacity of the star's substance), and this in turn tells us at what rate energy must be generated inside the star for it to be able to remain in equilibrium in the configuration in question. It now becomes possible to calculate the way in which the luminosity of a star depends on the mass and diameter of the star. This, in turn, provides us with an explanation of the fact, already mentioned on p. 47, that two stars usually differ much more in luminosity than in mass; a little difference in mass often entails a great difference in luminosity. By making certain assumptions as to the conditions in stellar interiors, Eddington was able to calculate a theoretical relation between the mass and the luminosity of a star, and this is found to be approximately true, at least for main-sequence stars—so much so that it is occasionally used to form an estimate of the mass of a star of which the luminosity is known. The relation is generally known as the "mass-luminosity law"; it is expressed by a somewhat complicated mathematical formula, but it may, without any loss of accuracy, be replaced by the simpler statement that a star's luminosity is proportional to the cube of its mass—if one star has twice the mass of another, it will have eight times the luminosity, and so on.

Let us now consider a star in which the matter is so loosely packed that the electrons and broken atoms move as freely as in a perfect gas, collisions being rare events, and the distances between consecutive electrons and broken atoms being large in comparison with their linear dimensions. It will be convenient to refer to this as the "gaseous" state, because the interior of the star behaves like a gas with electrons and broken atoms replacing the molecules of an ordinary gas.

According to Kramers' theory, the opacity of matter depends on the atomic numbers and atomic weights of the atoms of which it is built, a large clot of matter in the form of a massive atomic nucleus being far more effective in absorbing radiation than a large number of small clots of the same total weight. Everyday terrestrial experience shows that this is so. It is for this reason that the physicist and surgeon both select lead as the material with which to screen their X-ray apparatus; they find that a ton of lead is far more effective in stopping unwanted X-rays than a ton of wood or of iron. If we knew the total intensity of energy emitted by an X-ray apparatus, and the total weight of shielding material round it, we could form a very fair estimate of the atomic weight of the shielding material by measuring the amount of X-radiation which escaped through it.

A very similar method may be used to determine the atomic weights of the atoms of which the stars are composed. A star is in effect nothing but a huge X-ray apparatus. We know the weights of many of the stars, and the rate at which they are generating X-rays is merely the rate at which they are radiating energy away into space. If we could cut each atomic nucleus in a star into two halves, we should halve the opacity of the star, so that radiation would travel twice as far through the star before being absorbed. If the star were wholly gaseous, this would result in its expanding to four times its original diameter, and in its surface-temperature being halved. It follows that we can calculate the atomic weight of the atoms of which a star is composed from the weight, luminosity and surface-temperature of the star.

If we suppose that a star does not consist in large part of hydrogen, then the atomic weights of a number of stars, calculated on the supposition that the stars are wholly "gaseous," come out in practically every case higher than that of uranium, which is the weightiest atom known on earth. They not only prove to be higher, but enormously higher; so high indeed, as to seem utterly improbable.

If on the other hand we suppose that the stellar matter may consist in large part of hydrogen, there is an alternative solution which requires that some stars at least should consist almost exclusively of hydrogen, while others contain a considerable proportion of hydrogen. There is nothing intrinsically improbable in this, for the only stellar matter whose composition we know with any accuracy—namely the atmospheres of the sun and stars—is found to consist almost entirely of hydrogen.

We must accordingly conclude that the stars consist largely

of hydrogen. Stromgren and Eddington find that all the relevant facts can be reconciled by supposing that main-sequence stars contain one-third or more of hydrogen. For the sun the most probable proportion is about 35 per cent., although for the giant blue stars at the top of the main sequence the proportion may be as high as 80 per cent. Our knowledge as to the composition of the non-gaseous white dwarfs is less definite, but it seems clear that their hydrogen content is at least not negligible.

THE EVOLUTION OF THE STARS

We shall be led to conjecture below (p. 224) that the stars were born as flecks of gaseous spray thrown off by spinning nebulae, having previously acquired separate existences as condensations in the outer fringes of these nebulae. When they first came into being these condensations would, from the mode of their formation, be of all sorts and sizes, subject only to the restriction that none could be below a certain limit of mass. All would have one feature in common—they would be of extreme tenuity, their density being comparable with that of the nebula itself.

We must now try to picture the series of changes they would experience under the play of natural forces.

If the sun radiated as at present through a life of 3,000 million years, it would lose a 5000th part of its mass in the form of radiation. So small a loss is negligible for the purpose of our present discussion, so that we may properly suppose that the sun has retained the same mass throughout the whole of its existence. Turning to the diagram on p. 190, we see that at every period of its life, the sun must have occupied a position somewhere on the line marked "mass = 1." It must, then, be possible to represent all the changes the sun has experienced by a motion along this line, together of course with the uncharted part of it which lies to the left of the main sequence.

It is the same with the stars in general; the only possible course of evolution for a star is represented by motion along one or other of the lines of constant mass in this diagram. We must of course remember that the lines represent average properties rather than the properties of any individual star, but observation shows that the spread around the average is usually quite small, so that no great error is introduced by supposing that fig. 19 refers to individual stars, and the evolution of every individual star must be very approximately along one of the lines of constant mass in this diagram.

As the evolutionary process proceeds, the motion must in general be from right to left, this being the direction from low density to great, or from large diameter to small. When the star starts life as a condensation of extreme tenuity, it will be represented by a point out beyond the extreme right-hand edge of the diagram, and as it contracts under its own gravitation it moves to the left where densities are higher. During this contraction, the whole star gets hotter in accordance with the principles explained on p. 192. In time the central temperature will reach a point—perhaps about 200,000 degrees—at which thermo-nuclear reactions (p. 148) first become appreciable in amount, and so provide a substantial amount of radiation for the star. The time until this happens is at most a few million years, for we have seen that if there were no thermo-nuclear reactions at all to provide energy, the sun would have contracted down to its present size in about 50,000,000 years, and the shorter contractions we are now considering will of course require substantially less time than this.

The reactions which come into play first are the proton-proton reaction, in which protons combine with other protons to form deuterons and ultimately other heavier particles, and reactions of deuterons with protons and with one another. The first of these is a sluggish reaction and does not provide energy rapidly enough to replace that radiated away from the surface of the star; thus it may slow down the contraction, but cannot entirely inhibit it. The deuteron reactions may, however, provide energy enough to prevent contraction until no more deuterons are available, after which contraction will begin again and continue until temperatures are reached—of a few million degrees—at which protons begin to react with the nuclei of the light elements lithium, beryllium and boron. These reactions provide sufficient energy to check contraction of the star until the supply of light nuclei in the central regions of the star is exhausted.

All the stars to the right of the main sequence are very probably in one or other of the states just considered. Actually these stars are found to fall into three fairly distinct groups. To the extreme right in fig. 18 come the red giants (p. 180) followed by the Cepheid variables and then, farthest to the left and so nearest to the main sequence, the cluster variables (p. 53). Gamow and Teller find that the positions of these stars in the diagram of fig. 18 agree very well with those calculated from pure theory as the positions of stars in which the reactions just described are in progress. The group of stars to the extreme right—the red giants—is exactly in the position which ought to be occupied by stars in which the energy is provided by the reactions of deuterons with protons and other deuterons. The next group—that of Cepheid variables—is rather less definite; there seem to be three overlapping groups corresponding to the reactions of protons with the nuclei of lithium, beryllium and boron of atomic weight 11. Finally the cluster variables occupy the positions appropriate to stars in which the main reaction is that of protons with the nuclei of boron of atomic weight 10.

A time must finally come when the light nuclei in the central regions of the star have all been consumed, and the star is left with no source of energy beyond its contraction and the sluggish proton-proton reaction, which does not provide enough energy for the radiation of the star. The star accordingly contracts until it has reached a temperature high enough for new thermo-nuclear reactions to come into operation. The first to occur is that of protons with carbon nuclei (p. 149). This occurs at a temperature of about 20,000,000 degrees and, if the star was abundantly provided with hydrogen in the first place, can provide energy for a very long period indeed—about 100,000 million years for a star with the mass and luminosity of the sun. During this phase of its existence the star is a main-sequence star, and the long continuance of this phase explains why so large a proportion of the stars are main-sequence stars.

At long last, the supply of hydrogen in the central regions of the star becomes exhausted, and again there is no source of energy except contraction. The star accordingly contracts—

passing to the left of the main sequence, and becoming a white dwarf or a sub-dwarf. These stars emit so little radiation that contraction alone can provide them with energy for many thousands of millions of years of radiation. Some of them may have no sources of energy beyond this, while others may have shrunk so far that new thermo-nuclear reactions have already come into operation, and are providing the energy for their radiation.

Thermo-nuclear reactions, as we have already noticed, are very sensitive to changes of temperature. For instance, under conditions such as prevail at the centre of the sun, calculation shows that the amount of energy generated by the proton-carbon reaction will vary approximately as the seventeenth power of the temperature, so that if the temperature is raised only four per cent., the generation of energy will almost double.

Yet we can see that this doubling cannot be instantaneous, since if it were the stars would be highly unstable. An infinitesimal increase in the central temperature of a star would cause energy to be generated more rapidly; this would raise the temperature still further, with vastly more generation of energy, and so on indefinitely—the star would be highly explosive.

Thus general principles show that there must be a time-lag in the adjustment between temperature and generation of energy; the generation of energy at any instant is not dependent only on the temperature at the instant, but on that at some past moment or moments. Not only so, but both theory and laboratory experiments show that such a lag must actually occur—the energy only becomes available after a sequence of transformations of radio-active type, and such transformations take their time; in the proton-carbon reaction, some of the transformations take millions of years. All this results in finite but stable fluctuations in the rate of generation of energy, and these cause periodical fluctuations in the luminosity of the star and also in its mechanical structure. In brief, we might expect all stars to be variable stars of the kind explained in Chapter I.

It is then noteworthy that practically all of the stars to the right of the main sequence are variable stars. Not only does their light fluctuate up and down with a perfectly regular periodicity, but spectroscopic observation shows that these fluctuations are accompanied by pulsations of the whole structure of the star; as the star's light gets brighter and fainter, its size gets larger and smaller.

Thus there is no longer a difficulty in understanding why the long-period variables, Cepheids and cluster variables exhibit fluctuations of luminosity; the difficulty is to understand why the main-sequence stars do not exhibit similar fluctuations. Various suggestions have been made, but before we can pass judgment on them, we probably ought to have more detailed knowledge than now, both on the thermo-nuclear reactions themselves and on the structure of stellar interiors.

To reconcile this view of stellar evolution with the conclusions we reached on p. 204, we must suppose that the hydrogen in the outer layers of a star is not consumed in the main-sequence stage, but persists into the later white-dwarf stage. Hydrogen is burned up only in the central regions of the star, and Schönberg and Chandrasekhar consider that as the hydrogen is burned up here, the convective core gradually changes its quality, and finally becomes a core in which the matter is all at the same temperature, so that convection no longer occurs. They find that not more than about ten per cent. of the total hydrogen content of the star can be burned up before the star leaves the main sequence. Even to burn up this much requires a period of about 10,000 million years for the sun, although substantially less for more massive stars.

In any case it seems probable—although not certain—that the stars cannot all be of the same age; different births of stars must have occurred at different epochs. A white dwarf of solar mass, such as Sirius *B*, can hardly have existed for less than 10,000 million years, while a sub-dwarf which is still less massive and less luminous seems likely to have had an even longer life. On the other hand, a massive and highly luminous red giant cannot conceivably have had a life of anything like this duration; its radiation has been provided partly by a gravitational contraction, which could hardly provide radiation for a million years, and partly by the burning up of a small amount of hydrogen (with perhaps a little lithium), which could only supply radiation for a very few million years.

But the hypothesis that the stars are of different ages meets with difficulties from many directions; we shall consider some of these in the next chapter. We have to admit that there is still a good deal of uncertainty and even mystery about the whole problem, but we must remember that the whole subject is a growth of the last few years; order is emerging very rapidly out of chaos, and there is every reason to hope that all difficulties may be cleared up before long.

CHAPTER V

Carving out the Universe

We have now explored space to the farthest depths to which our telescopes can probe, and have explored into the intricacies of the minute structures we call atoms, of which the whole material universe is built. These in turn have proved to be formed of still more fundamental units—the minute charged particles we call electrons and positrons, protons, neutrons and possibly others. An unthinkably great number of these—according to Eddington's estimates about 10^{79} protons and an equal number of electrons—have somehow fallen together to form a universe. They have not fallen into mere random chunks or agglomerations of matter, but into distinctive and characteristic formations—stars, nebulae, etc. It is natural to inquire why these special formations were formed rather than others.

We have commented on the surprising emptiness of space: six specks of dust in Waterloo Station about represent the extent to which it is occupied by stars in its most crowded parts. The comment might well have taken another form. Six specks of dust contain, let us say, a thousand million million molecules. Our model of space is empty because this great number of molecules happens all to be aggregated into as few as six lumps. In the real space of astronomy the unit of aggregation is the star, and an average star contains about 10^{56} molecules—a number so large that it is quite useless to try to imagine it. The emptiness of space does not originate from any paucity of molecules; it originates from the circumstance that, apart from those forming the tenuous clouds of gas which stretch from star to star, the molecules are aggregated together in the huge colonies we call stars, with about 10^{56} members to each. Why should the molecules in space herd together in this way, when the molecules in the rooms in which I am writing and you are reading do not?

Following a well-tried scientific method, we may attempt to discover why these aggregates have formed, by first examining what keeps them together now that they have formed. The earth's atmosphere consists of about 10^{44} molecules. Why do they stay pressed down into an atmosphere instead of spreading out through space? The answer is of course provided by the earth's gravitation. A bullet fired from the earth's surface with a speed of 6·93 miles a second or more will fly off into space, because the earth's gravitational pull is inadequate to hold it back when it moves with so high a speed. But a bullet fired with a speed of less than 6·93 miles a second does not leave the earth; its speed is inadequate to take it clear of the earth's pull. Thus the molecule-bullets which form the earth's atmosphere, which are almost all flying with speeds of less than a mile a second, have no chance at all of getting away. The earth's gravitation continually pulls them back to earth, and in this way the earth retains its covering of air.

At rare intervals a molecule may experience a succession of exceptionally lucky collisions with other molecules, and so attain a speed of more than 6·93 miles a second. A molecule which happens to arrive at the outside of the earth's atmosphere with such a speed will leave the earth altogether, and join the interstellar crowd of stray molecules. The earth is continually shedding a minute fraction of its atmosphere in this way, but calculation shows that the loss, even in thousands of millions of years, is quite insignificant, so that we may regard the earth's atmosphere as permanent.

It is the same with the sun. The sun's heat has broken up the molecules of its atmosphere into their constituent atoms, and these move with an average speed of about 2 miles a second. But an atom-bullet would have to move at about 380 miles a second to escape altogether from the sun, so that again the solar atoms remain to form an atmosphere.

If all the molecules of air in an ordinary room were collected into a bunch at the centre of the room, the ball of air so formed would of course exert a gravitational pull on its outermost molecules, of the same kind as the earth and sun exert on the molecules of their atmospheres. But, because the weight of this ball of air is relatively so small, the intensity of its gravitational pull would also be small; indeed, it would be so feeble that a speed of about a yard an hour would be enough to take the outermost molecules clear of it. As the molecules of ordinary air move with an average speed of about 500 yards a second, such a ball of air would immediately scatter through the whole room. On the other hand, if the room were big enough to contain the sun, all its molecules could stay in a ball at the centre, just as they do in the sun. The outermost molecules would need a speed of at least 380 miles a second to escape, so that their actual speeds of 500 yards a second or so would be of no service to them.

PLANETARY ATMOSPHERES. In general the question of escape or no escape depends on the outcome of a conflict between the molecular speeds of the outermost molecules, and the intensity of the gravitational hold which the remainder of the mass exerts on them. We shall come upon many examples of this later (p. 260 ff.). The moon has only a twenty-third as much gravitational hold over the molecules of an atmosphere as the earth has, with the result that any atmosphere the moon may ever have had, has escaped by now. Mercury has only a tenth of the earth's gravitational hold, and also, owing to its nearness to the sun, its sunward surface is very hot, with the consequence that most or all of its atmosphere also has escaped. The hold of Mars on its molecules is only a fifth of the earth's, but its surface is cooler. Calculation shows that water-vapour and heavier molecules ought to remain, while the lighter molecules of helium and hydrogen ought to have escaped. This probably represents what has actually happened. The largest satellite of Saturn and the two largest satellites of Jupiter would exercise about the same gravitational hold as the moon, but as their surfaces must be enormously colder than that of the moon, they ought to be able to retain atmospheres. Some observers claim to have seen indications of atmospheres on all three satellites. All the four major planets exert stronger gravitational holds over their molecules than the earth, and so retain their atmospheres with ease, while Venus, with approximately the same gravitational hold as the earth, also retains an atmosphere.

These considerations amply explain why the molecules of the stars must necessarily remain aggregated now that the aggregates have once been formed, but the question of how and why these aggregates formed in the first instance is far more complex. What, for instance, determined that there should be about 10^{56} molecules in each star rather than 10^{54} or 10^{58}?

GRAVITATIONAL INSTABILITY

It is natural to enquire whether the forces which now keep a star together may not also have been responsible for its falling together in the first instance. This leads us to study the aggregating power of gravitation in some detail.

Five years after Newton had published his law of gravitation, Bentley, later Master of Trinity College, wrote to him, raising the question of whether the newly discovered force of gravitation would not account for the aggregation of matter into stars, and we find Newton replying, in a letter of date December 10, 1692:

It seems to me, that if the matter of our sun and planets, and all the matter of the universe, were evenly scattered throughout all the heavens, and every particle had an innate gravity towards all the rest, and the whole space throughout which this matter was scattered, was finite, the matter on the outside of this space would by its gravity tend towards all the matter on the inside, and by consequence fall down into the middle of the whole space, and there compose one great spherical mass. But if the matter were evenly disposed throughout an infinite space, it could never convene into one mass; but some of it would convene into one mass and some into another, so as to make an infinite number of great masses, scattered great distances from one to another throughout all that infinite space. And thus might the sun and fixed stars be formed, supposing the matter were of a lucid nature.

Exact mathematical investigation not only confirms Newton's conjecture in general terms, but also provides a method for calculating what size of aggregates would be formed under the action of gravitation.

THE FORMATION OF CONDENSATION. You stand in the middle of a room and clap your hands. In common language you are making a noise; the physicist, in his professional capacity, would say you are creating waves of sound. As your hands approach one another, they expel the intervening molecules of air. These stampede out, colliding with the molecules

of outer layers of air, which are in turn driven away to
collide with still more remote layers; the disturbance originally
created by the motion of your hands is carried on in the form
of a wave. Although the individual molecules have an average
speed of 500 yards a second, the zig-zag quality of their
motions reduces the speed of the disturbance, as we have
already seen, to about 370 yards a second—the ordinary
velocity of sound. As the disturbance reaches any point, the
number of molecules there becomes abnormally high, for the
stampeding molecules add to the normal quota of molecules
at the point. This of course produces an excess of pressure.
It is this excess pressure acting on my ear-drum that transmits
a sensation to my brain, so that I hear the noise of your clap-
ping your hands.

This excess of pressure cannot of course persist for long,
so that the excess of molecules which produces it must rapidly
dissipate. It is thus that the wave passes on. Yet there is one
factor which militates against its dissipation. Each molecule
exerts a gravitation pull on all its neighbours, so that where
there is an excess of molecules, there is also an excess of
gravitational force. In an ordinary sound wave this is of
absolutely inappreciable amount, yet such as it is, it provides
a tiny force tending to hold the molecules back, and preventing
them scattering as freely as they otherwise would do. When
the same phenomenon occurs on the astronomical scale, the
corresponding forces may become of overwhelming importance.

Let us speak of the gas in any region of space where the
number of molecules is above the average of the surrounding
space, as a "condensation." Then it can be proved that, if a
condensation is of sufficient extent, the excess of gravitational
force may be sufficient to inhibit scattering altogether. In
such a case, the condensation may continually grow through
attracting molecules into it from outside, whose molecular
speeds are then inadequate to carry them away again.

Whether this happens or not will depend of course on the
speed of molecular motion in the gas, as well as on the size
of the condensation. But it will not depend at all on the
extent to which the process of condensation has proceeded.
On doubling the extent to which condensation has proceeded,

we double the excess number of molecules in any condensation. In so doing, we double the gravitational pull tending to increase the condensation, but we also double the excess pressure which tends to dissipate it; we merely double the weights on each side of the balance, so that the balance still swings in the same direction. If once conditions are favourable to its growth, a condensation goes on growing automatically until there are no further molecules left for it to absorb.

The further a condensation extends in space, the more favourable conditions are to its continued growth. Other things being equal, a condensation two million miles in diameter will exert twice as much gravitational force on its outermost molecules as a condensation one million miles in diameter, but the excess pressures are the same in the two cases. Thus, the larger a condensation is the more likely it is to go on growing, and by passing in imagination to larger and larger condensations we must in time come to condensations of such a size that they are bound to keep on growing. Nature's law here is one of unrestricted competition. Nothing succeeds like success, and so we find that condensations which are big to start with have the capacity of increasing still farther, while those which are small merely dissipate away.

Suppose now that an enormous mass of uniform gas extends through space for millions of millions of miles in every direction. Any disturbance which destroys its uniformity may be regarded as setting up condensations of every conceivable size.

This may not seem obvious at first; it may be thought that a disturbance which only affected a small area of gas would only produce a condensation of small extent. Such an argument overlooks the way in which the gravitational pull of a small body acts throughout the universe. The moon raises tides on the distant earth, and also tides, although incomparably less in amount, on the most distant of stars. Each time the child throws its toy out of its baby-carriage, it disturbs the motion of every star in the universe. So long as gravitation acts, no disturbance can be confined to any area less than the whole of space. The more violent the disturbance which creates them, the more intense the condensations will be to begin with, but even the smallest disturbance must set up condensations, although these may be of extremely feeble intensity. And we have seen that the fate of a condensation is not determined by its intensity but by its size. No matter how feeble their original intensity may have been, the big condensations go on growing, the small ones disappear. In time nothing is left but a collection of big condensations. The mathematical analysis already referred to shows that there is a definite minimum weight such that all condensations below this weight merely dissipate away into space. This minimum weight is such that if approximately a tenth of this weight of gas were isolated in space, and all the rest of the gas annihilated, the molecules would just and only just fail to escape from its surface.*

We may say that the original uniformly distributed mass of gas was "unstable" because any disturbance, however slight, causes it to change its configuration entirely; it had the dynamical attributes of a stick balanced on its point, or of a soap-bubble which is just ready to burst.

PRIMAEVAL CHAOS. These general theoretical results may now be applied to any mass of gas we please. Let us begin by applying them to Newton's hypothetical "matter evenly disposed throughout an infinite space" (p. 213). We return in imagination to a time when all the substance of the present stars and nebulae was spread uniformly throughout space; in brief, we start from the primaeval chaos from which most scientific theories of cosmogony have started.

We have already seen (p. 81) that if all the substance of the present universe—nebulae, stars, stray matter and everything else—were uniformly scattered through space, there

---

* This is near enough, but not absolutely accurate. Exact mathematical analysis shows that the weight of the minimum condensation M is given by

$$M = (\tfrac{1}{3}\pi\kappa)^{\frac{3}{2}} \frac{C^3}{\gamma^{\frac{3}{2}}\rho^{\frac{1}{2}}},$$

where C, γ, ρ, κ are the molecular velocity, gravitation constant, initial density, and ratio of specific heats, whereas the weight from which molecules moving with velocity C just fail to escape is given by

$$M = \frac{3}{4\pi} \frac{C^3}{\gamma^{\frac{3}{2}}\rho^{\frac{1}{2}}}.$$

With $\kappa = 1\tfrac{2}{3}$ the minimum weight of condensation is 9·7 times the weight which is just adequate to retain the molecules.

would be something like 10^{-28} gramme of matter to the cubic centimetre, so that this is the kind of density we must assign to the hypothetical primaeval nebula. It is almost inconceivably low. In ordinary air, at a density of one eight-hundredth that of water, the average distance between adjoining molecules is about an eight-millionth part of an inch; in the primaeval gas we are now considering, the corresponding distance is nearly a yard. If the amount of air which occupies the space of a pinhead in our atmosphere were reduced to this density, it would occupy a hundred million cubic miles—a cube 460 miles each way. The contrast again leads back to the theme of the extreme emptiness of space.

We must, however, not forget that the universe appears to be expanding very rapidly, and changing its mean density of matter in space. The mean density of the primaeval chaos may have been greater or less than now according as space has increased or decreased its volume in the meantime. Assuming the Friedmann-Lemaître cosmology, Eddington has estimated that the mean density of matter in the original Einstein space must have been about 10^{-27}.

We proceed to inquire what is the minimum weight of condensation that would persist in a primaeval gas of such densities.

Calculation shows that if ordinary air were attenuated to a density of 10^{-28}, so that its molecules were about a yard apart, no condensation could persist and continue to grow unless it had at least 640,000 times the mass of the sun; any smaller weight of gas would exert so slight a gravitational pull on its outermost molecules, that their normal molecular speeds of 500 yards a second would lead to the prompt dissipation of the whole condensation.

Hence if such a gas were spread uniformly in space, and disturbed in any way, all incipient condensations whose mass was less than that of 640,000 suns would be smoothed out, and the gas would ultimately break up in larger condensations each having 640,000 times the mass of the sun or more.

We can carry out similar calculations with reference to other assumed molecular velocities. The following table shows the weights of condensations which would be formed in primaeval masses of chaotic gas of this same density 10^{-28}, with the molecules moving at different speeds:

Speed (yards a sec.)	Where found	Minimum mass of condensation
500	Air in room	640,000 suns
2,000	Hydrogen at 0° C.	40 million suns
27,000	?	100,000 ,,
120,000	Free electron at 0° C.	9,000,000 ,,

If we make similar calculations for a density of 10^{-27} gramme per cubic centimetre, the masses prove to be only about one-third of those tabulated above.

All known stars have weights comparable with that of the sun. Thus if, as Newton conjectured, the stars first came into being as condensations of this kind, then the entries in this table ought to be comparable with unity. Newton's conjecture, in the form in which we have just considered it, is clearly untenable, since the calculated weights are of the order of millions of times that of the sun. If there ever existed a primaeval chaos of the kind we are now considering, it would not condense into stars, but into enormously more massive condensations, each having the weight of millions of stars.

THE BIRTH OF THE GREAT NEBULAE

Obviously, then, it is significant that bodies are known in space having weights equal to those just calculated, namely the great extra-galactic nebulae, of which the masses are of the order of 100,000 million suns.

Thus it is to the great nebulae and not to the stars that we must look for masses comparable with those just tabulated. The general magnitude of nebular masses is such as to suggest that the condensations which would first be formed out of the primaeval nebula must have been the great extra-galactic nebulae, and not mere stars. It is of course at best only a conjecture that the great nebulae were formed in this manner— if for no other reason because we can never know whether the hypothetical primaeval nebula even existed—but it seems the most reasonable hypothesis we can frame to explain the fact that the present nebulae exist. These nebulae are so generally similar to one another that it seems likely that they must all have been produced by the action of the same agency, and that which we have just considered provides a reasonable explanation which, apart from the postulated existence of the continuous primaeval nebula, is based on *verae causae*.

We may notice that if the nebulae came into being in this way, the molecules must have moved with very high speeds— possibly of the order of 27,000 yards a second, or more than fifty times the molecular speed of ordinary air. The molecules of ordinary air can never attain such speeds as this, for the heat would break the molecules up into their atoms before they reached speeds of 27,000 yards a second; indeed it would break up the atoms themselves before they attained such speeds, setting free a few of the outermost electrons.

If, then, we imagine the nebulae to have formed as condensations in a primaeval chaos, this chaos cannot have consisted of complete molecules nor even of complete atoms. It must have consisted of a mixture of loose electrons and atoms with possibly a few complete molecules. Starting from such a primaeval chaos, it is quite easy to suppose the nebulae to have formed as gravitational condensations, precisely as imagined by Newton. The temperature of the primaeval matter need not have been very high. Even at ordinary room temperatures, free electrons move at an average speed of 120,000 yards a second, so that the presence of even a few free electrons raises the average speed of a mixture very substantially, and the needed average speed of 27,000 yards a second may be attained in a mixture of quite reasonable composition.

The great nebulae are of course not all exactly similar to one another, and our next inquiry must be as to the origin of their differences.

If the condensations in the primaeval gaseous nebula had formed and contracted in an absolutely regular fashion, the final product would be an array of perfectly equal and similar masses of gas spaced with perfect regularity. But we seldom find nature behaving with such perfect regularity as this; and we need not be surprised that the observed nebular array is not evenly spaced, or that its members are neither equal in weight, nor symmetrically arranged. As the original condensations in the primaeval gas contracted, they must have produced currents, and these would hardly be likely to occur absolutely symmetrically. If the motion in each mass of condensing gas had been directly towards the centre of the condensation at every point, the final result would have been a spherical nebula devoid of all motion, but any less symmetrical system of currents would result in a spin being given to each contracting mass. This spin would no doubt be very slow at first, but the well-known principle of "conservation of angular momentum" requires that, as a spinning body contracts, its rate of spin must increase. Thus, when the process of condensation was complete, the final product would be a series of detached gaseous masses rotating at different rates.

ROTATING MASSES OF GAS. The great nebulae are no longer rotating masses of gas; they would probably be better described as rotating clusters of stars. But the considerations just mentioned suggest that they may have begun their lives as simple masses of rotating gas which somehow, in the course of time, have changed into clusters of stars such as we observe in the extra-galactic nebulae and our own galactic system.

A mass of gas which was wholly devoid of rotation and of all internal movement would of course assume a perfectly spherical shape under its own gravitational forces; it would be just a big ball of gas with the density increasing towards the centre where the pressure was greatest. But masses of gas which are rotating will assume different shapes, the exact shape depending on the amount of rotation. These shapes can be calculated mathematically, and it is highly significant that the calculated shapes agree almost perfectly with the observed shapes of the actual nebulae. The agreement is so complete that it will be convenient to enumerate the shapes calculated for rotating masses of gas at the same time as those observed for the actual nebulae.

We may suitably start from the spherical shape which is associated with no rotation. A spherical nebula would of course be seen as a circular patch of light against the background of the sky, but we must not say that a nebula which looks circular is necessarily spherical in shape—a dinner plate

PLATE XXVII

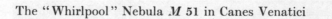

The "Whirlpool" Nebula *M* 51 in Canes Venatici

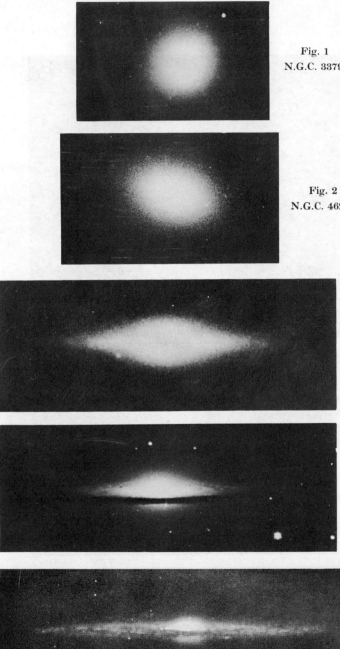

Fig. 1
N.G.C. 3379

Fig. 2
N.G.C. 4621

Fig. 3
N.G.C. 3115

Fig. 4
N.G.C. 4594
in Virgo

Fig. 5
N.G.C. 4565
in Berenice's
hair

Mt Wilson Observatory

A sequence of Nebular Configurations

stuck on a wall at the height of our eyes will look circular in outline, but is not spherical in shape. A number of nebulae are known which look circular, and although we cannot say that any particular individual of these is spherical, we can be sure that some of them must be. For if they were all non-spherical, it would only be by a rare accident that any particular one would appear circular in outline, and a simple statistical calculation shows that the number of nebulae which show circular outlines is far too great to be explained in this way. A typical nebula of circular outline is shown in fig. 1 on Plate XXVIII opposite.

A mass of gas which is in slow rotation will assume the shape of a slightly flattened ellipsoid—an orange-shaped figure like that of the earth or Jupiter. Nebulae of this shape are also known in abundance; an example is shown in fig. 2 on the same plate.

With a higher degree of rotation the degree of flattening increases, but theoretical calculation shows that the orange shape is soon departed from. The equator first begins to show a pronounced bulge, until finally, with sufficient rotation, this develops into a sharp edge, the rotating mass now being shaped like a double-convex lens. A large number of these lens-shaped nebulae are observed in the sky, a typical example being shown in fig. 3 on Plate XXVIII.

The next step is somewhat sensational. Further rotation does not, as might be expected, result in still further flattening. Up to now, each increase in rotation has increased the sharpness of the equatorial bulge, but this is now as sharp as it can be. Theory shows that the flattening also has proceeded to the utmost possible limit, and that the next stage must consist in matter being ejected through the sharp edge of the equator and spread throughout the equatorial plane. Here again observation conforms with theory; figs. 4 and 5 on Plate XXVIII show types of nebulae actually observed, the former being the nebula N.G.C. 4594 in Virgo which we have already had under discussion (p. 74).

The comparatively thin layer of gas which now lies in the equatorial plane is similar in one respect at least to the matter "evenly disposed throughout an infinite space" from which

Newton imagined the stars to be born. Disturbances can be set up in it in a variety of ways, and any disturbance, no matter how slight, must result in the creation of a series of condensations. As before, those below a certain limit of size disappear of themselves, while those above this limit continually increase in intensity until they have absorbed all the gas in the equatorial plane. Again, as with the hypothetical primaeval chaos, we can calculate the minimum size of condensation which can be expected to have a permanent existence, and once again the result proves to be highly significant.

We have already seen (p. 177) that there are about 40 stars lying within a distance of 16 light-years of the sun. These are mostly smaller and less massive than the sun, their average mass being perhaps half that of the sun. If we assume that there is a total mass of 20 suns lying within 16 light-years of the sun, we can calculate that the average density in the neighbourhood of the sun is 3×10^{-24}. Nearer to the centre of the galaxy, the average density must of course be higher.

Indeed, from the single well-established datum that the rotation-period of the sun in the galaxy is 250 million years, it is possible to deduce with fair certainty that the average density of matter inside the orbit of the sun must be of the order of 3×10^{-23}, or ten times that just calculated for the immediate proximity of the sun, the main uncertainty in the calculation arising from our inadequate knowledge as to how the stars are distributed inside this orbit.

Similar calculations can be performed for all nebulae of which the period of rotation is known. We find, for instance, that the central region of the Andromeda nebula must have a density of the order of 5×10^{-21}, and there are very similar results for other nebulae.

With these figures before us, we may perhaps take 10^{-22} as a reasonable estimate for the density of matter in the equatorial plane of the primaeval gaseous nebula. If we now proceed to calculate the weights of the smallest condensations which could form and persist in a gas of this low density, we obtain the results shown in the following table. The molecular velocities are taken rather low, so as to allow for the cooling which must occur when the gas is spread out in the equatorial plane of the nebula.

Molecular speed	Mass of condensation in terms of Sun
100 yards a second	5
300 „ „	140
500 „ „	640
1000 „ „	5000

Again the masses of the condensations are given in terms of that of the sun. And most of the entries in the table represent masses comparable with that of the sun; the condensations which must form in the outer regions of the great nebulae will be of stellar mass.

THE BIRTH OF STARS

And indeed it seems a reasonable conjecture that the process we have just been considering is that of the birth of stars. Even a casual glance at photographs of nebulae suffices to show that the matter which has been ejected into the equatorial plane of a nebula does not lie uniformly spread out in that plane; it is seen to have fallen into bunches, knots or condensations. These are apparent enough in many of the nebular photographs already shown, but they can be seen still more clearly in nebulae which are viewed nearly full on, such as for instance the striking nebulae shown in Plates XXVII (p. 220) and XXIV (p. 77).

These bunches are invariably too large to be interpreted as single stars; they are more probably groups of stars. In the largest telescopes they break up into great numbers of points of light in the way already exhibited in Plate V (p. 22). We have already mentioned the reasons which compel us to regard these points of light as actual stars, the principal being that some of them show the characteristic light-fluctuations of the Cepheid variables. It is not altogether clear whether the stars are formed directly as condensations in the equatorial plane of the nebula, or whether larger condensations form first, namely the bunches observable in nebular photographs, which subsequently form smaller condensations, the stars. On the whole it seems likely that there may be two processes involved—first the break-up of the nebular matter into big condensations, and then the break-up of these big condensations into stars. Such a succession of processes might well accompany a gradual cooling of the matter, and it is of course possible that even more than two processes are involved. There is no need to form a final opinion on this at present, as it is in no way essential to the progress of the main argument.

A collection of nebular photographs enables us to follow nebular evolution from the earliest stages shown in Plate XXVIII (p. 221), through the first formation of the equatorial ring of matter, and the appearance of granular bunches, such as are shown in Plate XXVII (p. 220), and the first distinct appearance of stars shown in Plate V (p. 22), down to the later stages, such as are shown in Plate XXXI (p. 252), in which the nebula appears to be but little more than a cloud of stars. Hubble has found it possible to follow the sequence still farther, and can trace a continuous transition from the nebulae of this last type to pure star-clouds such as the Greater and Lesser Magellanic Clouds shown in Plate XIII (p. 30).

Thus the stars appear to have been born in much the same way as we have conjectured that their parents, the great nebulae, had been born before them, namely, through the operation of what is generally known as "Gravitational Instability." This causes any mass of chaotic gas to break up into detached condensations, and, the more tenuous the original gas was, the more massive the condensations that are formed out of it. The original primaeval nebula was of such low density that the condensations which formed in it were thousands of millions of times as massive as the sun. These increased their density so much in contracting that when their rotation caused them to eject gaseous matter, this condensed into bodies of stellar mass which we believe actually to be stars.

We have less certain knowledge of the former process than of the latter. Our only reason for thinking that the former process ever occurred at all is that the extra-galactic nebulae now exist, and that the hypothesis of the previous existence of a primaeval chaotic nebula leads to a satisfactory explanation of the present nebulae existing as they do. On the other hand, we not only know that the stars exist, but also that masses of matter exist, or have existed, out of which the stars might well be born through the operation of natural forces—namely the fringes of the extra-galactic nebulae.

STAR CLUSTERS

A substantial proportion of the stars, whether of our own galaxy or of the extra-galactic nebulae, do not travel through space alone, but congregated in bunches or clusters. The globular clusters, which are observed both in our system (p. 58) and in the nearer nebulae, provide the most obvious instance of this. They seem to be bunches of stars which are, and always have been, too compact to suffer disintegration through the interaction of other stars, and so have assumed a globular shape under their own attraction, just as the molecules of a mass of gas would do. In our own system these clusters are found to lie somewhat outside the galactic plane; it may be, as Shapley has suggested, that they are broken up in travelling through this plane, where they would meet many other stars, or it may be simply that the obscuring matter in this plane is too opaque for us to see whatever clusters there may be.

By contrast, the groups of stars of the type generally described as moving clusters (p. 38)—the Pleiades, the Hyades, the stars of the Great Bear and a crowd of others voyaging in company with them through space—are generally found to move in the galactic plane. These may possibly represent the final vestiges of globular clusters which have been broken up by interaction with other stars, all except the most massive members having been knocked out of formation. As already mentioned, mathematical analysis shows that the interaction between the stars of such moving clusters and other stars in the galactic plane would cause each cluster to assume the shape of a flat biscuit or watch, of diameter equal to $2\frac{1}{2}$ times its thickness. It is significant that the majority of the moving clusters show a flattening of this kind, its amount agreeing tolerably well with the calculated value.

All clusters of stars, whether globular or open, seem *prima facie* to consist of groups of stars which are kept together by their mutual gravitational attraction, and so move together through space as a permanent group. The globular clusters contain great numbers of stars, but the open clusters contain fewer, there being no known limit to the fewness of their members. Indeed there is a continuous transition from the largest of open clusters to clusters containing very few stars indeed.

To take an extreme instance, the stars α Centauri and Proxima Centauri, which have already been mentioned as being the stars nearest to the sun, may be regarded as a cluster containing only three members—three, since α Centauri is itself a binary system (p. 172). The three constituents are now moving through space together, permanently locked together by their mutual gravitational attractions. In the same way, binary systems—Sirius, Procyon, etc.—may be treated as clusters of only two members.

Three possible reasons suggest themselves why a small group of stars should be permanently locked together in this way, and so travel together through space:

(1) they may have started as independent and independently moving stars, but subsequently have come under one another's influence and not separated since—a massive star, for instance, may have captured a less massive one;

(2) they may be the broken up remains of what was once a single star;

(3) they may have originated as contiguous condensations in the original nebula, and remained neighbours ever since.

Let us examine these three possibilities in turn.

BINARY SYSTEMS AS THE RESULT OF CAPTURE

A large proportion of the binary systems in the sky seem at a glance to consist of very ill-assorted pairs. In the very short table given on p. 45, two out of the four systems might fairly be described in this way, namely the systems of Sirius and Procyon, in each of which a fairly massive and highly luminous star is associated with a much less massive and enormously less luminous companion. And the proportion of odd pairs in the whole of space is probably not very different. An extreme case is the system of *o* Ceti, in which a star having about 300 times the diameter of our sun is accompanied by a companion hardly larger than the earth; we may think of an elephant and a flea pairing off to travel through space together. We are tempted to conjecture that in such oddly assorted pairs the smaller members must be celestial "pick-ups"—the result of capture. Yet we must remember that there are only two ways in which one star can capture another. One is by collision, the other is through a third star acting as intermediary. For it is well known that two stars which merely pass near to one another without contact, and without a third star being quite near, merely pull each other, to a greater or less degree, out of their rectilinear paths and continue their journeys through space in new paths. But it is an exceedingly rare event for one star to collide with another—so rare that each star can expect it to occur only once in thousands of millions of millions of years—while the near conjunction of three stars is even more rare. Only a very minute fraction of the whole number of the stars can ever have been involved in either a collision or a triple encounter, and no appreciable fraction of binary systems can have been formed in this way.

Even if we could strain the probabilities to the extent of supposing that Sirius and Procyon had both been formed in this way—in spite of adverse odds of innumerable millions to one—we should only encounter graver difficulties in such systems as o^2 Eridani. This system consists of a main star which is rather like the sun, and two less massive stars of entirely different quality. It would be ludicrous to imagine that the main star of this system could have made two captures in succession; such systems must clearly have some other origin.

BINARY SYSTEMS AS THE RESULT OF FISSION

Let us now examine the second possibility. When we were discussing the way in which nebulae might be born out of chaos, we noticed that the existence of currents in the primordial medium would endow the resulting nebulae with varying amounts of rotation. For the same reason the children of the nebulae, the stars, must also be endowed with rotation at their birth. There is a further reason for such rotation. The general principle of the "conservation of angular momentum" requires that rotation, like energy, cannot entirely disappear. Its total amount is conserved, so that when a nebula breaks up into stars, the original rotation of the nebula must be conserved in the rotations of the stars. Thus the stars, as soon as they come into being, are endowed with rotations transmitted to them by their parent nebula, in addition to the rotations resulting from the currents set up in the process of condensation.

Their continual radiation of energy causes the physical conditions of the stars to change, and we saw in the preceding chapter that this change generally involves a shrinkage of the star's diameter. The same principle of "conservation of angular momentum" now requires that, as a star shrinks, its speed of rotation shall increase. In brief, as a star ages, it spins faster and faster.

We have already seen (p. 36) how the rotations of stars can be detected and measured by spectroscopic methods. The method has so far been confined mainly to the largest stars, and here the law just mentioned appears to be confirmed. The largest stars of all—the "red giants" described on p. 187— show little or no evidence of rotation, while the blue stars of substantially smaller size show rapid rotation, with velocities ranging up to 200 miles a second and more at their equators.

We have seen how nebulae which were initially endowed with rotation would continually increase their speed of rotation under shrinkage, until finally their rotation broke them up and ultimately produced a family of stars out of each. The question now obviously arises whether, as the speed of rotation of the stars increases, these are likely to break up in the same way, and produce yet a third generation of astronomical bodies. We might expect that mathematical analysis would apply to large and small bodies equally, irrespective of scale. And a detailed examination of the problem shows that in actual fact the process we have had under consideration would repeat itself, and again bring a further generation of smaller bodies into being, provided the physical conditions were suitable.

The physical conditions, however, prove not to be suitable;

they certainly fail in one respect at least. Although a rotating star may eject gaseous matter in its equatorial plane, the whole process will be on a much smaller scale than in the nebulae. We might expect the ejected matter to form condensations as before, but calculation shows that, unless the molecular velocity is extraordinarily low, no condensation can survive unless it has a weight greater than the whole weight of the star! This means that with any reasonable molecular velocity, the ejected gas would not form condensations at all; it would merely scatter into the surrounding space, forming an atmosphere without any distinct condensations.

Such is the course of events if the stars, like the nebulae before them, are treated as pure masses of gas. Another alternative must, however, be considered.

THE FISSION OF LIQUID MASSES. We have seen how a mass of gas which was entirely devoid of rotation would assume a strictly spherical shape under its own gravitational attraction, while slight rotation would cause it to flatten into an orange shape, like the earth. The earth also has assumed this shape on account of its rotation, although its internal structure is very different from that of a mass of gas.

It can be shown that this flattened orange shape must be common to all slowly rotating bodies, regardless of their internal composition; gases, liquids and plastic bodies assume it equally, so long as they are rotating slowly. But if they rotate more rapidly their shape will depend very greatly on their internal arrangement and constitution, being especially affected by the extent to which the weight of the body is concentrated near its centre.

As a consequence of the high compressibility of gases, this central concentration of weight reaches its extreme limit in a purely gaseous mass. The opposite extreme is reached in a mass of uniform incompressible liquid such as water, in which there can be no appreciable central concentration.

As a mass of this latter type increases its speed of rotation, the slightly flattened orange shape merely gives place to the shape of a more flattened orange. The tendency which is shown by a gaseous mass, to form a sharp edge round the equator, is entirely absent, and the cross-section of its figure remains elliptical throughout. At a still higher speed of rotation the equator loses its circular shape and it too becomes elliptical. The figure has now three unequal diameters, but every cross-section is strictly elliptical; the figure is an "ellipsoid." After this, its longest diameter begins to elongate until the mass, still ellipsoidal in shape, has formed a cigar-shaped figure with a length nearly three times its shortest diameter.

A new series of events now begins. The mass of liquid gradually concentrates about two distinct points on its longest diameter, a waist or furrow forming across its middle. This furrow deepens, and finally cuts the body into two detached masses, which finally rotate in orbital motion about one another and form a binary star. The sequence of events is shown in fig. 20.

For comparison the sequence of shapes assumed by a rotating mass of gas is shown in fig. 21, this being identical with the sequence of observed nebular shapes which is actually observed, and is illustrated photographically in Plate XXVIII (p. 221).

The two chains of configurations shown in figs. 20 and 21 represent, it will be remembered, the two extreme cases of a rotating body whose substance is distributed with complete uniformity, and of a rotating body whose substance is very highly condensed towards its centre. As the constitutions of actual astronomical bodies must lie somewhere between these two extremes, we might naturally expect such a body to follow a series of configurations intermediate between the two shown in figs. 20 and 21. Theory shows that as a matter of fact it does not. All bodies having less than a certain critical degree of central condensation follow the sequence shown in fig. 20, or a sequence differing only immaterially from this; all bodies having more than this critical amount of central condensation follow the sequence shown in fig. 21. Thus, when this critical degree of central condensation is reached there is a sudden swing over from fig. 20 to fig. 21. In brief, every rotating body conducts itself either as if it were purely liquid, or as if it were purely gaseous; there are no intermediate possibilities.

The sequence shown in fig. 20 ends in two detached masses which revolve around one another like the two components of a binary system. The conjecture has often been made that the binary systems came into existence in this way, but it has long been recognised that there are difficulties in it, and these do not lessen as knowledge grows.

The principal difficulty is as follows. We have already seen how modern experimental physics has provided us with the knowledge necessary for a study of the structure of the interiors of

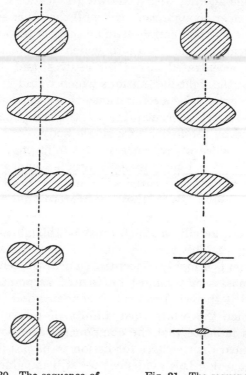

Fig. 20. The sequence of configurations of a rotating mass of liquid.

Fig. 21. The sequence of configurations of a rotating mass of gas.

the stars (p. 199), and the more we study the problem the more certain it seems that most of the stars behave as though their interiors were wholly gaseous, so that they would follow the series of changes shown in fig. 21, and could never produce a binary system. Knowing what we now know of the theory of stellar interiors, it is hard to imagine a star as massive as the sun having its substance spread with sufficient uniformity to produce a binary system through rotational fission. Yet in many binary systems each component is more massive than the sun.

A certain amount of direct evidence confirms this. In the ordinary eclipsing binary (p. 49), two stellar bodies of known masses revolve round one another at a known distance, and so act on one another with a known gravitational pull. If the masses are near enough, each will pull the other substantially out of shape by tidal action. The amount of distortion will of course depend on the degree to which the substance of the masses is concentrated near their centres, and it is possible to calculate the light-fluctuations which would correspond to different degrees of concentration; those actually observed indicate too much concentration for the components to have been formed by the fission of a single body.

A second piece of evidence is the following. If the two constituents of a binary system are far enough from one another for both to be treated as points, the orbit of each will be a perfect ellipse. But if they are nearer to one another than this, the orbits will no longer be perfect ellipses; each is nearly an ellipse, but an ellipse which must be thought of as turning round in space. This turning will be slow if the substance of the components is highly concentrated near the centre, because then the masses may almost be treated as points; it will be more rapid if there is less central condensation of mass. The rate at which the orbits turn admits of measurement, and the results indicate that the components are too highly concentrated near their centres for fission to be possible.

If, disregarding this evidence, we still imagine the binary stars to have been formed by the fission of single masses, we encounter further difficulties in studying the changes which will occur after the supposed fission has taken place. Obviously the two components cannot be expected to continue revolving round one another for ever in the positions shown in fig. 20, and binary stars would not be explained if they did, for these are observed to have their components at all sorts of distances, up to millions of diameters apart. How then, we wish to know, does the sequence shown in fig. 20 continue, and does it end up with masses at millions of diameters apart? Can we discover natural causes which would result in the masses separating to such distances as are found in the majority of binary systems?

The whole question is governed by the circumstance that to separate two stars to a great distance from one another requires a very large amount of energy. If the two components of a binary system are to move far from one another in the course of time, this energy must be supplied from somewhere, and where is it to come from?

Some might of course be provided by other stars, but this could only happen at times of close approach, and we have already seen (p. 97) that close approaches by other stars must be exceedingly rare events; a simple mathematical calculation shows that the energy which could be provided from such sources in a few thousands of millions of years would be quite negligible.

Thus if the two components of a close binary system are to separate, the energy must be found within the system itself— the system has only its own stores of energy to draw upon, again like a ship on an empty ocean. Only one available source of energy is known—the energy of rotation of the components. The process by which this becomes available is as follows.

TIDAL FRICTION. We have seen that when the components of a binary system are close to one another, they may exert such forces on one another that both are pulled seriously out of shape. The process is identical, except for scale, with that by which the moon raises tides on the earth. The nearness of the moon is an essential feature in the production of these tides. A very distant moon would exert a gravitational pull which would be uniformly the same at all parts of the earth. With the moon reasonably near to the earth, the pull on those parts of the ocean which are nearest to, and so directly under the moon, is substantially greater than the average pull exerted on the solid earth as a whole, while the pull on the antipodally opposite parts of the ocean—those farthest away from the moon—is substantially less. If the earth was not rotating, the difference in these pulls would cause the water to be exceptionally near to the moon at the former point, and exceptionally far from it at the latter. In other words there would be two points of high tide, one just under the moon and one antipodally opposite. The combination of this effect and the earth's rotation produces the complicated phenomenon of our ocean tides.

In the same way, when a rotating astronomical mass breaks up to form a binary system, the two components are at first so close that they necessarily raise tremendous tides in one another. These tides complicate the gravitational pulls between the two bodies enormously, and produce a series of effects which Sir George Darwin studied under the name of "Tidal Friction." He showed that the new forces set up by the tides must drive the two bodies apart, and equalise their rates of rotation in so doing. After these processes have been in operation for millions of years, the rates of rotation of the two bodies and their rate of revolution about one another must all become equal, so that each body perpetually turns the same face to its companion, and the two rotate about one another like the two spheres of a dumb-bell kept apart by an invisible arm. When this stage is reached, the separation has reached its limit, since there is no more energy available to effect a further separation.

If the system consists of two bodies of very unequal mass, the energy set free by the slowing down of the rotation of the larger mass may produce big results in the smaller mass, possibly driving it very far away. But when the two bodies are comparable in mass, as they usually are in a binary system, this cannot occur; the available energy can only produce a very limited separation, perhaps to a distance equal to a few diameters of either mass.

Now we have already noticed that the separation in binary systems may be anything from a fraction of a diameter to millions of diameters. If a binary has been produced by the fission of a single mass, its constituents would be separated by only a fraction of a diameter at first; tidal friction is quite inadequate to increase this to millions of diameters, and no other source of energy is available. Thus, even apart from the difficulties already mentioned, it seems highly improbable that binary systems in general can have been produced by fission.

This last objection does not apply to close binary systems. A large proportion of these consist of constituents which are not only fairly similar in both mass and size, but also exhibit similar spectra, which suggests that they are of similar physical constitution. The same tendency can be observed in wider systems, but in a far less degree—so much less that close and wide binaries may almost be said to form two distinct classes.

Because of this, it has often been conjectured that close and wide binary systems may have had different origins, the close systems—or at least those of similar constitution and spectral type—having been formed by fission, and the others in some other way. But both parts of this conjecture are open to grave objections. The conjecture that close systems were formed by fission meets the difficulties already mentioned on p. 232, while so far as we can at present see, the only possible origins for the wider systems are capture, which we have already dismissed as untenable, and adjacent condensations in the original nebula, which we shall now discuss and find to be untenable.

BINARY SYSTEMS AS ADJACENT CONDENSATIONS

The remaining possibility is that the two constituents of a binary system may have started as adjacent or near condensations in the primaeval nebula; they were perhaps originally held so firmly together by each other's gravitational pull that they have never been able to escape from one another to travel through space as independent separate stars.

We have seen that the condensations which form in a mass of nebulous gas may be of all sizes above a certain limit. Thus there is no reason to expect that adjacent condensations will be of equal or nearly equal size, and no difficulty is presented by the fact that the constituents of a binary or multiple system are often very dissimilar stars.

On the other hand, if binary systems had the origin we are now considering, the two or more constituents must be of the same age, whereas we have already noticed (p. 226) that the constituents of many binary systems—Sirius, Procyon, o Ceti, etc.—are to all appearances of very different ages. According to the theory of stellar evolution propounded in the last chapter, the white dwarfs and the faint red stars must be very old, while the red giants and the massive main-sequence stars are much younger.

This is only one aspect of a difficulty which besets the whole problem of stellar evolution. We have seen how the most massive stars radiate the most energetically—not only absolutely, but also per unit mass of their substance. On the main sequence, for instance, the radiation varies approximately as the cube of the mass, so that a star with ten times the mass of the sun has 1000 times the luminosity of the sun, and so uses up its store of energy 100 times as fast as the sun. Thus, as a general rule, the more massive stars are running through their energy far more rapidly than the less massive; old age comes upon them more quickly. If, then, the stars were all of the same age, we should expect to find that the most massive were in the most advanced state of old age, while the least massive were still in the full vigour of youth. Exactly the reverse is of course found to be the case, so that formidable difficulties stand in the way of supposing the stars all to be of the same age.

Reverting to the special problem of binary systems, it is hard to see how the two constituents can be of the same age, and yet they can only be of different ages if they have come together as the result of capture, a contingency which is so improbable that it can be ruled out as a possible origin for the normal binary system.

Obviously similar difficulties surround the problem of the origin of larger groups of stars, as well as of the globular clusters, and indeed of the galactic system as a whole. Clearly some piece of the puzzle is missing here.

CHAPTER VI

The Solar System

THE ORIGIN OF THE SYSTEM

Cosmogony first came into being as an attempt to discover the origin of the solar system. The reasons why it limited its efforts to this particular problem are chronological, in the early days of cosmogony, astronomy was barely conscious of anything outside the solar system.

EARLIER HYPOTHESES. From the earliest times men had remarked on the regularity of arrangement and motion in the solar system, and the more serious-minded tried to discover a reason for it. The earliest attempts of all were purely arithmetical or geometrical, having no reference to evolutionary development under the play of natural forces. Plato, for instance, believed that the distances of sun, moon, and planets were in the "proportions of the double intervals," by which he meant the ratio $1 : 2 : 3 : 4 : 8 : 9 : 27$. Two thousand years later Kepler claimed to have discovered that the distances of the planets from the sun were determined by the geometry of the regular solids. If spheres were drawn round the sun as common centre, with one of the planetary orbits lying in the surface of each, he believed that one of the regular solids could be made to fit exactly between each pair of adjacent orbits— i.e. placed so that one sphere should be inscribed in it, and the other circumscribed around it.

Kepler thought very highly of this theory for a time, and then abandoned it for a later view that the planetary distances stood to one another in ratios which were the frequency-ratios of consonant musical intervals.

Guided by a similar line of thought, Bode in 1772 pointed out a simple numerical relation connecting the distances at which the various planets moved round the sun. This is obtained as follows: Write first the series of numbers

0	1	2	4	8	16	32	64	128	256

in which each number after the first two is double the preceding. Multiply each by three, thus obtaining

0	3	6	12	24	48	96	192	384	768

and add four to each, giving

4	7	10	16	28	52	100	196	388	772

These numbers are very approximately proportional to the actual distances of the planets from the sun, which are (taking the earth's distance to be 10):

3·9	7·2	10·0	15·2	26·5	52·0	95·4	191·9	300·7	395
Mercury	Venus	Earth	Mars	Asteroids	Jupiter	Saturn	Uranus	Neptune	Pluto

The law was enunciated before Uranus and the asteroids had been discovered, so that it is somewhat remarkable that these fit so well into their predicted places. On the other hand, the law fails completely for Neptune and the still more recently discovered Pluto, so that it seems more than likely that it is a mere coincidence with no underlying rational explanation.

Modern science is no longer concerned to look for numerical order in the distances of the planets, but is very much concerned to see whether the various observed regularities can be explained on evolutionary lines as the result of the operation of natural forces.

Newton tells us that Plato had imagined the planets to be created at some infinitely remote point in space and allowed to fall sunward from the hand of their Maker, gaining speed all the time from their fall, until they reached their appointed orbits; then their motion was suddenly turned through a right angle without change of speed. Plato thought that this would account for the more rapid motion of the inner planets, but Newton showed that the speeds gained in this way would not permit of the planets describing circular orbits; these would only be possible if the sun's pull on each of the planets had been suddenly doubled at the moment when the planet's direction of motion was changed.

In 1750 Buffon conjectured that the planets had been formed by the collision of a comet with the sun, chunks of matter being splashed out of the sun, and condensing to form the planets.

The first theory which was truly evolutionary was due to Immanuel Kant the philosopher, who started his intellectual life as a scientist. He acknowledged his indebtedness to an English writer, Thomas Wright of Durham, but Wright seems to have done little more than pull a trigger. In 1751 Wright had published a book with the title *Original Theory or New Hypothesis of the Universe, founded upon the Laws of Nature, and solving by Mathematical Principles the general Phenomena of the visible Creation.*

Kant appears to have seen nothing of the book beyond its title and a review in a Hamburg periodical, but these set his mind to work, so that he began to think out for himself in what way the astronomical universe might have assumed its present form through the operation of natural laws. He published the result of his meditations four years later, under the title *Allgemeine Naturgeschichte und Theorie des Himmels.* In this he pictured the primaeval universe as a chaotic cloud of specks of dust and particles of matter of various kinds, either standing at rest or darting hither and thither in purely random motion. It was the same hypothetical beginning of things as Newton had already postulated some sixty years earlier (p. 213), but there is no reason for thinking that Kant was acquainted with Newton's speculations.

Kant went on to picture order as gradually emerging out of such a chaos; the primaeval matter began to cohere, until finally the whole picture is occupied by a vast continuous mass, which will ultimately form the sun. Kant imagined that the mass would be set into rotating by the mere act of cohering into a single body, but here he went wrong. He further supposed that it gradually cooled, that as it cooled it contracted, and that this caused it to rotate faster and faster, until finally its speed of rotation was so great that it could no longer hold together as a single body, and burst—like an over-driven fly-wheel. Masses of gas were thrown off its equator, and as these cooled further, they became first liquid and then solid. These solidified masses, according to Kant, formed the planets of which our earth is one.

LAPLACE'S NEBULAR HYPOTHESIS. Laplace advanced what was practically the same hypothesis independently in 1796—independently, because he says that, so far as he knew, no one except Buffon had previously thought about these problems. Laplace was an incomparably better mathematician than Kant, so that he knew better than suppose that the mere act of condensing could set his nebular mass into rotation—the mass could have no more angular momentum than it possessed at the outset. Thus he postulated a nebulous mass which was in a state of rotation from the beginning. This was in no way objectionable, for we have seen that most of the nebulae in the sky are in a state of rotation. Cooling, contraction and speedier rotation now supervene, just as in Kant's theory. Laplace traced out the detailed changes which were to be expected with mathematical precision. He showed how, as its shrinkage made it spin ever faster and faster, the rotating mass would gradually flatten out, develop the lenticular form we have already discussed (fig. 3 of Plate XXVIII, p. 221), and then proceed to eject matter in its equatorial plane, or rather to leave it behind as the shrinkage of the main mass continued. At this stage it would look somewhat like the nebulae shown in figs. 4 and 5 of Plate XXVIII, although Laplace, being unacquainted with nebulae of this type, adduced Saturn surrounded by its rings as an example of the formation to be expected at this stage (Plate XXXII, p. 253). Laplace imagined that the fringe of abandoned gas would then condense and form a single planet. As the main mass shrank further, more gas was abandoned in the equatorial plane, which in due course condensed into another planet, and so on, until the sun left off shrinking and no more planets were born. A repetition of the same process, but on a far smaller scale, resulted in the satellites being born out of the planets.

That the hypothesis is *prima facie* plausible, is evident from its having survived, and indeed been generally accepted, for nearly a century before it encountered any serious opposition. Recently criticisms have accumulated, of so vital a nature as to make it clear that the hypothesis must be abandoned.

The sun, according to Laplace, broke up and gave birth to planets through excess of rotation. But, as angular momentum is conserved, the angular momentum of the primaeval sun must persist in the rotation of the present sun, and in the revolutions of the planets around it. The total we obtain on adding together the contributions from all of these must represent the angular momentum of the primaeval sun. In strictness a further contribution ought to be added to represent the momentum of all the radiation which the sun has emitted since the planets were born. We can calculate the amount of this contribution, because we know the age of the earth with tolerable accuracy, but it proves to be entirely negligible.

The total angular momentum of the primaeval sun can be calculated with very fair accuracy, because something like 95 per cent. of the total angular momentum of the present solar system resides in the orbital motion of the four major planets, Jupiter alone contributing 60 per cent. The contributions from these four planets can of course be calculated with great exactness, so that some uncertainty in the minor contributions which make up the remaining 5 per cent. can have but little influence on the total.

When this total is calculated, we find that the primaeval sun cannot have had enough rotation to cause break-up at all. It is clear that the sun is very far from being broken up by its present rotation. Flattening of figure is the first step towards break-up, and the sun's figure is so little flattened by its present rotation that refined modern measurements have so far failed to detect any flattening at all. On adding the further angular momentum now represented in the motions of Jupiter and all the other members of the solar system, we arrive at a primaeval sun rotating about as fast as Jupiter or Saturn now rotate, and showing about the same degree of flattening of figure as Jupiter—enough to measure quite easily in a telescope, or even to detect with the eye alone, but nothing like enough to cause break-up. Thus the sun cannot have broken up, as Laplace imagined, through excess of rotation; indeed, it can never have possessed more than a quite tiny fraction of the amount of rotation needed to break it up.

Laplace's hypothesis is open to a further objection of a somewhat different character. Laplace was a very great mathematician, and there was nothing the matter with his abstract mathematical theory, so far as it went. More refined modern analysis has confirmed it at every step, and observation does the same, as photographs of rotating nebulae (Plate XXVIII) bear witness. These photographs exhibit a process taking place before our eyes, which is essentially identical with that imagined by Laplace, except for a colossal difference of scale. Everything happens qualitatively as Laplace imagined, but on a scale incomparably grander than he ever dreamed of. In these photographs the primitive nebula is not a single sun in the making, but contains substance sufficient to form hundreds of millions of suns; the condensations do not form puny planets of the size of our earth, but are themselves suns; they are not eight or so in number, but must be counted in millions.

We may ask whether the same thing cannot happen on the smaller scale imagined by Laplace—for are not the conclusions of mathematics applicable independently of the size of the body with which we are dealing? The answer has in effect been given already (p. 216). Everything happens on the smaller scale according to plan until we come to the formation of the condensations; here the question of scales proves to be vital. We have seen (p. 211) how the molecules which form the sun have condensed into a star because of their great number; the molecules in a room do not condense into anything at all because they are too few. In the same way, the molecules left behind by the slow shrinkage of a sun (assuming this for the moment to rotate rapidly enough to leave molecules behind) would not condense, because at any instant there would be too few of them available for condensation. They would be shed by driblets, and a driblet of gas does not condense but scatters into space—like the gas escaping from a leaking gas-burner. A mathematical calculation decides the question definitely; it is of a kind which Laplace could not make, since he was unacquainted with the molecular properties of gases. The decision is entirely adverse to his hypothesis. Apart from minor details, the process imagined by Laplace explains the birth of suns out of nebulae; it cannot explain the birth of planets out of suns.

All recent investigations have confirmed these objections to Laplace's conjectures, and to every other conjecture which attributes the genesis of the planets to one star alone. It is now clear that two bodies must have been involved; the planets must have had a father as well as a mother.

TWO-BODY HYPOTHESES

This conjecture is one which has often been made on its own merits. We have seen how Buffon imagined that the sun's family had come into existence through a collision between the sun and a passing comet—bits of the sun were splashed off, and condensed to form the present planets. In 1880 Professor Bickerton of New Zealand propounded a theory which was similar, except that Buffon's comet was replaced by a star and his head-on crash by a grazing collision. He imagined the *débris* of the collision to form a third nebulous body, condensations in which formed the planets. He showed how the resistance which the planets would encounter as they moved through the surrounding nebula would gradually make their orbits more circular, and so account for their present nearly circular shapes. Ten years earlier the English writer, R. A. Proctor, had advanced similar ideas, although with less precision. In recent years, H. Jeffreys of Cambridge has returned to the same train of thought.

Yet all theories of this type are open to a very serious objection. The two giant planets Jupiter and Saturn are surrounded by satellites, and in each case the planet with its satellites forms an almost exact replica, in miniature, of the main solar system of sun and planets. The resemblance is so marked that it seems fantastic to attribute different origins to the three systems, and yet it is straining the probabilities too much to suppose that three grazing collisions can have occurred, one to form each system—a single collision which merely grazes is a highly improbable event, and for any theory to postulate three is simply asking too much.

TIDAL THEORIES. In 1898 a Cambridge mathematician, W. F. Sedgwick, replaced the concept of material collision by that of tidal action, propounding a theory according to which the planets were pulled out of the sun by the tidal force of a passing star. In 1901 I independently advanced a similar speculation. Still a third speculation on these lines was put forward in 1905 by Professors Chamberlin and Moulton of the University of Chicago. They supposed that, in some remote past age, the sun had been liable to eruptions similar to those which now show themselves as prominences, but of far greater intensity. Then a wandering star happened to pass so close that these eruptions were enormously intensified by its tidal action, and puffs of gas were ejected so forcibly that they broke clear altogether of the sun's atmosphere, and ultimately condensed into solid bodies to which the name "planetesimals" was assigned. These were of far below planetary size, but in due course large numbers of them fell together and by their aggregation formed the present planets. This theory suffers from the defect that puffs of gas of planetesimal size would not condense into solid bodies; their internal gas-pressure would cause them to expand, and finally they would merely scatter into space like the dribbles of gas which figure in Laplace's theory (p. 242).

These various theories were little more than speculations, usually uncontrolled by mathematical tests, and showing but little capacity for explaining the more salient features of the solar system; none of them, for instance, explained why the larger planets in the solar system are accompanied by families of satellites, all much smaller than themselves.

In 1916 I tried to solve the purely mathematical problem of discovering what events would actually occur when a second star approached fairly close to the sun, and found that the tidal action of the second star might be sufficient of itself to break up the sun and produce a family of planets; there seemed to be no need to call in any intermediate mechanism such as eruptions and planetesimals. The process is briefly as follows.

The proximity of the moon raises tides in our atmosphere, on our oceans, and even in the solid body of the earth, and the proximity of a second star would raise tides in the same way in the gaseous sun. The tides which the moon raises in the earth are minute, partly because the moon is much smaller than the earth, and partly because it is at the relatively great distance of about sixty of the earth's radii away from the earth—and tidal effects diminish as the cube of the distance. But if a second star, at least as massive as the sun, were to

PLATE XXIX

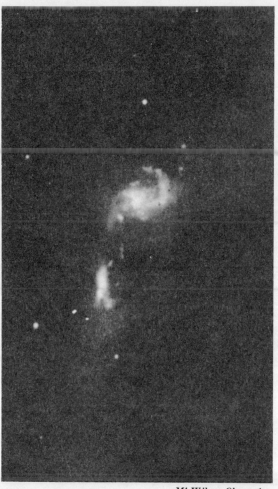

Two Nebulae (N.G.C. 4395, 4401) suggestive
of Tidal Action

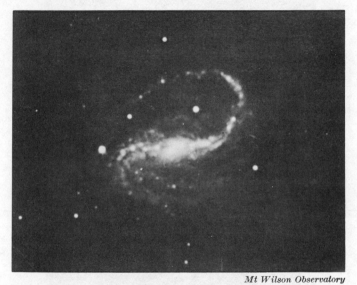

Mt Wilson Observatory

The Nebula N.G.C. 7479

approach to within two or three radii of the sun, its tidal effects would be immense. Calculation shows that, in place of the mild elevation of surface we find in terrestrial tides, a huge mountain of gas would rear itself up on the sun as the other star approached, its rate of growth increasing almost without limit until it finally darted out as a long tongue of gas—pulled out of the sun by the gravitational attraction of the second star and pointing towards the second star.

Now any column of gas, provided only it is on a sufficiently large scale, is unstable through the operation of what we have called gravitational instability. Thus condensations begin to form in this long tongue of gas, in the way already described (p. 214). As before, the smaller condensations are dissipated, while the larger increase in intensity until the filament finally breaks up into a number of detached masses. Calculations of the kind explained on p. 216 show that these would have masses comparable with those of the planets of the solar system, so that we may henceforth describe them as planets. The pairs of nebulae which are shown in Plate XXIII (p. 76) and Plate XXIX (p. 244) are very probably under one another's tidal influence, and may serve to suggest the general nature of the process we are now considering, although it must be remembered that the whole picture is on an enormously greater scale than that of the solar system—if it were not, the telescope would be utterly unable to show it to us.

CATACLYSMIC DÉBRIS. When the new-born planets first begin to move as separate and independent bodies, they are acted on by the gravitational pulls of both stars, and so describe highly complicated orbits. Gradually the bigger star recedes until its gravitational effect becomes negligible, and the planets are left describing orbits around the smaller star alone. If the planets moved in a clear field of empty space, these orbits would be exact ellipses. But the great cataclysm which has just occurred must have left all sorts of *débris* behind. Comets, meteors and other minor bodies which still survive in the solar system may represent a small part of it, but probably the main part was left in the form of dust or gas, so that the new-born planets had at first to plough their way through a medium which offered some resistance to their motions. Under these circumstances their orbits would not be strict ellipses. It can be proved that a resistance of the kind just described would change the shape of the orbits, these becoming more circular with the progress of time, and finally becoming absolutely circular if the medium should last long enough.

The *débris* of gas and dust would, however, continually be swept up by the planets and would disappear completely in time, probably leaving the planetary orbits something short of absolute circles. If this is the true origin of the solar system, very little of the original *débris* can now remain, its·last vestiges being probably represented by the particles of dust which are responsible for the zodiacal light. Nevertheless, the resisting medium appears to have existed for long enough to make the orbits, both of the planets and of their satellites, very nearly circular for the most part.

The exceptional cases are fully as significant as the cases of conformity. Comparatively elongated orbits still exist in just those regions where we should expect the primaeval resisting medium to have been most sparsely spread in space, namely on the outermost confines of the solar system and of the various satellite systems. Pluto, the outermost planet of all, has a more elongated orbit than any other planet. Again, in the systems of Jupiter and Saturn, the satellites with the most elongated orbits are those which are farthest away from their primaries. In addition to this, a general tendency may be discerned for elongated orbits to be associated with small masses, both in planets and their satellites. Mercury, with only a twenty-fifth of the mass of the earth, has a quite elongated orbit, as also to a less degree has Mars, with a ninth of the mass of the earth. An explanation of this has been suggested by Jeffreys. Massive planets such as Jupiter and Saturn must have collected a large mass of the resisting medium round them, and carried it through space with them as a far-reaching envelope. The massive planets would have their motion checked by the interaction of the whole of this big envelope with the remainder of the medium, and so would attain circular orbits more rapidly than the lighter planets with their smaller envelopes. And the same, with the appropriate modifications, is true of the satellite systems (p. 248).

Jeffreys has calculated the rate at which planetary orbits would change their shape under the action of this resisting medium. The data of the problem are necessarily uncertain, and this uncertainty naturally affects his conclusions, but we have already seen (p. 156) that his study has confirmed other estimates of the length of time which has elapsed since the planets were born.

PLANETARY EVOLUTION. We may next turn our attention to the physical changes which must all this time be affecting the various planets. The long filament of matter pulled out of the sun is likely to have been richest in matter in its middle parts, these parts having been pulled out when the second star

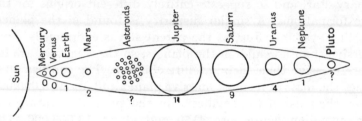

Fig. 22. Diagrammatic scheme showing the birth of planets out of a cigar-shaped filament of gas. The number of satellites is indicated under each planet (see p. 249).

was nearest and its gravitational pull was strongest. Diagrammatically at least, we may think of this filament as shaped like a cigar—thick near the middle, thin at the ends—so that when condensations begin to form, those near the middle are likely to be richer in matter than those at the ends. This probably explains why the two most massive planets, Jupiter and Saturn, occupy the middle positions in the sequence of planets.

Fig. 22 shows the planets arranged in the order of their distances from the sun, with their sizes drawn roughly to scale. The thousands of asteroids whose orbits now fill the space between the orbits of Mars and Jupiter are represented as a single planet, it being generally supposed that these asteroids were formed by the break-up of what was originally a single planet in a way we shall shortly describe.

If we surround the planets by a continuous outline, as in the diagram, we can reconstruct in imagination the cigar-shaped filament out of which they were produced, and we see at once how the biggest planets were produced where matter was most abundant.

The tidal theory which predicts all these features had been propounded, and its consequences worked out, many years before Pluto had been discovered. Valuable support for the theory may thus be found in the circumstance that Pluto behaves in every way according to the requirements of the tidal theory.

THE BIRTH OF SATELLITES. We have already noticed how the great disparity of weight between the sun and planets distinguishes the sun-planet formation from that of the normal binary star, and so suggests entirely different origins for the two formations. A similar disparity is found in the planet-satellite systems. Just as the parent sun is enormously more massive than its children the planets, so these in turn are far more massive than their satellite children. The sun has 1047 times the mass of its most massive planet and about 6,000,000 times the mass of the smallest. In the system of Saturn the corresponding figures are 4150 and about 16,000,000. The nearest approach to equality of mass is provided by the earth-moon system, the earth having only 81 times the mass of the moon. And, like the planetary system of the sun, the satellite systems of Saturn and, to a lesser degree, of Jupiter show a general tendency for the masses of the various satellites to increase up to a maximum as we pass outwards from the planet, and then to decrease again. This again suggests formation out of a cigar-shaped filament with matter occurring most richly near the middle. In conjunction with the repetition of the great disparity of masses between primary and secondaries, this suggests very forcibly that the satellites of the planets have been born by the same type of process as had previously resulted in the birth of their parents.

We can imagine the process in a general way. Immediately after their birth, the planets must begin to cool down. The larger planets, such as Jupiter and Saturn, naturally cool most slowly and the smallest most rapidly. The smallest planets of all may lose heat so speedily that they liquefy, and perhaps even solidify, almost immediately after their birth.

While these events are in progress, the planets are still pursuing somewhat erratic orbits, in describing which they may pass so near to the sun that a second series of tidal disruptions occurs. In these the sun itself plays the *rôle* originally played by the passing star from space, the planets playing the part originally taken by the sun. The sun may now tear long filaments of matter out of the surfaces of the planets, and these, forming condensations, may give birth to yet another generation of astronomical bodies, the satellites of the planets. In some such way the tidal theory imagines the planetary satellites to have come into being.

Mathematical investigation shows that the more liquid a planet was at birth, the less likely it would be to be broken up by the still gaseous sun. If, however, such a break-up occurred, the masses of primary and satellites would be more nearly equal than if the planet had been more gaseous. Thus, on passing from wholly gaseous planets to planets which liquefied at or immediately after their birth, we should expect at first to find planets with large numbers of relatively small satellites, and then, after passing through the border-line cases of planets with small numbers of relatively large satellites, we should expect to come to planets having no satellites at all.

We have already seen that the big central planets, Jupiter and Saturn, ought to have remained gaseous for longest and the smaller planets to have liquefied earliest; we now see that this prediction of theory exactly describes what is actually found in the solar system. Starting from Jupiter and Saturn, with eleven and nine relatively small satellites, we pass Mars with only two satellites, and come to the earth with its one relatively large satellite, followed by Venus and Mercury which have no satellites at all. Proceeding in the other direction we leave Jupiter and Saturn with their eleven and nine tiny satellites, to discover Uranus with four small satellites and Neptune with one comparatively big satellite. The number placed under each planet in fig. 22 gives the number of its satellites. When the numbers are exhibited in this way, the law and order in the arrangement of the satellite systems becomes very apparent, and this arrangement is seen to be exactly in accordance with the prediction of the tidal theory. The cigar-shaped arrangement applies not only to the sizes of the planets, but also, as it ought, to the numbers of their satellites.

The earth and Neptune, with only one satellite each, and those comparatively large ones, form the obvious lines of demarcation between planets which were originally liquid and those which were originally gaseous. This leads us to conjecture that Mercury, Venus and Pluto must have become liquid or solid immediately after birth, that the earth and Neptune were partly liquid and partly gaseous, and that Mars, Jupiter, Saturn and Uranus were born gaseous and remained gaseous at least until after the birth of their families of satellites.

We may perhaps find further evidence confirmatory of the tidal theory in the circumstance that the masses of Mars and Uranus are abnormally small for their positions in the sequence of planets. If, as we have supposed, the planets were all born out of a continuous filament of matter, the mass of Mars at birth would in all probability have been intermediate between those of the earth and Jupiter, and the mass of Uranus intermediate between those of Neptune and Saturn. But if, as we have already been led to suppose, the two anomalous planets Mars and Uranus were the two smallest planets to be born in the gaseous state, they would be likely to lose more of their substance than the other planets through their outermost layers of molecules dissipating away into space before they had cooled down into the liquid state. If Mars and Uranus are supposed to be mere relics of planets which were initially far more massive than they now are, the anomalies begin to disappear and the pieces of the puzzle to fit together in a very satisfactory manner.

ORBITAL PLANES. Every rotating mass, whether gaseous, liquid or solid, has a definite axis of rotation, and, perpendicular to this, a definite equatorial plane which divides the mass symmetrically into two exactly equal and similar halves. When a mass breaks up under its own rotation, the equatorial plane and the symmetry still persist. Illustrations of this can be found in any set of photographs of rotating nebulae, as, for instance, those shown in Plates XI (p. 26) and XXI (p. 74). In more humble life an illustration is provided by the splashes of mud thrown off by a spinning bicycle-wheel, which all keep in the plane in which the wheel is spinning.

If the sun's equatorial plane had proved to be a plane of symmetry for the solar system, so that the whole system was similarly arranged as regards the two sides of this plane, it might have been possible to explain the system as the result of a rotational break-up. But the sun's equatorial plane is not a plane of symmetry. The planets do not move in it; most of them move in a plane which makes an angle of 5 or 6 degrees with it. In terms of our homely analogy, the splashes of mud are not flying about in the plane in which the bicycle-wheel is spinning.

The hypothesis that the planets came into being through a rotational break-up of the sun fails completely before this fact, but the tidal theory provides a simple explanation of it at once. The sun is still rotating much as it was before the planets were born, and so retains its original equatorial plane. The quite different plane in, or very close to, which the planets are describing orbits must clearly be the plane in which the long tidal filament was originally drawn out by the passing star. Thus the plane in which the outer planets now move must record the position of the plane in which the two stars— the sun and the second parent of her family of children— described orbits around one another something like 3000 million years ago. It is the only clue the latter has left of his identity, and is of course far too slight for identification to be possible after such a lapse of time.

Such is the tidal theory of the genesis and evolution of the solar system, which can obviously account for a large number of the observed features of the system. But it only occupies one minute corner of the canvas on which we attempt to portray the evolution of the universe as a whole.

We made the conjecture in Chapter v that the stars first came into being as condensations in nebulae of almost inconceivable tenuity; these condensations would contract until they had formed stars of the kind we know.

Through the whole of their histories, these stars would be wandering about, mostly independently, through space, so that pairs of them would occasionally come close enough to one another to produce families of planets in the way we have just described.

For a long time it was thought that the process of contraction of new-born stars would proceed so rapidly that there would be no appreciable chance of planets being born while it was in progress. But this overlooked that the new-born stars, owing to their immense size and tenuous texture, would be especially vulnerable to tidal action. Leaving the solar system entirely out of consideration for the moment, it seems reasonably certain that a great number of planetary systems must have been formed by tidal action of the kind just described, and that a very great proportion of these must have been formed while their suns were still in a semi-nebulous state; all this is a mere matter of statistical calculation. Our own solar system contains intrinsic evidence that it was born in the same way as this majority, the sun being still of immense size when it was born. No other hypothesis can explain its immense extent in space; if the planets had been born when the sun had already shrunk to its present size, no available force could have carried matter out from the sun to the orbit of Pluto, and neither could any known agency have caused the planets to rotate as fast as they now do.

It was, nevertheless, supposed for a long time that any planets that there might be in the sky had been produced mainly by stars in their present shrunken states; it would then be very rare for two stars to approach near enough to one another for planets to be produced. On these grounds it used to be supposed that planetary systems must be rare objects in the sky. But we now see that a far greater number of effective encounters must have taken place while the stars were large, and that planetary systems must be far commoner than was previously thought. A fair, although probably still small, proportion of the stars must be accompanied by planets; the birth of a family of planets is still not the normal fate of a star, but it is much less abnormal than we used to think, and it must have befallen a fair proportion of the stars. The total number of stars in space is so immense—at the lowest computation greater than the number of blades of grass on the whole surface of the earth—that the number of planetary

PLATE XXXI

Mt Wilson Observatory

The Nebula *M* 101 in Ursa Major

PLATE XXXII

Saturn in 1916

Saturn in 1917

Lowell Observatory

Saturn in 1921

Saturn and its System of Rings

systems in the whole of space must be almost unthinkably great. Millions of millions of these must be almost exact replicas of our solar system, and millions of their planets must be almost exact replicas of our earth.

ROCHE'S LIMIT

The reign of gravitational instability must end with the birth of planetary satellites, since gaseous bodies of less weight than these could not hold together. Even under the most favourable circumstances their feeble gravitational pulls would be unable to restrain their outermost molecules from escaping, so that the whole mass would speedily scatter into space. Yet astronomy provides many instances of smaller bodies; we have already mentioned the asteroids, meteors or shooting-stars, and the particles of Saturn's rings. As all these are too small to have been born in the gaseous state, we must suppose them to be broken-up fragments of larger masses. This accords with the circumstance that these small bodies as a rule do not occur individually but in swarms.

The asteroids occur as a single swarm. If these were found scattered throughout the solar system, their origin might present a difficult problem. As things are, the whole swarm can be explained quite simply as the broken fragments of a primaeval planet. Saturn's rings again admit of a natural explanation as the fragments of a former shattered moon of Saturn. Comets, which we have hardly had occasion to mention so far, are in all probability swarms of minute bodies which are just held together sufficiently by their mutual gravitational attraction to describe a common orbit in space. At its apparition in 1909, Halley's comet was estimated to reflect as much of the sun's light as a single body 25 miles in diameter. Yet its apparent surface was 300,000 times that of such a body, and was quite transparent. It is difficult to resist the conclusion that the comet consisted of a widely spaced swarm of small bodies, and such a swarm again admits of a simple explanation as the broken fragments of a single mass.

Shooting-stars, or meteors, also are encountered in swarms. As we shall see later, the motion of many of these swarms makes it possible to identify them as broken-up comets. Thus the broken fragments which compose a comet are identical with the meteors which we see as shooting-stars when they penetrate into the earth's atmosphere. Shapley has estimated that the earth's atmosphere must catch thousands of millions of shooting-stars every day, of which at most only one in a hundred is bright enough to be visible to the naked eye. Generally they dissolve into vapour long before they reach the earth's surface, but occasionally one is so big that the earth's atmosphere fails to dissipate it entirely, and what remains of it strikes the earth as a solid body—a meteorite. Every shooting-star and meteorite may be regarded as a miniature comet, consisting of only a single fragment. On occasions a whole group of fragments, moving in parallel paths at only small distances apart, may strike the earth's atmosphere and appear as a "fireball." Generally speaking all the small fry of the solar system move in swarms, and can be naturally interpreted as the broken-up fragments of larger bodies.

It is easy to see how larger bodies might be broken up into swarms of meteors. We have supposed the sun to have been broken up, at least to the extent of ejecting a family of planets, by the tidal pull of a passing star. What would have happened if the passing star had not passed, but had come to stay? So long as it remained within a certain distance of the sun, its tidal forces were pulling the sun to pieces. We can imagine how a longer visit from it would have resulted in a greater upheaval in the sun, and the birth of a larger family of planets. Finally a visit of unlimited duration would have shattered the sun into fragments.

In 1850 Roche gave a mathematical investigation of this process of tidal break-up. His discussion dealt only with solid or liquid bodies, but the underlying mechanism is the same whether the bodies are solid, liquid or gaseous. We have seen that the smaller of the two bodies involved in a tidal encounter suffers the most. Roche dealt only with the case in which one body was very small in comparison with the other; in such a case the small body was completely broken up, while the larger one remained unscathed. Roche imagined the small body to describe an orbit of gradually decreasing size around the big body. He calculated that if the two bodies were of equal density, the small body would be broken up as soon as the radius of its orbit fell to 2·45 times the radius of the large body. If the bodies are different in density the matter is slightly more complicated. We must imagine the larger body to expand or contract until it has the same average density as the smaller body; the critical distance is then 2·45 radii of the larger body in its imaginary expanded or contracted state

This distance is generally known as Roche's limit. A satellite can describe a circular orbit about its primary with safety so long as this orbit lies beyond Roche's limit, but it is broken into fragments as soon as it trespasses within the limit. The following figures confirm Roche's mathematical analysis:

Radius of Saturn's outermost ring	2·30 radii of Saturn
Roche's limit	2·45 *radii of primary*
Radius of orbit of Saturn's innermost satellite	3·11 radii of Saturn
Radius of orbit of Jupiter's innermost satellite	2·54 radii of Jupiter
Radius of orbit of Mars' innermost satellite	2·79 radii of Mars

They also suggest very forcibly that Saturn's rings are the broken-up fragments of a former satellite which ventured into the danger-zone marked out by Roche's limit. We speak of rings in the plural, because two circular gaps cause an appearance of three detached rings. There is a tendency to jump to the hasty inference that the rings are the shattered remains of three distinct satellites, but it is not so. Certain orbits around Saturn appear to be rendered unstable by the motions of the larger satellites of Saturn, so that no particle could permanently remain in such an orbit. Now the positions of these unstable orbits can be calculated theoretically, and the calculated positions are found to agree exactly with the positions of the observed divisions between the rings. We conclude that Saturn's rings were almost certainly produced by the breakage of a single satellite.

Roche's fundamental idea can be extended in many directions and admits of varied applications. There must, for instance, be a danger-zone, marked off by a Roche's limit, surrounding the sun. The distance of this danger-zone from the sun depends on the density of the body for which it is dangerous (p. 255). For a body having the low density of a comet the distance will be very great indeed. Whatever the distances of their danger-zones, comets must occasionally pass through them and become broken up in so doing. Two comets, Biela's comet (1846) and Taylor's comet (1916), were observed actually to break in two while at about the earth's distance from the sun, and in 1882 a comet was seen to divide into four parts. Biela's comet returned in due course (1852) in the form of two distinct comets a million and a half miles apart, since which time neither part of the original comet has been seen again. The orbit of this comet was identical with that of the Andromedid meteors, which make a display of shooting-stars in the earth's atmosphere on favourable 27ths of November, so that it is likely that these shooting-stars are the broken remains of Biela's comet. Other conspicuous swarms of shooting-stars also move in the tracks of comets—the Leonids, which used to make a magnificent show every 33 years, move in the track of Comet 1866 I, the Perseids in the track of another Comet (1862 II), and the Aquarids in the track of Halley's famous comet. In each case there can be little doubt that the shooting-stars are scattered fragments of the comets. Besides this there are several families of comets whose members follow one another round and round in the same orbit, as though they had originally formed a single mass.

In the same way a Roche's limit must surround the planet Jupiter, so that comets and other bodies may be broken up through getting inside the danger-zone marked off by this limit. Jupiter's innermost satellite is already perilously near it. But the greatest interest of this particular danger-zone is that it probably accounts for the existence of the asteroids. In the early days of the solar system, when the orbits of the planets were less nearly circular than they now are, a primaeval planet between Mars and Jupiter may well have described an orbit so elongated as to take it repeatedly within the danger-zone of Jupiter. If so, we need look no further for the origin of the asteroids. It is significant that the average orbit of all the asteroids agrees almost exactly with that of the planet which

Bode's law (p. 237) would require to exist between Mars and Jupiter.

As a final illustration, such a danger-zone must also surround the earth. The moon is at present well outside it, but will not always be so. For we shall see almost immediately (p. 258) that the final fate in store for the moon is to be dragged back, under the influence of the earth's tides, towards the earth from which it originally came. When it has been dragged down to within about 8000 miles of the surface of the earth, the tides raised by the earth in the solid body of the moon will shatter the latter into fragments. These will form a system of tiny satellites revolving around the earth in the same way as the particles of Saturn's rings revolve around Saturn, or as the asteroids revolve around the sun.

Moonlight will be replaced by the light reflected from the earth's ring of satellites. This will be far brighter than our present moonlight because there will be a far greater surface to reflect the sun's light.

TIDAL FRICTION

When once the planets are in existence as detached, independent bodies, tidal friction will operate in the way explained on p. 234. Each planet will be driven away from the sun, and there will be a tendency for the rate of rotation of each to approximate to that of the sun, so that the planet tends always to show the same face to the sun.

It is almost certainly through the operation of tidal friction that Mercury always turns the same face to the sun, and that Venus rotates so nearly at the same speed as the sun that it turns the same face to the sun day after day, and probably also week after week. As we pass farther away from the sun the effects of tidal friction diminish rapidly but it is probably significant that the nearer planets, Earth and Mars, have days of nearly twenty-four hours each, while the remote planets Jupiter, Saturn and Uranus each have days of only about 10 hours. The periods of rotation of Neptune and Pluto are unknown. Apart from these we find, in a general way, that the farther we recede from the sun the more rapidly the planets rotate, which is precisely the effect that ought to be produced by tidal friction.

In the same way, tidal friction has in all probability been mainly responsible for the present configuration of the earth-moon system, driving the moon away to its present distance from the earth and causing it always to turn the same face towards us. Tidal friction must of course still be in operation. As the moon raises tides in the oceans of the earth, these exert a pull on the solid earth underneath, and so slow down its speed of rotation, with the result that the day is continually lengthening, and will continue to do so until the earth and moon are rotating and revolving in complete unison. When, if ever, that time arrives, the earth will continually turn the same face to the moon, so that the inhabitants of one of the hemispheres of the earth will never see the moon at all, while the other side will be lighted by it every night. By this time the length of the day and the month will be identical, each being equal to about 47 of our present days.

After this, tidal friction will no longer operate in the sense of driving the moon farther away from the earth. The joint effect of solar and lunar tides will be to slow down the earth's rotation still further, the moon at the same time gradually lessening its distance from the earth, until finally it meets the fate described above (p. 257).

Jeffreys has made a study of the length of time needed for all these processes to occur, with results that have already been mentioned (p. 156). He estimates that it must have required something like 4000 million years for the earth-moon system to reach its present configuration; he has further estimated that about another 50,000 million years will be required before day and month become identical in length, so that the earth always turns the same face to the moon.

THE PHYSICAL CONDITION OF THE PLANETS

We have conjectured that the planets begun life as condensations in a filament of tenuous gas; after this, they first gradually contracted, and then liquefied and solidified, until they assumed their present physical conditions. Let us now examine these conditions, and see if we can discover in detail how they were attained. There are two main lines of study; the first is to measure the total amount of radiation we receive from each planet, the second is to analyse it spectroscopically.

PLANETARY TEMPERATURES. We see the planets by the sunlight which is reflected back to us by their surfaces. Besides this radiation, these surfaces also emit a certain amount of radiant heat—just like any other surface which is not perfectly cold (i.e. at the absolute zero of temperature). The amounts emitted by the various planets can be measured by the bolometer, and observations which have been conducted with great precision in recent years have shown that each planet gives out just as much energy, in the form of light and heat together, as it receives from the sun. Thus the planets can have but little heat of their own, and are hot only to the extent that they are warmed by the sun. It follows that those planets are hottest that are nearest to the sun and conversely.

But distance from the sun only settles the average temperature of a planet; the range about this average will depend on the physical state of the planet. For instance, the earth and moon are at the same distance from the sun, so that their average temperatures are approximately the same, but their physical conditions are widely different. The moon, with no atmosphere, no water, no vegetation or life of any kind, is a dead world in which mountains of volcanic rock rise from plains of lava and ash. The earth on the other hand possesses an atmosphere, ample water, and teems with life. The consequence is that the earth's temperature remains fairly steady through the alternations of day and night, while the moon rushes from one extreme to another. We can see this last effect in miniature at a lunar eclipse, when the earth intervenes between the sun and moon, so that the sun's radiation is shut off from the surface of the moon. Pettit has found that a point directly under the sun is at a temperature of about 101° C., so long as the sun's rays are uninterruptedly falling upon it. As soon as the earth begins to shut off these rays, the temperature begins to fall rapidly, and has fallen to −73° C.—a fall of 174 degrees —by the time totality is reached, and no radiation falls on the point in question. A further hour of darkness reduces this to −91° C., and when the sun begins to reappear after 4¾ hours of totality, the temperature has fallen to −117° C. With the sun's rays falling upon it, the moon now gets warm with the same rapidity with which it had previously got cold.

Such terrific variations of temperature are unknown on the surface of the earth, during either the minutes of an eclipse or the hours of night. When the sun's rays are cut off, the earth benefits from the stores of heat in its atmosphere and soil. The moon has no such stores on which to draw; it has no atmosphere and its surface is an almost perfect non-conductor of heat, calculation showing that the heat which the moon gives out during an eclipse comes from a layer less than an inch in thickness.

PLANETARY ATMOSPHERES. We have already seen (p. 212) how the moon's absence of atmosphere results directly from the smallness of the moon's mass; its gravitational pull is inadequate to retain an atmosphere against the tendency of its molecules to stream off into space.

On earth a molecule at sea-level travels for only about a 400,000th of an inch before it collides with another molecule, and starts off on a new path. In the higher levels of the atmosphere, where molecules are less numerous, the length of their path is correspondingly greater, and finally, at the top of the atmosphere, it is possible for a molecule to travel many miles and even thousands of miles before meeting another. A molecule moving in these regions in the right direction and at the right speed—from 4·9 to 7 miles a second—may travel several times round the earth unmolested, forming in effect a miniature satellite of the earth—just like the moon, except for the difference in size (p. 41). If it is travelling at more than 7 miles a second, it will escape from the earth altogether and become a wanderer in space.

As the molecules which form the earth's atmosphere have an average speed of only about a third of a mile a second, there can be but few with speeds in excess of 7 miles a second. But there are always some, with the result that a steady trickle of molecules is for ever escaping from the earth's atmosphere and becoming lost to it for ever. Those molecules which escape do not, however, form a fair sample of the whole. We have seen (p. 107) how the lighter molecules in a mixed gas move with high speeds while the more massive move with low speeds. Thus the lighter are far more likely to attain to speeds in excess of 7 miles a second and the escaping gas will consist mainly or wholly of molecules of the lighter kinds.

A simple calculation shows that under present conditions no kind of gas would escape from the earth's atmosphere at an appreciable rate. On the other hand the moon exerts so feeble a hold on molecules at its surface that molecules which moved at a speed in excess of $1\frac{1}{2}$ miles a second could escape from its gravitational field. A detailed calculation shows that hydrogen, helium, water vapour, nitrogen, oxygen and argon would rapidly stream off into space. In the past, when the moon was hotter than now, and still in process of formation, even heavier gases would escape, so that we can readily understand how any atmosphere the moon may have then possessed has disappeared long ago.

Thus the moon has so slight a gravitational power that molecules of the commoner kinds would rapidly escape from it, but the earth has sufficient gravitational power to retain them all for an immense time. Intermediate cases may occur, in which a planet could retain the heavier kinds of molecules, but not the lighter. Such a case is Mars, which is larger than the moon but smaller than the earth. Calculation shows that hydrogen would escape from Mars at a great rate, helium much more slowly, and all heavier gases at a rate which is quite inappreciable. For each planet we can calculate which gases are debarred by their lightness from appearing in the atmosphere—although to know which actually do appear we must have recourse to observation.

Many of the smaller members of the solar system—Mercury, Mars and the moon in particular—show permanent clear-cut features which obviously belong to the solid surface of the body. The larger planets show no such features; what we see is neither clear-cut nor permanent and seems to consist of thick clouds, which may, however, be very different from terrestrial clouds. Whatever their nature may be, these clouds must of course have an atmosphere of some sort to support them.

To discover the composition of this atmosphere, we must have recourse to the second method of study, the spectroscopic.

As the planets emit no light of their own, they can only be studied by means of the sunlight they reflect. If the planet has an atmosphere, the light will have passed through it twice before reaching our instruments—once in going in and once in coming out. These journeys can of course add nothing to the sunlight, but may subtract something from it. The subtraction may show itself through the appearance of absorption bands in the spectrum of the light; if we can identify these we shall know what substances in the planet's atmosphere have obstructed the passage of the light, and can deduce the composition of this atmosphere, at least in part. If the atmosphere is so transparent that we can see to the planet's surface, there may be some loss of light resulting from reflection at this surface, for no substance reflects light perfectly. The proportion of lost light is different for different colours, and by comparing the reflecting powers of the surface, colour by colour, with those of known terrestrial substances, it may be possible to identify the material of which the surface consists. Lyot has recently found that the reflecting powers of the surfaces of Mercury, Mars and the moon are all identical with those of lava and pumice.

When light is reflected at a solid surface, it not only experiences a loss of quantity but also a change of quality. We say that light is "polarised" when its qualities are not the same for all the directions which are perpendicular to its direction of travel. Reflection usually changes the quality of polarisation of light, the amount of change depending on the colour of the light, and also on the nature of the reflecting surface.

The three surfaces just mentioned not only show the powers of reflecting light as lava and pumice, colour by colour, but also the same powers of changing the polarisation, so that we can hardly doubt that the surfaces of all these three bodies consist of the products of volcanic eruption in some form or other.

Such are the methods by which the astronomer investigates the physical conditions of the planets. Let us now consider the various planets in turn, commencing with those nearest to the sun.

MERCURY

Nearest to the sun and so hottest of all the planets is Mercury. Just as the moon always presents the same face to the earth, so Mercury always presents the same face to the sun. Thus on one hemisphere of Mercury there is perpetual day—and a very hot day—while on the other hemisphere it is always night. At the point directly under the sun, where it is always noon, the temperature is found to be about 650° F., a temperature at which lead and tin are both liquid. If we want to imagine Mercurians to exist, we may be sure that they do not inhabit this part of the planet's surface. They are more likely to live in a twilight zone some 90° away, where the sun is always near to the horizon and the heat more temperate. Yet even here they could hardly live in houses built above the ground, since the sun would immediately raise the temperature of every wall facing sunwards to about 650° F., and the inhabitants would be roasted as in an oven. Let us rather imagine them living in streets of trenches cut into the ground and raising a few feet of iron pipe above the ground here and there to boil their water and run their engines. But astronomy does not know of any single shred of evidence which suggests that there is life of any kind on Mercury.

It is still debatable whether Mercury possesses an atmosphere or not. It is the least massive of the planets, with less than a twentieth of the substance of the earth, so that its power of retaining an atmosphere is small. Under present conditions it would retain oxygen and heavier gases, but in the past, when it was presumably hotter even than now, all gases except the very heaviest would stream off into space. On the whole its surface markings are so permanent and clear-cut as to suggest that no appreciable atmosphere exists. Yet Schiaparelli noticed fifty years ago that some of the surface features were occasionally seen blurred, or even obscured, as though by some sort of cloud, and his observations have been confirmed and extended by Antoniadi. As the planet could not retain molecules of water-vapour, it has been suggested that the clouds may consist of particles of dust, set free possibly by falls of rock, but even so there must be some sort of atmosphere to save the dust particles from immediately falling back on to the surface of the planet.

VENUS

After Mercury comes Venus, the twin sister of the earth. The two planets are not entirely similar, since the earth has about three per cent. more diameter and about twenty-three per cent. more mass than its smaller sister. These small differences do not produce any appreciable difference in the atmosphere-retaining capacities of the two planets, so that Venus, like the earth, can retain all gases, including hydrogen. Thus if we study the problem merely in terms of the present state of the planets, we might reasonably expect Venus to exhibit an atmosphere similar to that of the earth, although perhaps somewhat smaller in amount.

Actually the two atmospheres are found to be very different. Something of this difference is suggested by the general appearance of Venus. An astronomer who observed the earth from Venus would see brilliant white clouds covering about half of the earth's surface, while gaps in the clouds would reveal the permanent features of sea, desert and fertile land. But an astronomer who examines Venus from the earth can discover no permanent features at all—only a continuous cloud-like surface. Gerasimovič has made a study of the brightness of this cloudy envelope and of the way in which it changes with the phases of the planet, and has shown that the envelope cannot be gaseous but must consist of large scattering particles—probably products of condensation, like the ice crystals which form the cirrus clouds in our own atmosphere. We have no means of exploring whatever atmosphere there may be below this stratum of clouds, but the "upper atmosphere" above it can of course be examined spectroscopically.

This proves to be in many ways the antithesis of the atmosphere of the earth. Hydrogen, nitrogen and the inert monatomic gases cannot in any case be detected spectroscopically, so that a study of the earth's atmosphere from Venus would reveal large quantities of oxygen, substantial quantities of water-vapour and minute quantities of carbon dioxide. A study of the upper atmosphere of Venus from the earth reveals no oxygen at all and no water-vapour, but an abundance of carbon dioxide. This does not necessarily mean that there is no oxygen or water-vapour at all, for the spectroscopic test is not infinitely sensitive, but it does mean that the amounts of oxygen and water-vapour must lie within definite assignable limits. If all the oxygen in the earth's atmosphere were collected and spread out in a layer at atmospheric pressure, this layer would be considerably over a mile in thickness, while if the carbon dioxide were treated in the same way it would form a similar layer only a very few feet thick. For the upper atmosphere of Venus, the corresponding thicknesses would be less than three feet of oxygen and about half-a-mile of carbon dioxide. In brief, when we pass from the earth to Venus, carbon dioxide and oxygen change places. Further, St John found that the total amount of water-vapour in the upper atmosphere of Venus is certainly less than that above the highest clouds on earth; if it were all precipitated in the form of rain, the rainfall would be less than a twenty-fifth of an inch.

It is perhaps rather surprising that two such similar planets should be surrounded by such different atmospheres. But it is the earth rather than Venus that provides the surprise. Oxygen combines eagerly with other substances, so that we might reasonably have expected to find but little free oxygen left on either planet. The free oxygen in the atmosphere of the earth is often attributed to the vegetation on the earth's surface; by breaking up compounds of oxygen, carbon dioxide in particular, this sets oxygen free in the air. But this can hardly be the whole story, for, although some biologists consider that life may have been generated spontaneously on earth under anaerobic conditions, it seems more likely that primitive life must have needed some free oxygen when it first appeared on earth. Tamman has suggested that the necessary free oxygen might have been set free through the heat of the primaeval earth breaking up molecules of water-vapour into the constituent atoms of oxygen and hydrogen. The hydrogen would stream off into space, the earth's gravitational pull being inadequate to hold it, and doubtless some of the oxygen would combine with the solidifying rock of the earth's crust, but vegetation would soon restore the balance. So long as we can assume the presence of both water-vapour and of vegetation, there is little difficulty in accounting for the presence of free oxygen.

If, then, free oxygen is lacking in the atmosphere of Venus, the reason may be a deficiency of vegetation, or of water-vapour, or of course of both. Let us begin by examining the first possibility—a deficiency or complete absence of vegetation.

It is conceivable that life came to our own planet as the result of some unusual accident, of some rare coincidence, or even—if we prefer—as a special creation confined to our own planet. The supposition that a similar event did not occur on Venus will then explain the whole situation—any store of free oxygen that Venus may once have possessed has long since combined with rocks and sediments, and there has been no vegetation to replace it. But it is also conceivable that life invariably appears when the physical conditions are favourable, and that favourable conditions have not yet appeared on Venus. Indeed it is reasonable to suppose that Venus has always been too hot for life. The small amount of carbon dioxide which is present in the atmosphere of the earth exercises a powerful "blanketing" effect, holding back the radiation which would otherwise stream outwards from the earth's surface, and so keeping the earth substantially warmer than it would otherwise be. The thousand times greater amount of carbon dioxide on Venus must form a far more potent blanket, so that estimates of the temperature of the surface of Venus range from 80° C. to 130° C. The atmospheric pressure is probably less than at the surface of the earth, so that water may well exist there only in the form of steam. If this is so, Venus must be highly unsuited to the support of life now, and must have been still more so in the past.

The alternative possibility, urged by Wildt, is that Venus may always have been deficient in water. As Venus was almost certainly formed out of the same store of matter as the earth—namely that which constituted the outer layers of the sun when its system of planets came into being—we might reasonably expect it to have started with the same proportion of water-vapour as the earth. But at a later stage the smaller mass and higher temperature of Venus might result in most of the molecules of water escaping from Venus, although similar molecules were being retained by the earth.

Out of its abundance of oxygen, the earth's atmosphere forms a layer of ozone which shields its lower parts from the destructive effects of the ultra-violet rays emitted by the sun. If the atmosphere of Venus contains no such abundance of oxygen, then there can be no such protection from the ultra-violet rays; these must permeate the whole atmosphere, and break up its molecules by photochemical action (p. 137). Under suitable conditions, atoms which had originally formed molecules of carbon dioxide (CO_2) and of whatever water-vapour (H_2O) there was, would re-combine to form molecules of free oxygen (O_2) and of formaldehyde (CH_2O). The oxygen would again be absorbed by the rocks, but the formaldehyde would stay in the atmosphere. Wildt at one time thought that the mysterious white clouds of the atmosphere of Venus might consist of a chemical combination of formaldehyde with water, but subsequently (1942) found this suggestion to be untenable. He finds that no trace of formaldehyde can be detected spectroscopically in the atmosphere of Venus.

However it may have originated, we may picture the present Venus as consisting of a hot dry surface, devoid of vegetation and probably of all life such as we know on earth, surrounded by an atmosphere in which there floats a layer of opaque clouds. Besides these clouds, the atmosphere contains a large amount of carbon dioxide, an unknown amount of nitrogen, and small amounts at most of water-vapour and free oxygen.

MARS

Next after Venus, still proceeding outwards from the sun, we come first to the earth, and then to planets which are colder than the earth. Mars, which comes first, is not enormously colder. The radiation it receives from the sun would give it an average temperature equal to 0·81 times that of the earth, or about −40° C. The temperatures actually observed are rather widely spread about this average, ranging from +10° C. at the equator on a Martian summer afternoon to −70° C. near the poles during the depths of the Martian winter.

Yet the temperatures would be even more widely spread if Mars were not surrounded by a fairly substantial atmosphere, and observation confirms the existence of such an atmosphere. W. H. Wright of Lick Observatory photographed the planet in infra-red light, which penetrates any atmosphere there may be, and so photographs the solid body of the planet, and also with ultra-violet light, which has very little penetrating power, and so photographs the surface not of the planet but of its atmosphere. He found that the ultra-violet image was measurably larger than the infra-red image, and thus obtained clear proof that Mars has an atmosphere, which he estimated to be from 50 to 60 miles high.

We still know very little of the constitution of this atmosphere. Spectroscopic analysis so far finds no definite evidence of either oxygen, carbon dioxide or water-vapour. Observations by W. S. Adams (1941) have shown that there cannot be a tenth as much water-vapour per square yard as there is in our own atmosphere. If the whole were precipitated in the form of a shower, the rainfall would certainly be less than a fiftieth of an inch.

The two poles of Mars are surrounded by white areas, generally known as "polar ice caps," which diminish in size in warmer weather and disappear almost entirely in summer. The name was given from analogy with the ice-caps on our own planet, but if they consist of ice, the ice must be very thin, since the chilly sun of the Martian summer does not provide enough heat to melt a thick layer of ice. It can be calculated that any ice there may be could not be more than a few inches thick, except perhaps quite close to the poles. The true nature of the caps is probably revealed by the photographs of W. H. Wright, already mentioned. It is found that the caps show very clearly in ultra-violet light, but are almost invisible in infra-red light. Layers of ice would of course behave in exactly the opposite way. The only possible inference would seem to be that the caps exist in the atmosphere, and not on the surface of the planet. They may consist of clouds of small solid particles, and so resemble the cirrus clouds in our own atmosphere as also perhaps the clouds which cover the surface of Venus.

The want of oxygen and carbon dioxide in the atmosphere of Mars suggests that this planet is like Venus in not possessing vegetation of the kind we know on earth. There are, however, certain dark areas on the surface of the planet which are observed to vary unmistakably as the seasons change, both in colour and extent. In the past these variations were frequently adduced as evidence of the presence of vegetation of some kind or other, but in the light of our present knowledge it seems more reasonable to interpret these also as meteorological phenomena—the results possibly of streams of water following the thaw of thin polar ice-caps, but more probably of the falling of rain on a desert of rock or ash. For we have seen that the reflecting and polarizing powers of the surface of Mars for lights of different colours suggest that the surface of Mars, like that of the moon, consists of volcanic ash and lava. The planet's surface is of a reddish hue, and this may indicate a certain degree of oxidation of the rocks and minerals, these having absorbed any free oxygen there may ever have been. Thus the general picture we form of Mars is that of a larger and colder moon, which, in virtue of its somewhat larger size and mass, has retained something of an atmosphere and so may still have rains, cloud and fog to vary its appearance.

The famous "Canals" on the surface of Mars are still the subject of debate, although less so than in the past. Some observers believe they have seen straight lines on the planet's surface; these generally seem to join up projecting features in the colour-scheme of the surface, and there has been a tendency to interpret them as the handiwork of intelligent beings who either inhabit the planet now, or did so in some past, and possibly warmer, epoch. Many considerations combine to cast doubt on this interpretation. For one thing similar lines are claimed to have been seen on the surface of Mercury and on the satellites of Jupiter, where it is highly improbable that intelligent life can have been at work, and even on Venus where we could in no case see any such work through the clouds, which completely conceal the planet's surface. One famous observer claimed to see double canals on Mars which were demonstrably too close together for the eye to see separately with the telescope he was using. There seems to be no room for doubt that when the human eye is straining to see an object by inadequate light, it tends to join conspicuous outstanding points by straight lines—just as school children are found to do if they are asked to copy a distant map in a bad light. It might seem easy to appeal to the camera, which has no such weakness, but unfortunately the camera is not altogether suited to settle the question. The coarseness of grain of photographic plates fixes a limit to the fineness of the detail which the camera can see, just as the finite wave-length of light fixes a limit to what the eye can see. The alleged Martian Canals are certainly so fine that the camera could not possibly see them; it can see certain brush-like markings, but these usually do not coincide with the canals claimed by visual observers. For such reasons as these, many astronomers have felt but little faith in the reality of the canals and have been inclined to regard them as subjective illusions, resulting from an over-conscientious enthusiasm to see everything there is to be seen.

In 1941, however, when Mars was to be seen under specially favourable conditions, Lyot and Gentili took a 38 cm. telescope to the observatory on the Pic du Midi, and made a series of observations, both visual and photographic, through the clear air of the mountain. The drawings in which they recorded their visual observations show features very similar to those seen by earlier observers, and in particular lines which look very similar to the alleged canals. But there was an essential novelty in their treatment of the photographic negatives. By combining hundreds of plates into a series of eighteen composite photographs, Lyot was able to eliminate the accidental effects which the coarseness of grain of the plates had introduced in the past. The observers consider that these composite photographs confirm the details they had seen visually and put into their drawings, and with these observations the Mars problem obviously enters upon a new phase of existence.

JUPITER AND SATURN

Mars is the last planet on which a solid surface can be seen, except that we do not know what we are looking at in the faint point of light we designate as Pluto. Still excepting Pluto, all the planets beyond Mars are much more massive than the earth, and, as they are also much colder than the earth, we should expect them to retain deep atmospheres; detailed studies make it clear that they do.

We have seen how different colours of light have different powers of penetrating atmospheric clouds and dust, infra-red radiation having the greatest power of all. The atmospheres of Jupiter and Saturn prove to be so opaque that even infra-red radiation cannot penetrate them; photographs taken with various colours of light, including infra-red, disclose no permanent features at all—only a succession of ever-changing vistas which are clearly of atmospheric origin. Jupiter has an average density which is only 1·34 times that of water, and Saturn the still lower density of 0·71. The lowness of these densities suggests that a large part of the volume of each planet is occupied by a gaseous atmosphere.

We can obtain further information from a study of the shapes of the planets as seen in a telescope. Both planets appear much flatter—more "orange-shaped"—than the earth. Now the degree of flattening of a rotating body depends on two factors—the period of rotation of the body, and the way in which its mass is distributed throughout its interior; it does not depend at all on the size of the body. Suppose that two bodies of any size A and B rotate at the same rate, but that the mass of A is fairly uniformly distributed throughout its interior, while the mass of B is much more concentrated round its centre. Then the body B will assume a much more flattened shape than A. Because of this, observation of the period of rotation of a planet, and of its degree of flattening of shape, can be made to yield information as to the interior structure of the planet.

The periods of rotation of both Jupiter and Saturn are easily measured, for each shows surface markings which, although not permanent, still persist through a very great number of rotations. Jupiter is found to make a complete rotation in just under 10 hours, and Saturn in about $10\frac{1}{4}$ hours. Calculation shows that if the earth were made to rotate at these speeds, it would not be as much flattened as Jupiter and Saturn are seen to be. We conclude that both planets must have their masses much more concentrated round their centres than the earth—as would be the case, to take an extreme case, if they consisted of a small solid core surrounded by a very extensive atmosphere.

Jeffreys considers that each planet consists primarily of an inner core of rock, coated by a thick layer of ice, the whole being enveloped by a very deep atmosphere. If so, Wildt has calculated, the rocky core of Jupiter will have a radius of about 22,000 miles, the coating of ice a thickness of about 16,000 miles, and the atmosphere a depth of about 6000 miles, the average density of this atmosphere being 0·78. The arrangement is shown in fig. 23.

The figures for Saturn are even more remarkable, as might be anticipated from its lower average density of 0·71. The rocky core must have a radius of 14,000 miles, the coating of ice a thickness of 6000 miles, and the atmosphere an average density of 0·41. This means that the rock and ice together occupy less than a fifth of the whole volume of Saturn; all the rest is atmosphere (fig. 24).

Judged by terrestrial standards, both of these atmospheres are exceedingly massive, and so must exert tremendous pressures. On Saturn the mass of atmosphere per square yard is about 1,000,000 times what it is on earth, and on Jupiter about 700,000 times. On both these planets, the force of gravity is greater than on earth, with the result that the greater part of both atmospheres must be at a pressure of at least a million terrestrial atmospheres.

Pressures of this order compress most substances to densities greater than that of water, but there are some exceptions. The principal are the two elements hydrogen and helium—the lightest of all the elements—and the compound substances methane, ethane and ammonia. All of these compounds have hydrogen as their principal constituent, which of course explains their low density under pressure. The lowness of the densities of the atmospheres of Jupiter and Saturn suggests that they must consist, in large part at least, of these five substances.

Both hydrogen and helium are likely to be present in profusion, for we know that they are abundant in the outer layers of the sun, and both planets are massive enough to retain them with ease, even at very high temperatures. Unfortunately it is impossible to test for the presence of these elements spectroscopically. Spectroscopic examination discloses only methane and ammonia—a foul and pestilent congregation

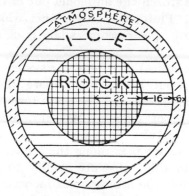

Mean density 1·34;
Atmospheric density 0·78
JUPITER
Fig. 23.

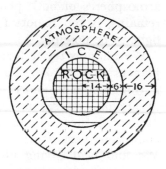

Mean density 0·71;
Atmospheric density 0·41
SATURN
Fig. 24.

of vapours. Ammonia is not found to occur in any great quantity, but methane occurs in profusion. It is remarkable that these two gases account for absolutely the whole of the absorption which is observed in the atmospheres of Jupiter and Saturn. Any other constituents which may be present are either in amounts too small to be observed or else, like hydrogen and helium, make no spectroscopic impression on light passing through them.

URANUS AND NEPTUNE

Still further away from the sun come Uranus and Neptune, which prove to be merely colder miniatures of Jupiter and Saturn. The observed temperature of Jupiter is −138° C. and of Saturn −153° C.; the temperature of Uranus is certainly lower than −183° C. and that of Neptune probably lower still, perhaps about −210° C. The ice layer on both planets may be about 6000 miles in thickness, while the overlying atmosphere may have a depth of 3000 miles on Uranus, and of 2000 miles on Neptune. Thus the two planets are similar to Jupiter and Saturn in their general structure. The spectra of their atmospheres are also of the same general nature as those of Jupiter and Saturn, both showing a great abundance of methane, although no ammonia has been detected as yet. But the extreme cold is likely to have frozen the ammonia out of the atmospheres of both planets. Pluto, the only planet which remains, is too remote for any spectroscopic analysis of its light to be possible.

We can now try to form a physical picture of the system of planets as a whole. Leaving out Pluto, because we know nothing about it, and reserving Venus and the earth for later discussion, we see a sequence of planets—Mercury, Mars, Jupiter, Saturn, Uranus and Neptune—in which the physical conditions vary continuously as we pass along the sequence. We find heat giving place to cold, absolute aridity to an abundance of water or ice, while the atmospheres increase in depth and extent and hydrogen probably increases from nil to a large amount, existing in the form either of free hydrogen or of its compounds, especially methane.

There are reasons known for all these changes. The planets near the sun are hottest simply because the planets depend solely on the sun for their heat; they are arid because they are too small and too hot—or have been too hot in the past—to retain water-vapour, and they are devoid of hydrogen for the same reason.

The twin planets, Venus and the earth, do not altogether fit into this sequence. This is partly because they are more massive than their immediate neighbours Mercury and Mars, and so retain more atmosphere. After allowing for this, Venus fits into the sequence fairly well, but the earth remains anomalous in having too much oxygen and water-vapour in its atmosphere. This, as we have already noticed, is probably a consequence of its clothing of vegetation. Life has come to the earth and thrown it out of its place in the regular sequence.

Not long ago it used to be thought that the sun was continually cooling and the planets with it. What the earth now is, it was said, Mars must have been in the not very remote past and Venus will be in the not very remote future; the earth may be the only planet on which life now exists, yet Mars may be the planet of spent life and Venus the planet of life yet to come. It may be so; certainly we have not sufficient knowledge to settle the question at present. But the view just described came from theories of stellar evolution which are now discarded, and our newly acquired knowledge suggests another approach to the problem.

We now believe that the sun obtains the energy for its radiation from sub-atomic rearrangement of its substance, light elements combining to form heavier, so that its chemical composition is continually changing, but without any substantial change of its vast mass. And we know that main-sequence stars which have the same mass as the sun all emit about the same amount of radiation as the sun. This suggests that a star of the sun's mass can only change the amount of its radiation slightly so long as it remains a main-sequence star. If so, the temperatures of the planets can also undergo but little change; Mars will have had its present cool temperature since those remote days when it was still warmed by the heat it had brought from the sun, and Venus will retain its present heat until the sun has used up its supply of light elements and begins to contract into a cooler and smaller "white dwarf." If this is so, the idea that life can progress along the planetary sequence is probably illusory. The earth is the planet of life, because it is at the right distance from the sun, but we have no reason for thinking that life of the kind we know on earth—life which requires hundreds of millions of years for its development—has either passed from Mars or will in due course appear on Venus; these planets are at the wrong distance from the sun.

CHAPTER VII

Beginnings and Endings

We have seen how the solid substance of the material universe is continually dissolving away into intangible radiation. Yesterday the sun weighed 360,000 million tons more than it does to-day, the difference being the weight of 24-hours' emission of radiation which is now travelling through space, and, so far as direct observation goes, is destined to journey on through space until the end of time. Less than a gramme of this radiation contains enough energy to take a liner across the Atlantic, while a pound of it would suffice to keep the whole British nation going for a fortnight—domestic fires, power-stations, factories, trains, ships and all. The same transformation of material substance into radiation is in progress in all the stars, and to a lesser degree on earth, while the cosmic radiation (p. 111) may be found to provide evidence that the transformation takes place on a far grander scale throughout the depths of interstellar space.

CYCLIC PROCESSES. It is natural to ask whether a study of the universe as a whole reveals these processes as part only of a closed cycle, so that the wastage which we see in progress in the sun and stars and on the earth is made good elsewhere. When we stand on the banks of a river and watch its current ever carrying water out to sea, we know that this water is in due course transformed into clouds and rain which replenish the river. Is the physical universe a similar cyclic system, or ought it rather to be compared to a stream which, having no source of replenishment, must cease flowing after it has spent itself?

THERMODYNAMICS

To this question, the wide scientific principle known as the second law of thermodynamics provides an answer in very general terms. If we ask what is the underlying cause of all the varied animation we see around us in the world, the answer is, in every case, energy—the chemical energy of the fuel which drives our ships, trains and cars, or of the food which keeps our bodies alive and is used in muscular effort, the mechanical energy of the earth's motion which is responsible for the alternations of day and night, of summer and winter, of high tide and low tide, the heat energy of the sun which makes our crops grow and provides us with wind and rain.

The science of thermodynamics deals primarily with energy and the various changes which it can undergo. It is based fundamentally on two laws which are generally known as the first and second laws of thermodynamics. These deal respectively with the quantity and quality of energy.

FIRST LAW OF THERMODYNAMICS. The first law of thermodynamics, which embodies the principle of "conservation of energy," teaches that energy is indestructible; it may change about from one form to another, but its total amount remains unaltered through all these changes, so that the total energy of the universe remains always the same. As the energy which is the cause of all the life of the universe is indestructible, it might be thought that this life would go on for ever undiminished in amount.

AVAILABILITY OF ENERGY. The second law of thermodynamics shows that this is not so. Energy is indestructible as regards its amount, but it continually changes in form, and generally speaking we may compare the two directions of change to journeys uphill and downhill. And it is the usual story. The descent is easy; but to retrace the steps—this is so difficult that we rightly treat it as impossible and think of energy as passing only in the one direction.

Actually it is not impossible, for the second law does not deal in certainties, but only in probabilities—and these of a somewhat unusual kind. It is perfectly in accordance with the laws of mechanics that energy should change its quality in the direction just described as upwards. But the odds against such a change in the energy either of the universe as a whole, or of any considerable part of it, are immense. The number of particles in the universe is perhaps of the order of 10^{79}, and the odds against such an occurrence as we have just mentioned are found to involve very high powers of 10^{79}.

When the odds are of this kind, we need not trouble to differentiate too closely between long odds and certainties.

For instance, both light and heat are forms of energy, and a million ergs of light-energy can be transformed into a million ergs of heat with the utmost ease; let the light fall on any cool, black surface, and the thing is done. But the odds against the reverse transformation are of the kind we have just described, so that we generally say that it is impossible; a million ergs which have once assumed the form of heat, can never again assume the form of a million ergs of light. This is a special example of the general principle that radiative energy tends always to change into a form of longer, not shorter, wave-length. In general, for instance, fluorescence increases the wave-length of the light; it changes blue light into green, yellow or red, but not red light into yellow, green or blue. Exceptions to the general principle are known, but they are of special type, admitting of special explanations, and do not affect the general principle.

It may be objected that the everyday act of lighting a fire disproves all this. Has not the sun's heat been stored up in the coal we burn, and cannot we produce light by burning coal? The answer is that the sun's radiation is a mixture of both light and heat, and indeed of radiation of all wavelengths. What is stored up in the coal is primarily the sun's light and other radiation of still shorter wave-length. When we burn coal we get some light, but not as much as the sun originally put into the coal; we also get some heat, and this is more than the amount of heat which was originally put in. On balance, the net result of the whole transaction is that a certain amount of light has been transformed into a certain amount of heat.

All this shows that we must learn to think of energy, not only in terms of quantity, but also in terms of quality. Its total quantity remains always the same; this is the first law of thermodynamics. But its quality changes, and tends to change always in the same direction; this is the second law of thermodynamics. Turnstiles are set up between the different qualities of energy; the passage is easy in one direction, impossible in the other. A human crowd may contrive to find a way round without jumping over turnstiles, but in nature there is no way round; energy flows always in the same direction, as surely as water flows downhill.

Part of the downward path consists, as we have seen, of the transition from radiation of short wave-length into radiation of longer wave-length. In terms of quanta (p. 137) the transition is from a few quanta of high energy to a large number of quanta of low energy, the total amount of energy of course remaining unaltered. The downfall of the energy accordingly consists in the breaking of its quanta into smaller units. And when once the fall and breakage have taken place, it is as impossible to reconstitute the original large quanta as it was to put Humpty-Dumpty back on his wall.

Although this is the main part of the downward path, it is not the whole of it. Thermodynamics teaches that all the different forms of energy have different degrees of "availability," and that the downward path is always from higher to lower availability.

And now we may return to the question with which we started the present chapter: "What is it that keeps the varied life of the universe going?" Our original answer "energy" is seen to be incomplete. Energy is no doubt essential, but the really complete answer is that it is the transformation of energy from a more available to a less available form; it is the running downhill of energy. To argue that the total energy of the universe cannot diminish, and therefore the universe must go on for ever, is like arguing that as a clock-weight cannot diminish, the clock-hand must go round and round for ever.

THE FINAL END OF THE UNIVERSE

Energy cannot run downhill for ever, and, like the clock-weight, it must touch bottom at last. And so the universe cannot go on for ever; sooner or later the time must come when its last erg of energy has reached the lowest rung on the ladder of descending availability, and at this moment the active life of the universe must cease. The energy is still there, but it has lost all capacity for change; it is as little able to work the universe as the water in a flat pond is able to turn a water-wheel. We are left with a dead, although possibly a warm, universe—a "heat-death."

Such is the teaching of modern thermodynamics. There is no reason for doubting or challenging it, and indeed it is so fully confirmed by the whole of our terrestrial experience, that it would be difficult to find any point at which it could be open to attack. It disposes at once of any possibility of a cyclic universe in which the events we see are as the pouring of river water into the sea, while events we do not see restore this water back to the river. The water of a river can go round and round in this way, just because it is not the whole of the universe; something extraneous to the river-cycle keeps it continually in motion—namely, the heat of the sun. But the universe as a whole cannot so go round and round. Short of postulating some sort of action from outside the universe, whatever this may mean, the energy of the universe must continually lose availability; a universe in which the energy had no further availability to lose would be dead already. Change can occur only in the one direction, which leads to the heat-death. With universes as with mortals, the only possible life is progress to the grave.

Even the flow of the river to the sea, which we selected as an obvious instance of true cyclic motion, is seen to illustrate this, as soon as all the relevant factors are taken into account. As the river pours seaward over its falls and cascades, the tumbling of its waters generates heat, which ultimately passes off into space in the form of heat radiation. But the energy which keeps the river pouring along comes ultimately from the sun in the form mainly of light; shut off the sun's radiation and the river will soon stop flowing. The river flows only by continually transforming light-energy into heat-energy, and as soon as the cooling sun ceases to supply energy of sufficiently high availability the flow must cease.

The same general principles may be applied to the astronomical universe. There is no question as to the way in which energy runs down here. It is first liberated in the hot interior of a star in the form of quanta of extremely short wave-length and excessively high energy. As this radiant energy struggles out to the star's surface, it continually adjusts itself, through repeated absorption and re-emission, to the temperature of that part of the star through which it is passing. As longer wave-lengths are associated with lower temperatures (p. 146), the wave-length of the radiation is continually lengthened; a few energetic quanta are being transformed into numerous feeble quanta. Once these are free in space, they travel onward unchanged until they meet dust particles, stray atoms, free electrons, or some other form of interstellar matter. Except in the highly improbable event of this matter being at a higher temperature than the surfaces of the stars, these encounters still further increase the wave-length of the radiation, and the final result of innumerable encounters is radiation of very great wave-length; the quanta have increased enormously in numbers, but have paid for their increase by a corresponding decrease in individual strength. Thus the main physical process of the universe consists in the energy of exceedingly high availability which is bottled up in atomic and nuclear structures being transformed into heat-energy at the lowest level of availability.

Many, giving rein to their fancy, have speculated that this low-level heat-energy may in due course re-form itself into new electrons and protons. As the existing universe dissolves away into radiation, their imagination sees new heavens and a new earth coming into being out of the ashes of the old. Science can give no support to such fancies. She cannot, it is true, prove that the fanciful will not happen—she can only calculate the odds against it happening. And these prove to be so enormous that we may disregard altogether the possibility of its occurrence. Perhaps it is as well; it is hard to see what advantage could accrue from an eternal reiteration of the same theme, or even from endless variations of it.

The final state of the universe will be attained when all the material mass which is capable of being transformed into radiation has been so transformed.

We have seen that matter is distributed in space at an average rate of something like 10^{-28} gramme per cubic centimetre. The transformation of a gramme of matter into radiation liberates 9×10^{20} ergs of energy, so that the transformation of 10^{-28} gramme of matter liberates 9×10^{-8} erg of energy. It follows that the complete transformation of all the substance of the existing universe would only fill space with energy at the rate of 9×10^{-8} erg per cubic centimetre. This would only raise the temperature of space from absolute zero to a temperature which is still well below that of liquid air; it would only raise the temperature of the earth's surface by about a tenth part of a degree Centigrade. The reason why the effect of annihilating a whole universe is so extraordinarily slight is of course that space is so extraordinarily empty of matter; trying to warm space by annihilating all the matter in it is like trying to warm Waterloo Station by burning a few specks of dust here and there inside it.

Such would be the final result of transforming the whole substance of the universe into radiation, but it is improbable that more than a small fraction of it can ever be transformed, so that the maximum result ever to be expected must be far below that just mentioned. As compared with any amount of radiation that is ever likely to be poured into it, the capacity of space is that of a bottomless pit.

Such is the final end of things to which, so far as present-day science can see, the material universe must inevitably come in some far-off age, unless the course of nature is changed in the meantime. It is a state of things in which life, as we know it on earth, could not possibly survive.

LIFE AND THE UNIVERSE

Let us now glance for a moment at the relation of life to this dying universe.

The old view that every point of light in the sky represented a possible home for life is quite foreign to modern astronomy. The stars have surface-temperatures of anything from 1650 degrees to 60,000 degrees or more and, as we have seen, are at far higher temperatures inside. A large part of the matter of the universe consists of stellar matter at a temperature of millions of degrees, its molecules being broken up into atoms, and the atoms broken up, partially or wholly, into their constituent parts. The rest consists, for the most part, of nebular gas or dust. Now the very concept of life implies duration in time; there can be no life—or at least no life at all similar to that we know on earth—where atoms change their make-up millions of times a second and no pair of atoms can ever stay joined together. It also implies a certain mobility in space, and these two implications restrict life to the small range of physical conditions in which the liquid state is possible. Our survey of the universe has shown how small this range is in comparison with that exhibited by the universe as a whole. It is not to be found in the stars, nor in the nebulae out of which the stars are born. Indeed, probably only an infinitesimal fraction of the matter of the universe is in the liquid state.

Actually we know of no type of astronomical body in which the conditions can be favourable to life except planets like our own revolving round a sun. Even these may be too hot or too cold for life to obtain a footing. In the solar system, for instance, it is hard to imagine life existing on Mercury or Neptune since liquids boil on the former and freeze hard on the latter.

Even when all the requisite conditions are satisfied, will life come or will it not? We must probably discard the at one time widely accepted view that if once life had come into the universe in any way whatsoever, it would rapidly spread from planet to planet and from one planetary system to another until the whole universe teemed with life; space now seems too cold, and planetary systems too far apart. Our terrestrial life must in all probability have originated on the earth itself. What we should like to know is whether it originated as the result of some amazing accident or succession of coincidences, or whether it is the normal event for inanimate matter to produce life in due course, when the physical environment is suitable. We look to the biologist for the answer, which so far he has not been able to produce.

The astronomer might be able to give a partial answer if he could find evidence of life on some other planet, for we should then at least know that life had occurred more than once in the history of the universe, but so far no convincing evidence has been forthcoming. There is no definite evidence of life anywhere in the universe, except on our own planet.

Apart from the certain knowledge that life exists on earth, our only definite knowledge is that, at the best, life must be limited to a tiny fraction of the universe. Millions of millions of stars exist which support no life, which have never done so and never will do so. Of the planetary systems in the sky, many must be entirely lifeless, and in others life, if it exists at all, is probably limited to a few of the planets. The three centuries and more which have elapsed since Giordano Bruno expressed his belief in an infinite number of worlds have changed our conception of the universe almost beyond description, but they have not brought us appreciably nearer to understanding the relation of life to the universe. We can still only guess as to the meaning of this life which, to all appearances, is so rare. Is it the final climax towards which the whole creation moves, for which the thousands of millions of years of transformation of matter in uninhabited stars and nebulae, and of waste of radiation in desert space, have been only an incredibly extravagant preparation? Or is it a mere accidental and possibly quite unimportant by-product of natural processes, which have some other and more stupendous end in view? Or, to glance at a still more modest line of thought, must we regard it as something of the nature of a disease, which affects matter when it has lost the high temperature with which most of the matter in the universe would at once destroy life? Or, throwing humility aside, shall we venture to imagine that it is the only reality, which creates, instead of being created by, the colossal masses of the stars and nebulae and the almost inconceivably long vistas of astronomical time?

Again it is not for the astronomer to select between these alternative guesses; his task is done when he has delivered the message of astronomy. Perhaps it is over-rash for him even to formulate the questions this message suggests.

THE EARTH AND ITS FUTURE PROSPECTS

Let us leave these rather abstract speculations and come down to earth. We feel the solid earth under our feet, and the rays of the sun overhead. Somehow, but we know not how or why, life also is here; we ourselves are part of it. And it is natural to enquire what astronomy has to say as to its future prospects.

The earth, which started life as a hot mass of gas, has gradually cooled, until it has now about touched bottom, and has almost no heat beyond that which it receives from the sun. This just about balances the amount it radiates away into space, so that it would stay at its present temperature for ever if external conditions did not change, and any changes in its condition will be forced on it by changes occurring outside. These changes may be either gradual or catastrophic.

Of the gradual changes which are possible, the most obvious is a diminution in the light and heat received from the sun. We have seen that if the sun consisted of pure hydrogen, it could lose one part in 150 of its whole mass through the transformation of hydrogen into helium. The energy thus set free would provide for radiation at the present rate through a period of 100,000 million years.

The sun does not consist of pure hydrogen, and has never done so, but a fair proportion of its present substance is probably hydrogen, and this ought to provide radiation for at least several thousands of millions of years, at the present rate. After all the available supplies of hydrogen are used up, the sun will, so far as we can guess, proceed to contract to the white dwarf state, probably to a condition resembling that of the faint companion of Sirius. The shrinkage of the sun to this state would transform our oceans into ice and our atmosphere into liquid air; it seems impossible that terrestrial life could survive. The vast museum of the sky must almost certainly contain examples of shrunken suns of this type, and some will have planets like our earth revolving round them. Whether these planets carry on them the frozen remains of a life which was once as active as our present life on earth we can hardly even surmise.

Such at least would be the normal course of events, the tragedy we have described happening after a time of the order of perhaps 10,000 millions of years. But a variety of accidents may intervene to bring the human race to an end long before any such interval has elapsed. To mention only possible astronomical occurrences, the sun may run into another star, any asteroid may hit any other asteroid and, as a result, be so deflected from its path as to strike the earth, any of the stars in space may wander into the solar system and, in so doing, upset all the planetary orbits to such an extent that the earth becomes impossible as an abode of life. It is difficult to estimate the likelihood of any of these events happening, but rough calculations suggest that none of them is at all likely to happen within the next 10,000 million years or so.

A more serious possibility is that the sun's light and heat may increase so much as to shrivel up all terrestrial life. We have seen how "novae" occasionally appear in the sky, temporarily emitting anything up to 25,000 times the radiation of the sun. It seems fairly certain that if our sun were suddenly to become a nova, its emission of light and heat would so increase as to scorch all life off the earth, but we are completely in the dark as to whether our sun runs any risk of entering the nova stage. If it does, this is probably the greatest of all the risks to which life on earth is exposed.

Many a nova has been proved to be an ordinary star which was visible as a very faint star long before it appeared as a nova, flashed into brilliance for a brief span of life, and then lapsed back into commonplaceness, and it seems reasonable to suppose that all novae are of this kind, although the star may often escape detection until it assumes its brilliant nova state. These apparitions are by no means rare; something like six are noticed every year in the galactic system alone. Let us suppose that a further six occur unnoticed. Then, if the galactic system contains about 300,000 million stars, it follows that the average star becomes a nova once every 24,000 million years. This purely statistical consideration suggests that there is a substantial danger that our sun may do the same before 10,000 million years have elapsed.

What we should like to know is whether our sun is in danger of becoming a nova—so far as can be told from the geological record, it does not seem to have done so for the last 1000 million years or so. So far there is no agreement among astronomers either as to the physical causes which turn an ordinary star into a nova, or as to the physical conditions which prevail in novae. Various suggestions are in the field, but none of them wins general acceptance. But it seems quite possible that the nova stage is merely what happens when an ordinary main-sequence star first begins to contract into a white dwarf —if so, we need not count our dangers twice over.

Apart from improbable accidents, it seems that if the solar system is left to the natural course of evolution, the earth is likely to remain a possible abode of life for thousands of millions of years to come.

If so, we may perhaps be glad that our lives have fallen in the beginning, rather than at the end, of this great stretch of time. We may well imagine that if man survives to the end of it, he will have infinitely more knowledge than now, but one thing he will no longer know—the thrill of pleasure of the pioneer who opens up new realms of knowledge. Disease, perhaps even death, will have been conquered, and life will doubtless be safer and incomparably better-ordered than now. It will seem incredible that a time could have existed when men risked, and lost, their lives in traversing unexplored country, in climbing hitherto unclimbed peaks, in fighting wild beasts for the fun of it. Life will be more of a routine and less of an adventure than now; it will also be more purposeless when the human race knows that within a measurable space of time it must face extinction and the eternal destruction of all its hopes, endeavours, and achievements.

The 10,000 million years which seems a possible future for the existence of life on earth is more than three times the past age of the earth, and more than 10,000 times the period through which humanity has so far existed on earth. Let us try to set these times in their proper proportion by the help of yet another simple model. Take a postage-stamp, and stick it on to a penny. Now climb Cleopatra's needle and lay the penny flat, postage-stamp uppermost, on top of the obelisk. The height of the whole structure may be taken to represent the time that has elapsed since the earth was born. On this scale, the thickness of the penny and postage-stamp together represents the time that man has lived on earth. The thickness of the postage-stamp represents the time he has been civilised, the thickness of the penny representing the time he lived in an uncivilised state. Now stick another postage-stamp on top of the first to represent the next 10,000 years of civilisation, and keep sticking on postage-stamps until you have a pile as high as the towers of Westminster Abbey. Such a pile still provides an inadequate representation of the length of the future which, so far as astronomy can see, probably stretches before civilised humanity, unless an accident cuts it short. The first postage-stamp was the past of civilisation; a column higher than the Abbey is its future. Or, to look at it another way, the first postage-stamp represents what man has already achieved; a pile which out-tops Westminster Abbey represents what he may achieve, if his achievement is proportional simply to his time on earth.

Up to now, we know that his achievement has not been simply proportional to his time. In some respects at least—the mechanical arts, for instance—we advance at an ever increasing tempo. The contributions of successive generations are not equal, but continually increase in geometrical progression, so that material civilisation advances more in a generation now than it did in a millennium when it was at its commencement. If this continual speeding-up were to persist throughout the whole astronomical future of the earth, it is impossible to imagine what the rate of advance would become before life disappeared from earth. But we can think of only too many factors which are likely to compel a slowing down before long.

We must remember too that we cannot count on such a length of future with any certainty. Accidents may happen to the race as to the individual. Celestial collisions may occur; shrinking into a white dwarf, the sun may freeze terrestrial life out of existence; bursting out as a nova it may scorch our race to death. Accident may replace our tower of postage-stamps by a truncated column of only a fraction of the height of which we have spoken. Even so, our race has an "expectation of life" which must be measured in terms of thousands of millions of years. It is a period which the human mind, as apart from the mind of the mathematician, can hardly conceive with any clearness. For all practical purposes the only statement that conveys any real meaning is that our race may look forward to occupying the earth for a time longer than any we can think of, and achieving incomparably more than anything we can possibly imagine.

Looked at in terms of space, the message of astronomy is at best one of melancholy grandeur and oppressive vastness.

Looked at in terms of time, it becomes one of almost endless possibility and hope. As inhabitants of a civilised earth, we are living at the very beginning of time. We have come into being in the fresh glory of the dawn, and a day of almost unthinkable length stretches before us with unimaginable opportunities for accomplishment. Our descendants of far-off ages, looking down this long vista of time from the other end, will see our present age as the misty morning of the world's history; they will see our contemporaries of to-day as dim heroic figures who fought their way through jungles of ignorance, error and superstition to discover truth, to learn how to harness the forces of nature, and to make a world worthy for mankind to live in. We are still too much engulfed in the greyness of the morning mists to be able to imagine, even vaguely, how this world of ours will appear to those who will come after us and see it in the full light of day. But by what light we have, we seem to discern that the main message of astronomy is one of hope to the race and of responsibility to the individual— of responsibility because we are drawing plans and laying foundations for a longer future than we can well imagine.

Index